AGS

Basic Math Skills

by
August V. Treff
and
Donald H. Jacobs

AGS®

American Guidance Service, Inc.
Circle Pines, Minnesota 55014-1796
800-328-2560

About the Authors

August V. Treff, M.Ed., is Chief of Educational Accountability for the Baltimore City Public Schools. He has been a mathematics teacher and also served as the Director of Research and Evaluation for the school district.

Donald H. Jacobs, M.Ed., teaches high school mathematics for the Baltimore City Public Schools. He has also been the coordinator of computer programming at the Talmudical Academy of Baltimore.

Photo Credits: p. x—David Young-Wolff/PhotoEdit; p. 34—Robert Brenner/PhotoEdit; p. 54—Lori Adamski Peek/Tony Stone Images; p. 84—Andrew Syred/Tony Stone Images; p. 114—FPG International; pp. 128, 176—Amy C. Etra/PhotoEdit; p. 158—David Barnes/The Stock Market; pp. 200, 280—Patterson Graphics; p. 224—William Taufic/The Stock Market; p. 240—Tony Freeman/PhotoEdit; p. 266—Michael Newman/PhotoEdit

Printed in the United States of America

ISBN 0-7854-0916-5-H (hardcover)

ISBN 0-7854-0442-2-S (softcover)

Product Number 90200 (hardcover)

Product Number 90201 (softcover)

A 0 9 8 7

Contents

Chapter

1

Whole Numbers

Everybody counts. From the time we first count candles on a birthday cake to when we count our life savings, we use mathematics to help us. We add when we find the total cost of groceries. We subtract when we write a check and find the new balance. Multiplication and division are the mathematical operations we perform when we find the earned run average of our softball pitcher.

In Chapter 1, you will learn ways to find the value of numbers and discover the similarities among addition, multiplication, subtraction, and division.

Goals for Learning

▶ To identify the place value of a digit in a number

▶ To write numbers in word form

▶ To round numbers

▶ To compute with whole numbers to solve word problems

Digit

One of the characters used to write a numeral.

In our number system the placement of each **digit** in a numeral is important. Each place has a certain value. Study the **place value** chart. Memorize the names of the places.

Hundred-millions	Ten-millions	Millions	Hundred-thousands	Ten-thousands	Thousands	Hundreds	Tens	Ones
					2	3	7	5

Place value

Worth based on position in a numeral.

EXAMPLE   2375

By looking at the place value chart, you can see that the number 3 is in the hundreds place.

Answer: 2375 — hundreds

Exercise A Write the name of the place for each underlined digit.

1) 52<u>6</u>
2) <u>4</u>015
3) 6<u>2</u>03
4) 5<u>1</u>781
5) <u>2</u>0902
6) 6230<u>0</u>

7) 2<u>3</u>4101
8) 1<u>5</u>52134
9) <u>2</u>003011
10) 5601<u>2</u>71
11) <u>9</u>7700310
12) 16<u>2</u>530000

Exercise B After each numeral is a place name. Copy the numeral on separate paper and underline the digit that is in that place.

1) 6308   ones
2) 42300   hundreds
3) 2830000   millions
4) 73000   thousands
5) 853726   tens

6) 4523306   millions
7) 25367000 ten-millions
8) 1563170   ten-thousands
9) 12623850 millions
10) 12647854 hundred-thousands

Whole numbers

The set of numbers 0, 1, 2, 3, 4, 5, 6, . . .

Reading and writing **whole numbers** can best be explained by using a place value chart. Notice the addition of the group names. Always read the numeral and then the group name. Read from left to right. Commas are inserted every three places to help identify place values.

EXAMPLE

	Hundred-millions	Ten-millions	Millions	Hundred-thousands	Ten-thousands	Thousands	Hundreds	Tens	Ones
A				8	2	0	5	6	7
B		2	5	0	0	8	3	0	1

A is read: Eight hundred twenty thousand, five hundred sixty-seven.

B is read: Twenty-five million, eight thousand, three hundred one.

Exercise A   Write the following numerals in words.

1) 465,721

2) 7,350,023

3) 26,003

4) 200,463

5) 91,008

6) 21,000,000

7) 14,005,006

8) 3,946

9) 315,621

10) 437

11) 12,400,600

12) 9,203,020

13) 535,000,495

14) 700,463,000

Occasionally, you may wish to round a whole number so that you will have simpler numbers to work with. To round to the nearest tens place, follow these steps:

Step 1 Find the place that you are rounding to.

Step 2 If the digit to its right is five or more, add one to the place that you are rounding to. If it is less than five, do not add anything.

Step 3 Change all of the digits to the right of the place to which you are rounding to zeros.

EXAMPLES	3,468	3,462
Step 1	3,4<u>6</u>8 Tens place	3,4<u>6</u>2 Tens place
Step 2	+1 3,46<u>8</u> 5 or more, add one	3,46<u>2</u> Less than 5, do nothing
Step 3	3,470	3,460

Exercise B Round each number to the nearest hundreds place.

1) 365

2) 9,127

3) 98

4) 23,091

5) 971

6) 5,209

7) 36,972

8) 23,068

Exercise C   The first number in each row is to be rounded to the nearest tens place. Write the number in the row that is correctly rounded.

1) **451:**   450   500   460

2) **3,169:**   3,100   3,160   3,170

3) **708:**   710   700   800

4) **1,509:**   1,510   1,600   1,500

5) **3:**   10   4   0

Write the number in each row that is correctly rounded to the nearest hundreds place.

6) **29,631:**   29,610   29,600   29,700

7) **6,309:**   6,310   6,400   6,300

8) **783:**   800   790   700

9) **49:**   150   100   0

10) **85:**   0   100   80

Round these numbers to the nearest tens place.

11) 375

12) 92

13) 96

14) 281

15) 3,516

Round these numbers to the nearest hundreds place.

16) 7,203

17) 861

18) 1,939

19) 2,065

20) 91

Exercise D Round these whole numbers to the nearest thousands place.

1) 56,266		**9)** 7,230	
2) 9,486		**10)** 27,864	
3) 13,472		**11)** 2,935	
4) 6,700		**12)** 11,906	
5) 98,716		**13)** 13,388	
6) 61,825		**14)** 20,635	
7) 22,464		**15)** 189	
8) 19,130		**16)** 38,612	

Exercise E Complete the chart by rounding to the place named.

		Tens	Hundreds	Thousands
1)	463		500	
2)	8,259			
3)	91,612			92,000
4)	83			
5)	915	920		
6)	9,200			
7)	36,155			
8)	3,919			
9)	16			
10)	623			
11)	18,800			
12)	499,792			
13)	30,209			
14)	92,314			
15)	68,197			

Addend
A number that is added to one or more numbers.

Addition
The arithmetic operation of combining numbers to find their sum.

Order
Sequence from smallest to largest.

Sum
The answer to an addition problem.

Zero
The first whole number.

Addition is combining numbers to form a total. Each number being added is an **addend**. The **order** in which you add two numbers does not change the answer, or the **sum**. Adding **zero** to a number does not change the number.

EXAMPLES   Add 7 and 5.

7		5 — addend
+ 5	OR	+7 — addend
12		12 — sum

Add 7 and 0.

7		0 — addend
+0	OR	+7 — addend
7		7 — sum

Exercise A   Add the following addends.

1) 4   2) 3   3) 6   4) 9   5) 8   6) 3   7) 7   8) 4   9) 4
   +6   +3   +5   +7   +8   +2   +0   +4   +0

10) 5 11) 5 12) 4 13) 7 14) 8 15) 9 16) 0 17) 3 18) 6
    +5   +0   +3   +9   +6   +1   +8   +0   +1

19) 8 20) 6 21) 0 22) 1 23) 3 24) 5 25) 7 26) 9 27) 2
    +1   +7   +1   +1   +4   +9   +8   +5   +0

28) 5 29) 5 30) 7 31) 9 32) 9 33) 8 34) 8 35) 7 36) 6
    +6   +3   +3   +2   +4   +3   +4   +4   +3

37) 4 38) 5 39) 2 40) 2 41) 6 42) 2 43) 2 44) 9 45) 8
    +5   +7   +5   +9   +8   +7   +6   +0   +5

When you are adding two-digit numbers, add the ones first. Then add the tens. Like place values must be added to like place values. If the sum of two numbers is more than 9, then add the ones column first, and carry over the tens to the tens column.

EXAMPLE

Add 38 + 5

$$\begin{array}{r} 1 \\ 38 \\ +5 \\ \hline 43 \end{array}$$

Add the ones first. 8 + 5 = 13
Write the 3 in the ones column.
Write the 1, which stands for 10, in the tens column. Add the tens.   1 + 3 = 4.

$$\begin{array}{r} 1 \\ 67 \\ +14 \\ \hline 81 \end{array}$$ 7 + 4 = 11

$$\begin{array}{r} 1 \\ 53 \\ + 79 \\ \hline 132 \end{array}$$ 3 + 9 = 12

Exercise B   Add the following problems.

1) $\begin{array}{r} 23 \\ +\ 6 \\ \hline \end{array}$
2) $\begin{array}{r} 54 \\ +\ 8 \\ \hline \end{array}$
3) $\begin{array}{r} 57 \\ +\ 9 \\ \hline \end{array}$
4) $\begin{array}{r} 68 \\ +\ 6 \\ \hline \end{array}$
5) $\begin{array}{r} 63 \\ +\ 5 \\ \hline \end{array}$
6) $\begin{array}{r} 24 \\ +\ 8 \\ \hline \end{array}$
7) $\begin{array}{r} 35 \\ +\ 7 \\ \hline \end{array}$
8) $\begin{array}{r} 64 \\ +\ 9 \\ \hline \end{array}$

9) $\begin{array}{r} 46 \\ +37 \\ \hline \end{array}$
10) $\begin{array}{r} 39 \\ +52 \\ \hline \end{array}$
11) $\begin{array}{r} 64 \\ +17 \\ \hline \end{array}$
12) $\begin{array}{r} 25 \\ +64 \\ \hline \end{array}$
13) $\begin{array}{r} 54 \\ +29 \\ \hline \end{array}$
14) $\begin{array}{r} 18 \\ +35 \\ \hline \end{array}$
15) $\begin{array}{r} 62 \\ +28 \\ \hline \end{array}$
16) $\begin{array}{r} 15 \\ +37 \\ \hline \end{array}$

Remember that when the whole numbers are added, all places of the same value must be kept in the same column.

EXAMPLE

Read the **horizontal** problem. Write the problem in **vertical** form.

Add 135 + 1,829 + 42.

$$\begin{array}{r} 135 \\ 1,829 \\ +\ \ \ 42 \\ \hline 2,006 \end{array}$$

Notice that 5, 9, and 2 are all in the ones place. They are all written in the same column.

Horizontal

Parallel to the horizon.

Vertical

Straight up and down.

Exercise C Write these problems in vertical columns as shown in the example. Then add.

1) 23 + 467 + 8
2) 98 + 29 + 435
3) 28 + 400 + 81
4) 731 + 42 + 100
5) 300 + 20 + 6
6) 9,213 + 84 + 172
7) 503 + 1,007 + 76
8) 1,551 + 2,003 + 8,711
9) 356 + 4,215 + 768
10) 3,005 + 23 + 36,011
11) 7 + 62 + 853 + 9,134
12) 10 + 235 + 10,062 + 3,412
13) 96 + 9 + 231 + 139 + 2,007
14) 1 + 11 + 1,101 + 2,011

Exercise D Find the sums.

1) 23, 693, 85
2) 353, 9, 72
3) 41, 603, 9143

4) 7, 703, 26, 4111
5) 31, 6211, 923
6) 9, 13, 831, 4111

7) 4, 35, 291, 6234
8) 52, 7, 206, 4110
9) 321, 6351, 8, 91

PROBLEM SOLVING

Exercise E Solve these word problems.

1) Baylor High School has 935 twelfth-grade students, 862 eleventh-grade students, and 1,036 tenth-grade students. What is the school's total enrollment?

2) Vaughn's family drove their economy car on their vacation. They used 15 gallons of gas on Monday, 16 gallons on Tuesday, and 18 gallons on Wednesday. How much gas did they use in all?

3) Konika's test grades during the first quarter are 75, 80, 92, 100, 83, 60, and 85. What is her test grade total for the first quarter?

4) Round each of the following numbers to the nearest hundred and then add: 2633, 493, 160, 55, 49.

5) A bowler bowls nine games. Her scores are 238, 93, 179, 217, 64, 278, 108, 76, and 240. What is her pin total?

Subtraction

The arithmetic operation of taking one number away from another to find the difference.

Subtraction and addition are opposite operations. The answer to a subtraction problem is the **difference**. You can check a subtraction fact by adding.

EXAMPLES

$9 - 4 = \blacksquare$

$$\begin{array}{r} 9 \\ -4 \\ \hline 5 \end{array}$$
Check:
$$\begin{array}{r} 5 \\ +4 \\ \hline 9 \end{array}$$

$17 - 5 = \blacksquare$

$$\begin{array}{r} 17 \\ -\ 5 \\ \hline 12 \end{array}$$
Check:
$$\begin{array}{r} 12 \\ +\ 5 \\ \hline 17 \end{array}$$

Difference

Answer to a subtraction problem.

Exercise A Subtract. Find the differences. Check your answers by adding.

1) $\begin{array}{r} 8 \\ -5 \\ \hline \end{array}$
2) $\begin{array}{r} 7 \\ -6 \\ \hline \end{array}$
3) $\begin{array}{r} 8 \\ -3 \\ \hline \end{array}$
4) $\begin{array}{r} 5 \\ -3 \\ \hline \end{array}$
5) $\begin{array}{r} 9 \\ -2 \\ \hline \end{array}$
6) $\begin{array}{r} 8 \\ -4 \\ \hline \end{array}$
7) $\begin{array}{r} 6 \\ -3 \\ \hline \end{array}$
8) $\begin{array}{r} 5 \\ -2 \\ \hline \end{array}$

9) $\begin{array}{r} 9 \\ -6 \\ \hline \end{array}$
10) $\begin{array}{r} 6 \\ -4 \\ \hline \end{array}$
11) $\begin{array}{r} 8 \\ -6 \\ \hline \end{array}$
12) $\begin{array}{r} 7 \\ -1 \\ \hline \end{array}$
13) $\begin{array}{r} 7 \\ -2 \\ \hline \end{array}$
14) $\begin{array}{r} 8 \\ -7 \\ \hline \end{array}$
15) $\begin{array}{r} 9 \\ -5 \\ \hline \end{array}$
16) $\begin{array}{r} 6 \\ -1 \\ \hline \end{array}$

17) $\begin{array}{r} 13 \\ -\ 6 \\ \hline \end{array}$
18) $\begin{array}{r} 15 \\ -\ 7 \\ \hline \end{array}$
19) $\begin{array}{r} 14 \\ -\ 4 \\ \hline \end{array}$
20) $\begin{array}{r} 12 \\ -\ 7 \\ \hline \end{array}$
21) $\begin{array}{r} 16 \\ -\ 8 \\ \hline \end{array}$
22) $\begin{array}{r} 14 \\ -\ 9 \\ \hline \end{array}$
23) $\begin{array}{r} 19 \\ -\ 5 \\ \hline \end{array}$
24) $\begin{array}{r} 15 \\ -\ 4 \\ \hline \end{array}$

25) $\begin{array}{r} 17 \\ -\ 6 \\ \hline \end{array}$
26) $\begin{array}{r} 15 \\ -\ 8 \\ \hline \end{array}$
27) $\begin{array}{r} 13 \\ -\ 8 \\ \hline \end{array}$
28) $\begin{array}{r} 16 \\ -\ 5 \\ \hline \end{array}$
29) $\begin{array}{r} 17 \\ -\ 5 \\ \hline \end{array}$
30) $\begin{array}{r} 17 \\ -\ 7 \\ \hline \end{array}$
31) $\begin{array}{r} 12 \\ -\ 8 \\ \hline \end{array}$
32) $\begin{array}{r} 12 \\ -\ 5 \\ \hline \end{array}$

33) $\begin{array}{r} 13 \\ -\ 5 \\ \hline \end{array}$
34) $\begin{array}{r} 14 \\ -\ 6 \\ \hline \end{array}$
35) $\begin{array}{r} 19 \\ -\ 7 \\ \hline \end{array}$
36) $\begin{array}{r} 12 \\ -\ 6 \\ \hline \end{array}$
37) $\begin{array}{r} 13 \\ -\ 3 \\ \hline \end{array}$
38) $\begin{array}{r} 15 \\ -\ 9 \\ \hline \end{array}$
39) $\begin{array}{r} 15 \\ -\ 6 \\ \hline \end{array}$
40) $\begin{array}{r} 12 \\ -\ 4 \\ \hline \end{array}$

41) $\begin{array}{r} 14 \\ -\ 3 \\ \hline \end{array}$
42) $\begin{array}{r} 16 \\ -\ 3 \\ \hline \end{array}$
43) $\begin{array}{r} 13 \\ -\ 4 \\ \hline \end{array}$
44) $\begin{array}{r} 14 \\ -\ 7 \\ \hline \end{array}$
45) $\begin{array}{r} 16 \\ -\ 4 \\ \hline \end{array}$
46) $\begin{array}{r} 15 \\ -\ 3 \\ \hline \end{array}$
47) $\begin{array}{r} 19 \\ -\ 3 \\ \hline \end{array}$
48) $\begin{array}{r} 18 \\ -\ 5 \\ \hline \end{array}$

Sometimes you must **rename** tens and ones to subtract.

EXAMPLE	45 − 8 = ■

```
  45
−  8
```

You cannot subtract 8 from 5. The ones must be renamed to 15.

```
45 = 4 tens + 5 ones          3 tens + 15 ones
− 8 =           8 ones   or            8 ones
                              3 tens +  7 ones = 37
```

Here is a shorter way to rename:

```
  3 15
  4̸5̸
−  8
  37
```

Exercise B   Subtract.

1) 23
    − 5

2) 34
    − 6

3) 48
    − 9

4) 32
    − 8

5) 21
    − 5

6) 37
    − 8

7) 36
    − 7

8) 25
    − 7

9) 31
    − 4

10) 46
    − 8

11) 52
    − 5

12) 63
    − 6

13) 26
    − 9

14) 42
    − 7

15) 55
    − 8

16) 72
    − 6

17) 67
    − 9

18) 35
    − 9

19) 36
    −18

20) 42
    −15

21) 53
    −26

22) 31
    −15

23) 63
    −27

24) 81
    −18

25) 37
    −28

26) 40
    −39

27) 54
    −36

28) 46
    −27

29) 55
    −38

30) 74
    −36

31) 90
    −63

32) 54
    −25

33) 75
    −66

34) 82
    −54

35) 80
    −52

36) 21
    −18

37) 48
    −39

38) 35
    −17

39) 67
    −19

40) 72
    −36

When whole numbers are subtracted, all places of the same value must be placed in the same column. It is necessary to rename in this example.

EXAMPLE 4,537 − 249 = ■

$$
\begin{array}{r}
^{4\ 12\ 17} \\
4,\ 5\ 3\ 7 \\
-\quad\ \ 2\ 4\ 9 \\
\hline
4,\ 2\ 8\ 8
\end{array}
$$

Exercise C Write these problems in vertical columns as shown in the example. Then subtract.

1) 2,803 − 532

2) 5,036 − 987

3) 7,260 − 463

4) 98,217 − 463

5) 40,317 − 8,234

6) 20,103 − 8,234

7) 12,665 − 2,666

8) 4,831 − 965

9) 20,398 − 8,643

10) 91,131 − 222

11) 1,200 − 268

12) 4,000 − 865

13) 29,143 − 9,269

14) 14,209 − 7,610

15) 25,311 − 3,167

16) 9,512 − 9,422

17) 23,716 − 1,875

18) 223,618 − 9,233

19) 112,130 − 16,832

20) 59,176 − 2,341

In subtraction problems, the number following "from" is always placed on top.

EXAMPLE From 4,627 subtract 968.

$$
\begin{array}{r}
^{3\ \ 15\ 11\ 17} \\
4,\ 6\ 2\ 7 \\
-\quad\ \ 9\ 6\ 8 \\
\hline
3,\ 6\ 5\ 9
\end{array}
$$

Exercise D   Write the problems in vertical columns and find the answers to these subtraction problems.

1) From 2,963 subtract 875.

2) From 39,002 subtract 8,723.

3) From 21,093 subtract 463.

4) From 4,238 subtract 829.

5) From 17,163 subtract 8,999.

6) Subtract 683 from 908.

7) Subtract 9,031 from 37,425.

8) Subtract 617 from 100,923.

9) Subtract 9,233 from 9,873.

10) Subtract 4,008 from 7,893.

PROBLEM SOLVING

Exercise E   Solve these word problems. Include the name of the units in your answer.

1) Tom weighed 136 pounds on Monday. At the end of two weeks of exercising, Tom weighs 128 pounds. How much weight did Tom lose?

2) Lakeside High School prints 15,000 raffle tickets. The twelfth grade sells 483 tickets. How many tickets are left?

3) Manuel, a plumber, has several pieces of pipe on his truck. He has a piece 6 feet long, a piece 7 feet long, one 9 feet long, and a piece 13 feet long. Find the total length of pipe in feet. If he uses 5 feet of pipe on a job, how many feet of pipe are left?

4) During inventory, the librarian finds that of the 2,482 books on the shelves, 482 are biographies, 726 are art books, and 534 are mysteries. The rest are fiction stories. How many books are fiction stories?

Multiplication

The arithmetic operation of adding a number to itself many times.

Addition and **multiplication** are similar. When you multiply a number, you simply add that number many times.

EXAMPLE

Addition:
$$
\begin{array}{r} 6 \\ 6 \\ +\,6 \\ \hline 18 \end{array} \Big\} \text{ three 6's}
$$

Multiplication: $\quad 3 \times 6 = 18$

$$
\begin{array}{r} 6 \text{ — factor} \\ \times\ 3 \text{ — factor} \\ \hline 18 \text{ — product} \end{array}
$$

Factors

Numbers that are multiplied in a multiplication problem.

Like addition, the order in which you multiply two **factors** does not change the **product**.

EXAMPLE

$$
\begin{array}{cc} 6 & 3 \\ \times 3 & \times 6 \\ \hline 18 & 18 \end{array}
$$

Product

Answer to a multiplication problem.

The product of any factor and zero is zero.

EXAMPLE

$$
\begin{array}{cc} 0 & 6 \\ \times 6 & \times 0 \\ \hline 0 & 0 \end{array}
$$

Exercise A   Multiply the following problems.

1) $\begin{array}{r}4\\ \times 5\end{array}$	**2)** $\begin{array}{r}6\\ \times 7\end{array}$	**3)** $\begin{array}{r}5\\ \times 6\end{array}$	**4)** $\begin{array}{r}3\\ \times 0\end{array}$	**5)** $\begin{array}{r}2\\ \times 8\end{array}$	**6)** $\begin{array}{r}4\\ \times 3\end{array}$	**7)** $\begin{array}{r}4\\ \times 2\end{array}$	**8)** $\begin{array}{r}2\\ \times 7\end{array}$	**9)** $\begin{array}{r}3\\ \times 6\end{array}$
10) $\begin{array}{r}7\\ \times 7\end{array}$	**11)** $\begin{array}{r}3\\ \times 5\end{array}$	**12)** $\begin{array}{r}6\\ \times 9\end{array}$	**13)** $\begin{array}{r}5\\ \times 9\end{array}$	**14)** $\begin{array}{r}0\\ \times 6\end{array}$	**15)** $\begin{array}{r}2\\ \times 5\end{array}$	**16)** $\begin{array}{r}4\\ \times 5\end{array}$	**17)** $\begin{array}{r}3\\ \times 4\end{array}$	**18)** $\begin{array}{r}7\\ \times 7\end{array}$
19) $\begin{array}{r}5\\ \times 8\end{array}$	**20)** $\begin{array}{r}9\\ \times 9\end{array}$	**21)** $\begin{array}{r}2\\ \times 4\end{array}$	**22)** $\begin{array}{r}5\\ \times 7\end{array}$	**23)** $\begin{array}{r}6\\ \times 4\end{array}$	**24)** $\begin{array}{r}5\\ \times 0\end{array}$	**25)** $\begin{array}{r}2\\ \times 9\end{array}$	**26)** $\begin{array}{r}3\\ \times 5\end{array}$	**27)** $\begin{array}{r}9\\ \times 5\end{array}$
28) $\begin{array}{r}8\\ \times 0\end{array}$	**29)** $\begin{array}{r}2\\ \times 3\end{array}$	**30)** $\begin{array}{r}6\\ \times 6\end{array}$	**31)** $\begin{array}{r}5\\ \times 1\end{array}$	**32)** $\begin{array}{r}6\\ \times 2\end{array}$	**33)** $\begin{array}{r}7\\ \times 3\end{array}$	**34)** $\begin{array}{r}8\\ \times 4\end{array}$	**35)** $\begin{array}{r}4\\ \times 9\end{array}$	**36)** $\begin{array}{r}3\\ \times 7\end{array}$

Exercise B   Practice your skills with multiplication.

1) 23 × 3	**2)** 42 × 4	**3)** 31 × 7	**4)** 73 × 3	**5)** 82 × 4	**6)** 61 ×8	**7)** 54 × 0	**8)** 70 × 7

9) 63 × 2	**10)** 52 × 3	**11)** 61 ×3	**12)** 72 × 4	**13)** 81 × 8	**14)** 63 × 3	**15)** 64 × 2	**16)** 64 × 1

17) 46 × 1	**18)** 32 × 4	**19)** 42 × 3	**20)** 51 × 7	**21)** 90 × 9	**22)** 84 × 0	**23)** 72 × 3	**24)** 81 × 7

25) 44 × 2	**26)** 53 × 3	**27)** 23 × 1	**28)** 41 ×9	**29)** 50 ×7	**30)** 61 ×6	**31)** 62 ×4	**32)** 85 ×0

When the product of the ones is greater than 9, you must rename the tens and ones. In the following example, notice that 48 ones were renamed as 4 tens and 8 ones. The 4 tens were added to the tens column.

EXAMPLE $36 \times 8 = \blacksquare$

$$36 = \qquad 3 \text{ tens and } 6 \text{ ones}$$
$$\times\ 8 = \times \underline{\qquad\qquad 8 \text{ ones}}$$
$$24 \text{ tens and } 48 \text{ ones } =$$
$$28 \text{ tens and } 8 \text{ ones } = 288$$

```
     36
  ×   8
     48   8 × 6  =   48 ⎫
  +240   8 × 30 = 240 ⎬ These products are added.
     288          288 ⎭
```

Here is a shorter way to multiply with renaming.

Step 1		**Step 2**	
	4		4
$8 \times 6 = 48$	36	$8 \times 3 = 24$	36
	× 8	and	× 8
	8	$24 + 4 = 28$	288

Exercise C Practice multiplying with renaming.

1) 34	**2)** 45	**3)** 67	**4)** 58	**5)** 79	**6)** 53	**7)** 62	**8)** 92
× 6	× 7	× 4	× 3	× 6	× 7	× 3	× 8

9) 64	**10)** 86	**11)** 49	**12)** 63	**13)** 47	**14)** 83	**15)** 24	**16)** 39
× 7	× 0	× 1	× 5	× 8	× 5	× 9	× 3

17) 64	**18)** 75	**19)** 75	**20)** 95	**21)** 48	**22)** 69	**23)** 57	**24)** 37
× 6	× 0	× 8	× 9	× 1	× 6	× 4	× 2

Sometimes you must multiply by a factor that contains two or more digits. Then you have to write **partial products**. The partial products must be written in the correct columns before they are added.

> ***Partial products***
>
> *Answers obtained by multiplying a factor by a digit in the other factor.*

EXAMPLE   53 × 32 = ■

Step 1
```
   53
 × 32
  106
```

Step 2
```
   53
 × 32
  106   partial product
 +159   partial product
```

In Step 1, you multiply by the 2 in 32. You write the first digit of the partial product in the *ones* place. The first digit is 6. 6 is written directly below the 2.

In Step 2, you multiply by the 3 in 32. You write the first digit of the partial product in the *tens* place. The first digit is 9. 9 is written below the first partial product and in the same column as the 3.

Step 3
```
    53
  × 32
   106 ⎫
 + 159 ⎬  Add these partial products.
 1,696    product
```

Exercise D   Multiply the following problems.

1) 45 **2)** 56 **3)** 47 **4)** 87 **5)** 35 **6)** 97 **7)** 75 **8)** 90
   ×57   ×45   ×90   ×54   ×34   ×63   ×21   ×51

9) 66 **10)** 83 **11)** 99 **12)** 75 **13)** 67 **14)** 34 **15)** 23 **16)** 75
   ×51   ×38   ×51   ×50   ×45   ×34   ×75   ×37

17) 40 **18)** 45 **19)** 63 **20)** 72 **21)** 83 **22)** 94 **23)** 77 **24)** 65
    ×66   ×74   ×34   ×45   ×56   ×67   ×85   ×91

Any number times zeros equals zero. When zero is part of a
factor, follow these steps.

EXAMPLES $26 \times 0 = 0$ $26 \times 30 = $ ■

Step 1   26   Multiply by 0.
             ×30   Write one 0 in the product below the 0
               0   you multiplied by.

Step 2   26   Multiply by the 3.
            × 30   Write the first digit of the product under 3.
             780

           35   56   75   787   567
         × 50   × 70   × 80   ×   10   × 100
          1,750   3,920   6,000   7,870   56,700

Rules   When you multiply a number by 10, write the number. Then write a
           zero at the end. $38 \times 10 = 380$

           When you multiply a number by 100, write the number. Then write two
           zeros at the end. $84 \times 100 = 8,400$

           When you multiply a number by 1,000, write the number, and write
           three zeros at the end. $23 \times 1,000 = 23,000$

Exercise E   Practice multiplying with zeros.

1) 45 **2)** 56 **3)** 86 **4)** 94 **5)** 35 **6)** 86 **7)** 75 **8)** 44
   ×40   ×50   ×70   ×40   ×30   ×10   ×70   ×40

9) 45 **10)** 56 **11)** 33 **12)** 675 **13)** 745 **14)** 455 **15)** 677 **16)** 897
   ×10   ×10   ×10   ×100   ×100   ×100   ×100   ×100

Multiplying With a 3-Digit Factor   When you multiply
whole numbers, you have to keep the digits in the partial
products lined up in the proper columns. The first digit of the
first partial product goes in the ones column. The first digit of
the second partial product goes in the tens column, one space
to the left. The first digit of the third partial product goes in the
hundreds column, two spaces to the left.

EXAMPLE $503 \times 137 = \blacksquare$

$$
\begin{array}{r}
503 \\
\times \quad 137 \\
\hline
3\ 521 \\
15\ 09 \\
+50\ 3 \\
\hline
68,911
\end{array}
$$

503 / 137 } factors

3 521 / 15 09 / +50 3 } partial products

68,911   product

Exercise F   Rewrite the following multiplication problems in
vertical form. Then multiply.

1) 741×16

2) 358×72

3) 539×41

4) 222×22

5) 465×55

6) 902×36

7) $1,103 \times 112$

8) $6,101 \times 270$

9) $3,817 \times 311$

10) $4,831 \times 717$

11) $9,613 \times 831$

12) $4,018 \times 763$

13) $8,106 \times 4,102$

14) $6,313 \times 7,011$

15) $1,202 \times 4,011$

16) $2,963 \times 6,291$

17) 237×462

18) 981×373

19) 425×631

20) 137×355

21) 239×414

22) 731×262

23) $5,821 \times 135$

24) $6,345 \times 217$

Exercise G Find the product of each pair of numbers.

1) 23 and 67

2) 854 and 68

3) 403 and 42

4) 679 and 73

5) 703 and 261

6) 785 and 362

7) 1,235 and 69

8) 6,304 and 390

9) 4,107 and 627

10) 8,931 and 3,007

11) 6,707 and 4,823

12) 4,113 and 6,305

13) 5,077 and 4,063

14) 2,011 and 3,579

15) 8,963 and 4,934

16) 5,169 and 4,551

Exercise H Round each factor to the nearest hundreds place. Then multiply.

1) 7,382
× 401

2) 4,600
× 2,030

3) 2,991
× 233

4) 20,909
× 2,016

5) 9,261
× 784

6) 40,101
× 30,102

PROBLEM SOLVING

Exercise I Find the answers to these word problems. Include the units in your answer.

1) Jennifer saves $13 a week. There are 52 weeks in a year. How much will she save in one year?

2) Mr. Tanaka's new car gets 52 miles on one gallon of gas. How many miles will he get from 260 gallons?

3) Nadine is figuring out the amount of money collected from ticket sales for the drama club's play. They sold 248 $3 tickets and 506 $2 tickets. What is the total amount of money they collected?

4) Each package of school duplicating paper contains 500 sheets of paper. How many sheets of paper are contained in 17 packages of paper?

5) Carlos makes $35 a week from his part-time job after school. How much money will he make over a 52-week period?

6) Laura's cat has five kittens. Each kitten eats 3 ounces of kitten food per day. How many ounces of food do the five kittens eat in 7 days?

Dividend

A number that is divided.

Division

The arithmetic operation that finds how many times a number is contained in another number.

Divisor

Number by which you are dividing.

Quotient

Answer in a division problem.

Division is the opposite of multiplication. The **dividend** is the number being divided. You may check division by multiplying the **quotient** by the **divisor**.

EXAMPLE $48 \div 6 = \blacksquare$

$$\begin{array}{r} 8 \text{ — quotient} \\ \text{divisor — } 6\overline{)48} \text{ — dividend} \end{array}$$

Check
$$\begin{array}{r} 8 \text{ — quotient} \\ \times\ 6 \text{ — divisor} \\ \hline 48 \text{ — dividend} \end{array}$$

Exercise A   Practice your skills with division facts.

1) $4\overline{)36}$

2) $2\overline{)14}$

3) $5\overline{)10}$

4) $4\overline{)16}$

5) $9\overline{)54}$

6) $4\overline{)32}$

7) $4\overline{)20}$

8) $7\overline{)14}$

9) $6\overline{)36}$

10) $2\overline{)6}$

11) $2\overline{)12}$

12) $8\overline{)16}$

13) $9\overline{)45}$

14) $5\overline{)15}$

15) $7\overline{)42}$

16) $9\overline{)81}$

17) $5\overline{)35}$

18) $5\overline{)30}$

19) $6\overline{)18}$

20) $4\overline{)20}$

21) $6\overline{)30}$

22) $8\overline{)48}$

23) $2\overline{)16}$

24) $7\overline{)49}$

25) $2\overline{)10}$

26) $8\overline{)64}$

27) $7\overline{)56}$

28) $7\overline{)21}$

29) $6\overline{)48}$

30) $3\overline{)18}$

31) $3\overline{)21}$

32) $5\overline{)25}$

33) $4\overline{)12}$

34) $3\overline{)6}$

35) $9\overline{)63}$

36) $8\overline{)40}$

37) $9\overline{)27}$

38) $2\overline{)8}$

39) $7\overline{)35}$

40) $4\overline{)24}$

41) $8\overline{)32}$

42) $3\overline{)27}$

43) $4\overline{)8}$

44) $5\overline{)40}$

45) $8\overline{)72}$

When you divide, place the digits correctly in the quotient.

EXAMPLES   138 ÷ 6 = ■

Step 1   The 2 is written above the 3 because the 6
         divides into 13.
Step 2   2 × 6 = 12. 12 is subtracted from 13.
Step 3   The 8 in the dividend is brought down and
         written next to the 1.
Step 4   6 divides into 18 three times. A 3 is placed in the
         quotient above the 8. 3 × 6 = 18. 18 is
         subtracted from 18. The remainder is 0.

Step 1   Step 2   Step 3   Step 4

     2   2   2   23
6) 138   6) 138   6) 138   6) 138
                   −12   −12   −12
                     1   18   18
                                                      −18
                                                        0

          432 ÷ 12 = ■

Step 1   Step 2   Step 3   Step 4

      3   3   3   36
12) 432   12) 432   12) 432   12) 432
                   −36   −36   −36
                     7   72   72
                                                      −72
                                                        0

Exercise B   Divide these problems.

1) 8) 568   **4)** 9) 108   **7)** 5) 165   **10)** 6) 258   **13)** 4) 108

2) 4) 52   **5)** 6) 126   **8)** 8) 248   **11)** 6) 108   **14)** 7) 322

3) 9) 207   **6)** 5) 85   **9)** 4) 248   **12)** 3) 282   **15)** 8) 504

Division With Remainders   Often, division problems have a **remainder**. Write the remainder after the quotient. Check the division by multiplying. Then add the remainder to the product.

Remainder
Amount left over when dividing.

EXAMPLES $324 \div 7 = \blacksquare$

```
    46 r 2
7 ) 324
   -28
    44
   -42
     2 remainder
```

Check
```
    46  quotient
×    7  divisor
   322
 +   2  remainder
   324  dividend
```

$157 \div 4 = \blacksquare$

```
    39 r 1
4 ) 157
   -12
    37
   -36
     1
```

Check
```
    39
×    4
   156
 +   1
   157
```

Exercise C   Divide and check your answers by multiplying.

1) $8) \overline{408}$ 9) $4) \overline{173}$ 17) $9) \overline{253}$ 25) $6) \overline{259}$

2) $5) \overline{338}$ 10) $2) \overline{369}$ 18) $7) \overline{278}$ 26) $6) \overline{435}$

3) $6) \overline{369}$ 11) $5) \overline{306}$ 19) $7) \overline{586}$ 27) $7) \overline{529}$

4) $6) \overline{228}$ 12) $9) \overline{888}$ 20) $8) \overline{508}$ 28) $8) \overline{419}$

5) $4) \overline{213}$ 13) $4) \overline{461}$ 21) $9) \overline{568}$ 29) $5) \overline{197}$

6) $6) \overline{837}$ 14) $7) \overline{298}$ 22) $7) \overline{268}$ 30) $7) \overline{598}$

7) $6) \overline{178}$ 15) $6) \overline{148}$ 23) $2) \overline{917}$ 31) $8) \overline{439}$

8) $7) \overline{376}$ 16) $8) \overline{651}$ 24) $9) \overline{699}$ 32) $7) \overline{449}$

Division of Numbers That Have Zeros

When you divide numbers that contain zeros, be sure that you keep your columns straight. Otherwise, you may leave a necessary zero out of the quotient.

EXAMPLE $2,080 \div 13 = \blacksquare$

$$
\begin{array}{r} 1 \\ 13\overline{)2,080} \\ -13 \\ \hline 7 \end{array}
\qquad
\begin{array}{r} 16 \\ 13\overline{)2,080} \\ -13 \\ \hline 78 \end{array}
\qquad
\begin{array}{r} 160 \\ 13\overline{)2,080} \\ -13 \\ \hline 78 \\ -78 \\ \hline 0 \end{array}
$$

Exercise D   Divide and show your work.

1) $4,550 \div 7$

2) $1,260 \div 3$

3) $27,720 \div 9$

4) $3,080 \div 7$

5) $1,600 \div 8$

6) $2,760 \div 23$

7) $21,730 \div 53$

8) $12,880 \div 46$

9) $2,520 \div 63$

10) $13,020 \div 42$

11) $27,200 \div 85$

12) $7,140 \div 17$

13) $14,300 \div 22$

14) $28,080 \div 72$

15) $8,010 \div 89$

16) $7,560 \div 63$

17) $9,690 \div 57$

18) $15,410 \div 23$

19) $17,220 \div 14$

20) $28,290 \div 41$

Keep your columns straight when you are dividing. This will help you write zeros in their proper place.

EXAMPLE $1,484 \div 14 = \blacksquare$

Step 1	$14 \div 14$ is 1. Write the 1 above the 4 in the quotient.	$\begin{array}{r} 1 \\ 14\overline{)1,484} \\ -14 \end{array}$
Step 2	The 8 is brought down. $8 \div 14$ is less than 1. Write a zero above the 8.	$\begin{array}{r} 10 \\ 14\overline{)1,484} \\ -14 \\ \hline 8 \end{array}$
Step 3	Then the 4 is brought down and written next to 8. Now $84 \div 14 = 6$. Write the 6 above the 4.	$\begin{array}{r} 106 \\ 14\overline{)1,484} \\ -14 \\ \hline 84 \\ -84 \end{array}$

Exercise E Divide and show your work.

1) $1,734 \div 17$ **6)** $3,366 \div 11$ **11)** $25,323 \div 23$

2) $4,466 \div 22$ **7)** $15,238 \div 19$ **12)** $44,142 \div 21$

3) $8,016 \div 16$ **8)** $21,624 \div 24$ **13)** $66,429 \div 33$

4) $13,938 \div 23$ **9)** $32,246 \div 46$ **14)** $16,032 \div 16$

5) $4,066 \div 38$ **10)** $25,888 \div 32$ **15)** $5,720 \div 55$

Exercise F Divide and show your work.

1) $26\overline{)5,278}$ **6)** $41\overline{)82,451}$ **11)** $13\overline{)40,391}$ **16)** $16\overline{)36,640}$

2) $35\overline{)23,100}$ **7)** $60\overline{)66,180}$ **12)** $28\overline{)12,320}$ **17)** $20\overline{)16,160}$

3) $39\overline{)5,850}$ **8)** $35\overline{)70,105}$ **13)** $32\overline{)29,056}$ **18)** $34\overline{)30,804}$

4) $89\overline{)10,680}$ **9)** $28\overline{)10,640}$ **14)** $57\overline{)96,957}$ **19)** $52\overline{)34,840}$

5) $29\overline{)14,674}$ **10)** $31\overline{)62,341}$ **15)** $28\overline{)64,568}$ **20)** $40\overline{)9,200}$

Exercise G   Solve these word problems.

1) Yuneng has a job after school. He earned $868 over a 14-week period. What is Yuneng's average weekly salary?

2) On Saturday, Jamal works with his father at the flour mill. They load 5,580 pounds of flour. If each bag of flour weighs 45 pounds, how many bags are loaded?

3) Ada's car gets 23 miles on a gallon of gas. How many gallons will she use to take a 4,715-mile trip?

4) Thumbtacks are sold on cards of 48 tacks each. How many cards must be bought if you need 1,104 tacks?

The quotient (answer) of a division problem may not always be a whole number. When this occurs, the remainder may be written as a fraction. The remainder is written over the divisor.

EXAMPLES

$$27\frac{8}{23} \quad \frac{\text{remainder}}{\text{divisor}}$$

$$\begin{array}{r} 23\overline{)629} \\ -46 \\ \hline 169 \\ -161 \\ \hline 8 \end{array}$$

$$250\frac{22}{38} \quad \frac{\text{remainder}}{\text{divisor}}$$

$$\begin{array}{r} 38\overline{)9,522} \\ -7\,6 \\ \hline 1\,92 \\ -1\,90 \\ \hline 22 \end{array}$$

Exercise H   Divide and write any remainders as fractions.

1) $35 \overline{)742}$

2) $11 \overline{)483}$

3) $63 \overline{)415}$

4) $39 \overline{)563}$

5) $91 \overline{)458}$

6) $19 \overline{)3,839}$

7) $22 \overline{)4,144}$

8) $9 \overline{)63,631}$

9) $38 \overline{)7,879}$

10) $45 \overline{)9,093}$

11) $16 \overline{)4,801}$

12) $23 \overline{)3,020}$

13) $18 \overline{)19,111}$

14) $23 \overline{)6,606}$

15) $51 \overline{)3,110}$

16) $18 \overline{)6,113}$

17) $24 \overline{)1,009}$

18) $47 \overline{)6,151}$

19) $31 \overline{)6,263}$

20) $8 \overline{)3,649}$

21) $17 \overline{)9,437}$

22) $29 \overline{)10,006}$

23) $26 \overline{)13,548}$

24) $36 \overline{)11,056}$

Exercise I   Divide and check by multiplying.

1) $29 \overline{)6,951}$

2) $69 \overline{)4,123}$

3) $12 \overline{)81,235}$

4) $8 \overline{)6,595}$

5) $12 \overline{)2,438}$

6) $33 \overline{)4,123}$

7) $28 \overline{)5,312}$

8) $36 \overline{)7,208}$

9) $42 \overline{)42,015}$

10) $125 \overline{)300}$

11) $8 \overline{)2,341}$

12) $6 \overline{)413}$

13) $17 \overline{)5,136}$

14) $10 \overline{)2,031}$

15) $81 \overline{)6,235}$

PROBLEM SOLVING

Exercise J   Solve these word problems.

1) Joe's new car averages 25 miles per gallon. How many gallons will he need to drive 455 miles?

2) Ms. Roland drives 650 miles on her vacation. If she drives for fourteen hours, how many miles will she average per hour?

3) Sandra paid $816 for heat last year. How much did she pay each month?

Average

The number obtained by dividing the sum of two or more quantities by the number of quantities.

The **average** of a set of numbers is found by adding all of the numbers and dividing their sum by the total number of numbers added.

EXAMPLE Jason's first-quarter test grades in mathematics are 65, 70, 75, 70, 80, and 90. What is Jason's average grade?

Step 1 Add

```
  65
  70
  75
  70
  80
+ 90
 450
```

Step 2 Divide

```
                              75 — average
number of scores —  6 ) 450  — sum
                            −42
                             30
                            −30
                              0
```

You may have a remainder when you divide. Write the remainder over the divisor to express the remainder as a fraction.

EXAMPLE Matt's mathematics test scores are 50, 52, 80, 60, 75, 90, and 75. What is Matt's average grade?

Step 1 Add

```
  50
  52
  80
  60
  75
  90
+ 75
 482
```

Step 2 Divide

```
         68 6/7  average
7 ) 482
   −42
    62
   −56
     6
```

Exercise A Find the average of each set of numbers.

1) 52, 55, 96, 87, 89, 75, 98, 97, 89

2) 95, 76, 53, 72, 63, 67, 94, 92, 50, 82, 75, 63

3) 37, 89, 71, 56, 92, 96, 83

4) 69, 76, 97, 81, 65, 74, 86

Exercise B   Solve these word problems about averages.

1) Gail's first-quarter grades are 85, 68, 90, and 75. Find her average.

2) Mr. Hiroshi receives these test scores in a course that he is taking: 83, 90, 77, 93, 67, and 70. What is Mr. Hiroshi's average in the course?

3) These temperatures are recorded in Seneca County: 75°, 75°, 82°, 63°, 91°, 72°, 60°, 59°. What is the average temperature?

4) In 18 basketball games, Sam scores 92 field goals (2 points each) and 60 foul shots (1 point each). What is the average number of points that Sam scored each game?

5) The five members of the twelfth-grade bowling team each bowl three games. Their scores are given in the chart below. Find the average for each member of the twelfth-grade team.

6) In the first football game of the season, the Fighting Irish gain 112 yards in 28 plays. What is the average number of yards gained on each play?

7) The airplane leaves Burtonville at 2 P.M. and arrives at Meadowfield, 1,095 miles away, at 5 P.M. Find the average speed of the airplane in miles per hour.

8) Anita's grades in her night school course are 93, 72, 85, 81, and 73. What is her average grade?

Team Member	Game 1	Game 2	Game 3
Nick	182	207	166
Eddie	201	106	200
Tony	145	203	102
Frank	225	198	207
Roberto	106	114	132

Calculator Practice

Use your calculator to find the average of a set of numbers. Remember to check each calculator entry to make sure the correct numbers have been entered. Round these averages to the nearest whole number.

EXAMPLE   Find the average of 236, 435, and 372.

Step 1   Add.
Press *236* + *435* + *372* =
The display reads *1043*.

Step 2   Divide by the total number of numbers.
Press ÷ *3* =
The display reads *347.66666*. Round to the nearest whole number. The average is 348.

Calculator Exercise   Use a calculator to find the average for each set of numbers.

1) 236, 414, 500, 502, 700, 308

2) 9063, 9060, 8021, 8913, 1006

3) 7000, 8000, 9000, 5000, 5555

4) 36200, 75120, 80602, 77314

5) 72000, 28000, 56100, 43900, 60105

6) 18, 26, 37, 17, 59, 49, 18

7) 412, 438, 319, 389, 372, 420, 422

8) 6, 54, 95, 83, 72, 61, 65, 64, 64

9) 17000, 22630, 29004, 19621, 20000

10) 5816, 5806, 5820, 5812, 5818, 2001

Exponent

Number that tells how many times another number is a factor.

Exponents make many math problems easier to write. The **exponent** tells how many times the same number is to be used as a factor.

EXAMPLES

4^2 means $4 \times 4 = 16$
4^3 means $4 \times 4 \times 4 = 64$
3^2 means $3 \times 3 = 9$
3^3 means $3 \times 3 \times 3 = 27$
3^4 means $3 \times 3 \times 3 \times 3 = 81$
5^3 means $5 \times 5 \times 5 = 125$
2^5 means $2 \times 2 \times 2 \times 2 \times 2 = 32$
12^3 means $12 \times 12 \times 12 = 1,728$

Exercise A Write each as a multiplication problem. Then find the product.

1) 3^2

2) 5^2

3) 6^3

4) 5^4

5) 8^2

6) 7^3

7) 8^3

8) 9^3

9) 6^2

10) 13^2

11) 3^5

12) 2^6

13) 8^4

14) 5^6

15) 4^4

16) 10^3

17) 10^4

18) 3^6

19) 11^2

20) 12^2

21) 15^2

22) 20^3

23) 17^2

24) 15^3

25) 30^2

26) 7^4

27) 16^2

28) 14^2

29) 50^3

30) 100^3

31) 1000^2

32) 60^3

33) 25^3

34) 40^2

35) 60^2

36) 2^7

37) 6^4

38) 5^5

39) 7^2

40) 2^8

When you have several operations in the same number statement, it is important that you perform the operations in the correct order. You should perform the operations in this order:

1. Evaluate any expressions with exponents.
2. Multiply and divide from left to right.
3. Add and subtract from left to right.

$2 + 4 \times 5$ is 22, not 30, because you multiply first before you add.

EXAMPLE

$$4^2 + 8 \times 3$$
$$= 16 + 24$$
$$= 40$$

$$2^3 + 6 \times 3 \div 2$$
$$= 8 + 18 \div 2$$
$$= 8 + 9$$
$$= 17$$

Exercise A Find the answers.

1) $12 - 18 \div 2$

2) $25 + 16 - 12 \div 2$

3) $5 + 6 \div 2 \times 3$

4) $2 + 8 \times 3 - 6 \times 2$

5) $16 - 9 \times 2 \div 3 + 3$

6) $25 - 4 \times 9 \div 2 + 12 \div 4 \times 2$

7) $12 + 6^2 \div 12 + 5 \times 2$

8) $2^4 + 2^2 \times 9 \div 6$

9) $8^2 - 4^2 \div 2 + 8^2 \div 2^2$

10) $9 - 6 \times 2 \div 2^2 - 6 \times 4 \div 8$

11) $8 + 5 \times 2 - 6 \times 3 \div 3^2 + 2$

Write the name of the place for each underlined digit.

1) 2<u>4</u>6
2) <u>5</u>103
3) 2019<u>6</u>
4) 8<u>4</u>1276

Write these numerals in words:

5) 25,602
6) 7,003,417
7) 32,001
8) 25,039,041

Round these whole numbers to the nearest . . .
Ten:

9) 351
10) 146

Thousand:

11) 31,056
12) 19,738

Solve these problems.

13) 26 + 209 + 3,512
14) 8 + 208 + 16
15) 1,803 − 736
16) From 90,123 subtract 8,341.
17) $3 \times 2^3 - 5 \times 2$
18) 457 × 203
19) 21,730 ÷ 53
20) 3,264 ÷ 16
21) 931 × 21
22) 2 + 5 × 4

Solve these word problems.

23) Miss Bonika drives 450 miles on her vacation. If she drives for 9 hours, how many miles does she average per hour?

24) Marshall pays $6.00 for a jar of coffee and $2.50 for a package of sugar. He also buys some cups for 85¢. If he gives the salesclerk $20.00, how much change will he receive?

25) Marina earns $75 a week from her part-time job. How much will she earn in 8 weeks?

Test Taking Tip Find out if you may use a calculator to check answers to problems.

Chapter 2

Number Theory

Many games and tricks that you can play with numbers are not what they seem. Rather, the fun of mathematics is often based upon the patterns that are found there. Art and architecture are pleasing to our eyes because of the patterns that the artist or designer uses. Patterns are only part of what is appealing about mathematics.

In Chapter 2, you will explore and discover some of the patterns in mathematics.

Goals for Learning

▶ To identify prime and composite numbers

▶ To factor numbers

▶ To find the least common multiple for pairs of numbers

▶ To find the greatest common factor for pairs of numbers

Whenever two or more numbers are multiplied together, each number is a factor of the product. The letter F represents factor.

$$1 \times 18 = 18 \qquad 2 \times 9 = 18 \qquad 3 \times 6 = 18$$

The factors of 18 are 1, 2, 3, 6, 9, and 18.

$$F_{18} = \{1, 2, 3, 6, 9, 18\}$$

You can find all of the factors of a number by trying the whole numbers in order. When the factors start to repeat, you have found all of them.

EXAMPLES

F_{16}
1 × 16
2 × 8
3 × No number works.
4 × 4 Factors repeat, so we stop.

$F_{16} = \{1, 2, 4, 8, 16\}$

F_{42}
1 × 42
2 × 21
3 × 14
4 × No number works.
5 × No number works.
6 × 7
7 × 6 Factors repeat, so we stop.

$F_{42} = \{1, 2, 3, 6, 7, 14, 21, 42\}$

Exercise A   Find the set of factors of each number.

1) F_{36}

2) F_{20}

3) F_{7}

4) F_{50}

5) F_{30}

6) F_{8}

7) F_{1}

8) F_{11}

9) F_{25}

10) F_{32}

11) F_{4}

12) F_{49}

13) F_{44}

14) F_{15}

15) F_{28}

16) F_{12}

17) F_{10}

18) F_{24}

19) F_{13}

20) F_{48}

Multiples	
The product of a given number and a whole number.	

The **multiples** of a number are the answers that you get when you multiply that number by the whole numbers.

EXAMPLE   The multiples of 6:

$$6 \times 0 \quad 6 \times 1 \quad 6 \times 2 \quad 6 \times 3 \quad 6 \times 4 \ldots$$
$$0 \qquad\quad 6 \qquad\quad 12 \qquad\quad 18 \qquad\quad 24 \ldots$$

Infinite
Without end or limit.

$M_6 = \{0, 6, 12, 18, \ldots\}$

The three dots show that the set of multiples continues forever. We say that the set is **infinite**.

Exercise A   Find the set of multiples of each number. Include 10 numbers in each set.

1) M_4

2) M_9

3) M_3

4) M_{12}

5) M_2

6) M_{10}

7) M_5

8) M_6

Calculator Practice   Use your calculator to find the set of multiples for any whole number.

EXAMPLE   Find the multiples of 17.
Write 0 because $17 \times 0 = 0$. Zero is the first multiple in each set.
Press $\boxed{+}$ 17 $\boxed{=}$
The display reads 17. Write 17 because $17 \times 1 = 17$.
Press $\boxed{=}$ $\boxed{=}$ $\boxed{=}$ $\boxed{=}$ $\boxed{=}$ $\boxed{=}$ $\boxed{=}$ and write the multiple after each $\boxed{=}$.
$M_{17} = \{0, 17, 34, 51, 68, 85, 102, 119, 136, 153, \ldots\}$

Calculator Exercise   Use a calculator to find the set of multiples of each number. List the first 10 numbers in each set.

1) M_{13}

2) M_{29}

3) M_{15}

4) M_7

5) M_{36}

6) M_{21}

Prime and Composite Numbers

Prime number

A number with only two factors.

If a number has exactly two factors, we say that it is a **prime number**. If a number has more than two factors, we say that it is a **composite number**.

Composite number

A number with more than two factors.

EXAMPLES   Look at the factors of these three numbers.

1

1×1 Factors repeat, so we stop.

$F_1 = \{1\}$

7	**10**
1×7	1×10
$2 \times$ No number works.	2×5
$3 \times$ No number works.	$3 \times$ No number works.
$4 \times$ No number works.	$4 \times$ No number works.
$5 \times$ No number works.	5×2 Factors repeat,
$6 \times$ No number works.	so we stop.
7×1 Factors repeat,	$F_{10} = \{1, 2, 5, 10\}$
so we stop.	
$F_7 = \{1, 7\}$	

$F_1 = \{1\}$ $F_7 = \{1, 7\}$ $F_{10} = \{1, 2, 5, 10\}$

7 is a prime number because it has exactly two factors.

10 is a composite number because it has more than two factors.

1 is neither a prime number nor a composite number because it has only one factor.

Exercise A   Find the set of factors of each number.

1) F_{12} 5) F_{18} 9) F_{21}

2) F_9 6) F_5 10) F_2

3) F_{13} 7) F_{20} 11) F_{15}

4) F_8 8) F_7 12) F_3

Exercise B   Answer the following questions.

1) Which of the numbers in Exercise A are prime numbers?

2) Which of the numbers in Exercise A are composite numbers?

The set of whole numbers is infinite. This set begins with zero and continues forever. You will use this set of whole numbers to find number patterns. This is the set of whole numbers:

$$\{0, 1, 2, 3, 4, 5, \ldots\}$$

Exercise A Follow the directions for each question.

1) The multiples of 2 are called even numbers. List the first six numbers in this set. Use three dots to show that the set is infinite.
Even numbers =

2) The rest of the whole numbers are called odd numbers. List the first six numbers in the set of odd numbers. Use three dots to show that the set is infinite.
Odd numbers =

3) If you begin with 0, and then add 1, and then add 2, to your answer, and then add 3 to your new answer, and continue in this manner, you get the set of triangular numbers. List the set of triangular numbers less than 100.
Triangular numbers = —, —, —, —, —, —, —, —, —, —,

—, —, —, —

4) If you multiply each whole number by itself, you get the set of square numbers. List the set of square numbers up to 100:
Square numbers = —, —, —, —, —, —, —, —, —, —, —

5) What set of numbers does each of these patterns suggests?
a) • •• ••• •••• etc.

b) • ∷ ∷∷ ∷∷∷ etc.

In the third century B.C., a Greek mathematician named Eratosthenes invented a way to find prime numbers. It is called the Sieve of Eratosthenes (ehr uh TAHS thuh neez). You may use his method to find the prime numbers less than 100. There are 25 of them. First, list the numbers from 1 to 100. Numbers that are not prime numbers are to be crossed out.

EXAMPLE   Follow these directions to make a Sieve of Eratosthenes and find prime numbers the way Eratosthenes did. Can you find all 25 of them? The numbers that you do not cross out are the prime numbers less than 100. The first two steps are done for you.

Step 1   1 is not a prime number, so it is crossed out.

Step 2   2 is the first prime number, so we circle it and cross out all of the other multiples of 2, like 4, 6, 8, 10, 12, . . .

Step 3   3 is a prime number. Circle it and cross out all of the other multiples of 3, like 6, 9, 12, . . .

Step 4   Circle 5 and cross out the other multiples of 5.

Step 5   Circle 7 and cross out the other multiples of 7.

1̸	②	3	4̸	5	6̸	7	8̸	9	1̸0̸
11	1̸2̸	13	1̸4̸	15	1̸6̸	17	1̸8̸	19	2̸0̸
21	2̸2̸	23	2̸4̸	25	2̸6̸	27	2̸8̸	29	3̸0̸
31	3̸2̸	33	3̸4̸	35	3̸6̸	37	3̸8̸	39	4̸0̸
41	4̸2̸	43	4̸4̸	45	4̸6̸	47	4̸8̸	49	5̸0̸
51	5̸2̸	53	5̸4̸	55	5̸6̸	57	5̸8̸	59	6̸0̸
61	6̸2̸	63	6̸4̸	65	6̸6̸	67	6̸8̸	69	7̸0̸
71	7̸2̸	73	7̸4̸	75	7̸6̸	77	7̸8̸	79	8̸0̸
81	8̸2̸	83	8̸4̸	85	8̸6̸	87	8̸8̸	89	9̸0̸
91	9̸2̸	93	9̸4̸	95	9̸6̸	97	9̸8̸	99	1̸0̸0̸

Exercise A   Answer these questions about prime numbers. Use your Sieve of Eratosthenes to help you.

1) List the prime numbers less than 100: 2, 3, . . . 97.

2) 3 and 5 are called twin primes because they are both prime numbers, and they are separated by only one number. What are the other seven twin primes less than 100?

3) What prime number is also an even number?

4) Why isn't the number 57 a prime number?

Mathematicians believe that any even number larger than 2 may be written as the sum of two prime numbers.

EXAMPLE	20 = 3 + 17, or 7 + 13
	However, we cannot use 5 + 15, because 15 is not a prime number.

Exercise B   Write each of these even numbers as the sum of two prime numbers. The first one has been done for you. Use your Sieve of Eratosthenes to help you.

1) 16 = 3 + 13	**5)** 84	**9)** 66
2) 44	**6)** 30	**10)** 42
3) 8	**7)** 52	**11)** 48
4) 28	**8)** 10	**12)** 80

Mathematicians also believe that any odd number larger than 5 may be written as the sum of three prime numbers.

Exercise C   Write each of these odd numbers as the sum of three prime numbers.

1) 17	**6)** 77
2) 25	**7)** 29
3) 59	**8)** 51
4) 41	**9)** 13
5) 21	**10)** 39

If one number divides into a second number and there is no remainder, then the second number is **divisible** by the first number.

Divisible

Able to be divided without a remainder.

EXAMPLE

$$
\begin{array}{r}
803 \\
7\overline{)5{,}621} \\
-56 \\
\hline
21 \\
-21 \\
\hline
0
\end{array}
$$

We can say that 5,621 is divisible by 7 because the remainder is zero.

Sometimes, you can tell if a number is divisible by another number by using a **divisibility** test instead of dividing by the number.

Divisibility

Able to be divided evenly.

EXAMPLE

Rule   A number is divisible by 2 if the digit in the ones place is an even number.

These are the multiples of 2:
0, 2, 4, 6, 8, 10, 12, 14, 16, 18, 20, . . .
They are all divisible by 2. Notice that the digit in the ones place is always 0, 2, 4, 6, or 8.

Exercise A   Use the divisibility test to tell which of these number are divisible by 2.

1) 16,287

2) 15,298

3) 6,750

4) 387,207

5) 4,393

Rule A number is divisible by 5 if the digit in the ones
place is 0 or 5.

Here are the multiples of 5:
0, 5, 10, 15, 20, 25, 30, 35, . . .

The digit in the ones place is always 0 or 5.

Exercise B Use the divisibility test to tell which of these
numbers are divisible by 5.

1) 48,295　　　　　　　　　**4)** 17,008
2) 50,553　　　　　　　　　**5)** 2,007
3) 160,280

The divisibility tests for 2 and 5 used the digit in the ones place
to tell if the number was divisible by 2 or 5. The divisibility test
for 3 uses all of the digits in the number.

EXAMPLE

Rule A number is divisible by 3 if the sum of its digits is
a multiple of 3.

Here are two large numbers: 21,474 and 3,051
These numbers are both divisible by 3.
Find the sum of the digits in each number.

21,474　　　　　　　　　　3,051
2 + 1 + 4 + 7 + 4 = 18　　　3 + 0 + 5 + 1 = 9

The sums of the digits are both multiples of 3.
M_3 = {0, 3, 6, 9, 12, 15, 18, . . .}

Exercise C Use the divisibility test to tell which of these
numbers are divisible by 3.

1) 48,296　　　　　　　　　**4)** 16,005
2) 52,872　　　　　　　　　**5)** 75,913
3) 30,782

Exercise D Use the divisibility tests for 2, 3, and 5. Fill in each space with *Yes* or *No* on a separate piece of paper.

	Number	Divisible by 2?	Divisible by 3?	Divisible by 5?
1)	128,295		Yes	
2)	486,394			
3)	308,460			
4)	268,465			
5)	758,484			
6)	254,751			
7)	396,730			

Any number less than 121 is a prime number if it is not divisible by 2, 3, 5, or 7. You may use the three divisibility tests and then try to divide the number by 7 to tell if a number less than 121 is a prime number or a composite number.

EXAMPLES
116
Divisible by 2.
Composite

95
Divisible by 5.
Composite

87
8 + 7 = 15
Divisible by 3.
Composite

91
Divisible by 7.
Composite

$$\begin{array}{r} 13 \\ 7\overline{)91} \\ -7 \\ \hline 21 \\ -21 \\ \hline 0 \end{array}$$

97
Not divisible by 2 or 5.
9 + 7 = 16
Not divisible by 3.

Not divisible by 7.
97 is a prime number.

$$\begin{array}{r} 13 \\ 7\overline{)97} \\ -7 \\ \hline 27 \\ -21 \\ \hline 6 \end{array}$$

Exercise E Tell whether each of these numbers is prime or composite. Use the divisibility tests and division by 7.

1) 115
2) 117
3) 107
4) 119

5) 120
6) 111
7) 101
8) 105

9) 106
10) 112
11) 103
12) 113

There are other divisibility tests that can be useful. These are the divisibility tests for 4, 9, and 10.

EXAMPLES

Rule A number is divisible by 4 if 4 divides evenly into the last two digits.
5,782 is not divisible by 4 because 4 does not divide evenly into 82.

Rule A number is divisible by 9 if the sum of the digits is a multiple of 9.
4,842 is divisible by 9 because 4 + 8 + 4 + 2 = 18, a multiple of 9.

Rule A number is divisible by 10 if the digit in the ones place is a zero.
57,680 is divisible by 10 because the ones digit is a zero.

Exercise F Use the divisibility tests for 4, 9, and 10. Fill in each space with *Yes* or *No* on a separate piece of paper.

	Number	Divisible by 4?	Divisible by 9?	Divisible by 10?
1)	45,666		Yes	
2)	65,320			
3)	73,980			
4)	84,350			
5)	32,436			
6)	88,650			
7)	52,324			

Prime Factorization

A number shown as the product of its prime numbers.

Every composite number can be written as the product of prime numbers. The expressed product of prime numbers is called the **prime factorization** of the number. One way to find the prime factorization of a number is to make a factor tree.

EXAMPLE

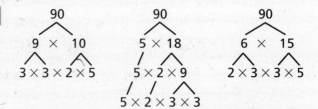

These three factor trees for the number 90 show that you will get the same factors in a different order if you begin with different factors of 90. You still have a 2, two 3's, and a 5 in the prime factorization of 90. You may think of other factor trees for 90 that all end with these same prime numbers.

Exercise A Use factor trees to do the prime factorization of the composite numbers below. Do not stop until the last row contains only prime numbers.

1) 40

2) 24

3) 15

4) 63

5) 54

6) 30

7) 28

8) 32

9) 16

10) 36

11) 42

12) 80

Another way to find the prime factorization of a composite number is to use short division and the divisibility tests. The only divisors to be used are 2, 3, 5, and 7. The prime factorization is all of the divisors and the last quotient.

EXAMPLE   Find the prime factorization of 420.

	7	Prime.	Stop.
	5) 35	Ends in 5.	Divide by 5.
	3) 105	1 + 0 + 5 = 6.	Divide by 3.
	2) 210	Even.	Divide by 2.
Begin here.	2) 420	Even.	Divide by 2.

$$420 = 2 \times 2 \times 3 \times 5 \times 7$$

Exercise B   Use division to find the prime factorization of these composite numbers.

1) 70

2) 96

3) 72

4) 27

5) 120

6) 84

7) 65

8) 91

9) 48

10) 51

11) 78

12) 110

13) 105

14) 112

15) 150

Least common multiple (LCM)

Smallest number that two numbers will divide.

There is always a *smallest* common multiple of two numbers. This number is called the **least common multiple (LCM)** of two numbers. Zero is a multiple of every number. This is because 0 times any number is always 0. If you look at the nonzero multiples of these numbers, you will see other common multiples.

EXAMPLES   You have found the multiples of 6 and 9:

M_6 = {0, 6, 12, 18, 24, 30, 36, 42, 48, 54, 60, . . .}
M_9 = {0, 9, 18, 27, 36, 45, 54, 63, 72, 81, 90, . . .}

These are the common multiples of 6 and 9: {18, 36, 54, 72, . . .}. There is always a least (smallest) common multiple of two numbers. The LCM (6, 9) = 18.

To find the LCM of two numbers, follow these steps:

Step 1   List the first few multiples of both numbers.

Step 2   Find the smallest nonzero number that is in both sets.

Step 3   If no nonzero number is in both sets, list more multiples of both numbers.

Find LCM (9, 15)
M_9 = {0, 9, 18, 27, 36, 45, . . .}
M_{15} = {0, 15, 30, 45, 60, . . .}
LCM (9, 15) = 45

Exercise A   Find the LCM of these pairs of numbers.

1) LCM (12, 18)

2) LCM (6, 8)

3) LCM (3, 9)

4) LCM (3, 7)

5) LCM (12, 15)

6) LCM (8, 20)

7) LCM (6, 15)

8) LCM (10, 8)

9) LCM (6, 12)

10) LCM (8, 9)

11) LCM (4, 6)

12) LCM (15, 18)

Common factors

For any two numbers, all the numbers that divide evenly into both numbers.

Greatest common factor (GCF)

Largest factor of two numbers.

You have listed all numbers that divide into a number evenly. These are the number's factors. Factors that occur for two numbers are **common factors**. The *largest* of these is the **greatest common factor** (GCF) of the two numbers.

EXAMPLE   List all of the factors of two numbers, 48 and 72.

48	72
1 × 48	1 × 72
2 × 24	2 × 36
3 × 16	3 × 24
4 × 12	4 × 18
5 × No number works.	5 × No number works.
6 × 8	6 × 12
7 × No number works.	7 × No number works.
8 × 6 Factors repeat, so we stop.	8 × 9
	9 × 8 Factors repeat, so we stop.

F_{48} = {1, 2, 3, 4, 6, 8, 12, 16, 24, 48}
F_{72} = {1, 2, 3, 4, 6, 8, 9, 12, 18, 24, 36, 72}

These two sets have numbers in common:
{1, 2, 3, 4, 6, 8, 12, 24}
GCF (48, 72) = 24

Exercise A   Find the GCF of these pairs of numbers.

1) GCF (10, 16)

2) GCF (16, 24)

3) GCF (4, 12)

4) GCF (10, 15)

5) GCF (8, 20)

6) GCF (7, 12)

7) GCF (18, 15)

8) GCF (16, 20)

9) GCF (8, 15)

10) GCF (12, 24)

11) GCF (4, 6)

12) GCF (16, 32)

13) GCF (16, 48)

14) GCF (2, 5)

Both the least common multiple and the greatest common factor of two numbers can be found by using the prime factorization of these two numbers.

EXAMPLE   Find the LCM of 12 and 40 by using prime factorization.

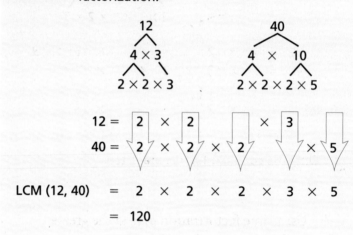

$$LCM\ (12,\ 40) = 2 \times 2 \times 2 \times 3 \times 5$$
$$= 120$$

Exercise A   Use prime factorization to find the least common multiple of these pairs of numbers.

1) LCM (8, 10)

2) LCM (6, 15)

3) LCM (10, 12)

4) LCM (6, 18)

5) LCM (15, 20)

6) LCM (8, 12)

7) LCM (12, 16)

8) LCM (8, 15)

9) LCM (8, 14)

10) LCM (6, 9)

11) LCM (15, 24)

12) LCM (10, 14)

13) LCM (6, 12)

14) LCM (9, 20)

The GCF of two numbers may also be found by using prime factorization. Use this method to find the GCF of 36 and 48. If there are no common factors, then the GCF is 1.

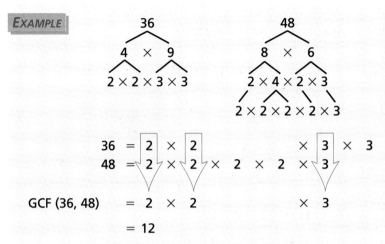

EXAMPLE

GCF (36, 48) = 2 × 2 × 3

= 12

Only the common factors are listed.

Exercise B   Use prime factorization to find the greatest common factor of these pairs of numbers.

1) GCF (24, 36)

2) GCF (15, 18)

3) GCF (4, 6)

4) GCF (30, 45)

5) GCF (14, 16)

6) GCF (24, 54)

7) GCF (26, 39)

8) GCF (12, 17)

9) GCF (12, 18)

10) GCF (24, 56)

11) GCF (36, 28)

12) GCF (15, 20)

13) GCF (24, 16)

14) GCF (50, 75)

List the set of all factors of these numbers:

1) F_{18}

2) F_{28}

3) F_{30}

List the set of multiples of these numbers:

4) M_8

5) M_{13}

6) M_{20}

Give the next three numbers in each pattern:

7) $\{0, 1, 3, 6, 10, \underline{\quad}, \underline{\quad}, \underline{\quad}, \ldots\}$

8) $\{1, 3, 5, 7, \underline{\quad}, \underline{\quad}, \underline{\quad}, \ldots\}$

9) $\{0, 1, 4, 9, \underline{\quad}, \underline{\quad}, \underline{\quad}, \ldots\}$

Answer the following questions:

10) Which of these are prime numbers?

| 45 | 37 | 16 | 53 |
| 117 | 2 | 57 | 19 |

11) Which of these are composite numbers?

| 4 | 57 | 31 | 59 |
| 9 | 49 | 101 | 27 |

12) Which number is divisible by 5?

2,431   4,307   2,503   1,760

13) Which number is divisible by 3?

2,871   4,303   9,286   4,009

Write these numbers as the sum of two prime numbers:

14) 42

15) 30

Give the prime factorization of these numbers:

16) 12

17) 24

18) 28

19) 36

Find the least common multiple (LCM) of each pair of numbers:

20) LCM (12, 16)

21) LCM (6, 8)

22) LCM (4, 12)

Find the greatest common factor (GCF) of each pair of numbers:

23) GCF (12, 16)

24) GCF (18, 25)

25) GCF (27, 36)

Test Taking Tip   When learning vocabulary, make flash cards with words and abbreviations on one side and definitions on the other side. Then use the flash cards in a game to test your vocabulary skills.

Fractions

D o you enjoy competing in sports? Think about the mathematics that are part of sports. Swimmers win races by fractions of a meter. Ice skaters win by fractions of a point, and runners win by fractions of a second. Sometimes we don't realize how often we use mathematics until we stop to think about it.

In Chapter 3, you will learn how to add, subtract, multiply, and divide fractions. Then, watch for the next time you use fractions while planning and enjoying your recreational activities.

Goals for Learning

▶ To compare fractions and determine which is more than or less than

▶ To simplify fractions

▶ To rename mixed numbers and improper fractions

▶ To compute with fractions and mixed numbers

Fraction

Part of a whole number.

This figure is divided into eight equal parts:

Numerator

The number of parts that are used; the number above the fraction bar.

Five of the eight parts are shaded. $\frac{5}{8}$ of the figure is shaded. We call $\frac{5}{8}$ a **fraction**. A fraction has a **numerator** and a **denominator**. The numerator tells how many parts are shaded. The denominator tells how many parts there are to the whole.

Denominator

The number of parts to the whole; the number below the fraction bar.

$$\frac{5}{8} \begin{array}{l} - \text{ Numerator} \\ - \text{ Denominator} \end{array}$$

Exercise A   Write a fraction to show what part of each figure is shaded.

1)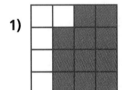

4)

7)

2)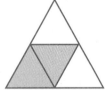

5)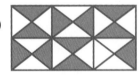

8)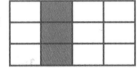

3)

6)

9)

You can tell which of two fractions is greater by using **cross products**.

EXAMPLE   Compare $\frac{2}{3}$ and $\frac{4}{5}$.

Step 1   10

$\frac{2}{3}$ $\frac{4}{5}$ The product of 2 and 5 is 10. $2 \times 5 = 10$

Step 2   10   12

$\frac{2}{3}$ $\frac{4}{5}$ The product of 3 and 4 is 12. $3 \times 4 = 12$

Step 3   10 < 12

$\frac{2}{3}$ $\frac{4}{5}$ 10 is **less than** 12, therefore,

Step 4 $\frac{2}{3} < \frac{4}{5}$ $\frac{2}{3}$ is less than $\frac{4}{5}$.

Exercise B   Tell whether the first fraction is less than ($<$) or greater than ($>$) the second fraction in each pair.

1) $\frac{2}{3}$ $\frac{3}{4}$ 8) $\frac{6}{8}$ $\frac{5}{6}$ 15) $\frac{5}{15}$ $\frac{2}{3}$ 22) $\frac{5}{17}$ $\frac{1}{3}$

2) $\frac{7}{8}$ $\frac{5}{6}$ 9) $\frac{2}{3}$ $\frac{4}{7}$ 16) $\frac{11}{15}$ $\frac{16}{17}$ 23) $\frac{6}{11}$ $\frac{1}{5}$

3) $\frac{2}{7}$ $\frac{3}{9}$ 10) $\frac{2}{9}$ $\frac{3}{10}$ 17) $\frac{7}{8}$ $\frac{14}{18}$ 24) $\frac{2}{13}$ $\frac{1}{6}$

4) $\frac{4}{7}$ $\frac{3}{8}$ 11) $\frac{5}{8}$ $\frac{4}{7}$ 18) $\frac{12}{17}$ $\frac{3}{4}$ 25) $\frac{18}{19}$ $\frac{17}{18}$

5) $\frac{3}{11}$ $\frac{4}{6}$ 12) $\frac{7}{8}$ $\frac{6}{7}$ 19) $\frac{2}{16}$ $\frac{1}{5}$ 26) $\frac{4}{30}$ $\frac{2}{8}$

6) $\frac{2}{5}$ $\frac{3}{7}$ 13) $\frac{5}{12}$ $\frac{2}{3}$ 20) $\frac{3}{18}$ $\frac{2}{3}$ 27) $\frac{5}{19}$ $\frac{2}{7}$

7) $\frac{5}{7}$ $\frac{4}{8}$ 14) $\frac{5}{6}$ $\frac{6}{7}$ 21) $\frac{5}{17}$ $\frac{3}{5}$ 28) $\frac{16}{17}$ $\frac{15}{16}$

You might need to express a fraction in higher terms before you can do an addition or a subtraction problem. You can raise a fraction to higher terms by multiplying the numerator and the denominator by the same number.

EXAMPLE Express $\frac{4}{5}$ as a fraction with a denominator of 30.

Step 1 $\quad \frac{4}{5} = \frac{\blacksquare}{30}$

Step 2 $\quad$ Divide 30 by 5. $\quad 30 \div 5 = 6$

Step 3 $\quad$ Multiply $\frac{4}{5}$ by $\frac{6}{6}$. $\quad \frac{4 \times 6}{5 \times 6} = \frac{24}{30}$

Step 4 $\quad \frac{4}{5} = \frac{24}{30}$

Exercise A Express these fractions in higher terms.

1) $\frac{2}{3} = \frac{\blacksquare}{6}$

2) $\frac{5}{7} = \frac{\blacksquare}{35}$

3) $\frac{7}{8} = \frac{\blacksquare}{32}$

4) $\frac{5}{6} = \frac{\blacksquare}{60}$

5) $\frac{11}{17} = \frac{\blacksquare}{51}$

6) $\frac{13}{14} = \frac{\blacksquare}{42}$

7) $\frac{5}{18} = \frac{\blacksquare}{72}$

8) $\frac{6}{13} = \frac{\blacksquare}{39}$

9) $\frac{17}{32} = \frac{\blacksquare}{64}$

10) $\frac{9}{32} = \frac{\blacksquare}{96}$

11) $\frac{11}{15} = \frac{\blacksquare}{45}$

12) $\frac{7}{9} = \frac{\blacksquare}{99}$

13) $\frac{11}{12} = \frac{\blacksquare}{36}$

14) $\frac{15}{23} = \frac{\blacksquare}{92}$

15) $\frac{12}{17} = \frac{\blacksquare}{34}$

16) $\frac{6}{19} = \frac{\blacksquare}{57}$

17) $\frac{11}{13} = \frac{\blacksquare}{52}$

18) $\frac{21}{32} = \frac{\blacksquare}{160}$

19) $\frac{9}{41} = \frac{\blacksquare}{123}$

20) $\frac{11}{33} = \frac{\blacksquare}{132}$

21) $\frac{10}{16} = \frac{\blacksquare}{48}$

22) $\frac{1}{7} = \frac{\blacksquare}{49}$

23) $\frac{1}{10} = \frac{\blacksquare}{100}$

24) $\frac{2}{8} = \frac{\blacksquare}{56}$

25) $\frac{19}{65} = \frac{\blacksquare}{130}$

26) $\frac{21}{70} = \frac{\blacksquare}{280}$

27) $\frac{221}{500} = \frac{\blacksquare}{4,000}$

28) $\frac{9}{375} = \frac{\blacksquare}{1,500}$

Simplest form

A fraction in which the numerator and denominator have no common factor greater than one.

When you are doing problems with fractions, you will often need to rename the answer in lowest terms. This is called **simplest form**. To **simplify** a fraction, divide the numerator and the denominator by the largest number that divides into both evenly.

EXAMPLES $\dfrac{14}{16} = \dfrac{14 \div 2}{16 \div 2} = \dfrac{7}{8}$ $\dfrac{36}{45} = \dfrac{36 \div 9}{45 \div 9} = \dfrac{4}{5}$

Simplify

To express in simplest form.

$\dfrac{17}{85} = \dfrac{17 \div 17}{85 \div 17} = \dfrac{1}{5}$ $\dfrac{20}{90} = \dfrac{20 \div 10}{90 \div 10} = \dfrac{2}{9}$

Exercise A   Rename these fractions in simplest form.

1) $\dfrac{4}{18}$ 9) $\dfrac{12}{42}$ 17) $\dfrac{27}{81}$ 25) $\dfrac{80}{100}$

2) $\dfrac{6}{18}$ 10) $\dfrac{16}{48}$ 18) $\dfrac{8}{16}$ 26) $\dfrac{28}{64}$

3) $\dfrac{8}{12}$ 11) $\dfrac{13}{39}$ 19) $\dfrac{8}{20}$ 27) $\dfrac{63}{72}$

4) $\dfrac{15}{20}$ 12) $\dfrac{26}{39}$ 20) $\dfrac{42}{60}$ 28) $\dfrac{16}{22}$

5) $\dfrac{16}{32}$ 13) $\dfrac{45}{50}$ 21) $\dfrac{38}{57}$ 29) $\dfrac{72}{81}$

6) $\dfrac{18}{24}$ 14) $\dfrac{28}{42}$ 22) $\dfrac{80}{120}$ 30) $\dfrac{75}{250}$

7) $\dfrac{24}{32}$ 15) $\dfrac{32}{64}$ 23) $\dfrac{12}{50}$ 31) $\dfrac{200}{3,000}$

8) $\dfrac{12}{15}$ 16) $\dfrac{42}{64}$ 24) $\dfrac{10}{16}$ 32) $\dfrac{55}{121}$

Exercise B   Rename these fractions in simplest form.

1) $\dfrac{16}{28}$ 4) $\dfrac{48}{56}$ 7) $\dfrac{14}{26}$ 10) $\dfrac{36}{90}$

2) $\dfrac{26}{52}$ 5) $\dfrac{52}{62}$ 8) $\dfrac{39}{42}$ 11) $\dfrac{44}{132}$

3) $\dfrac{18}{26}$ 6) $\dfrac{120}{130}$ 9) $\dfrac{78}{81}$ 12) $\dfrac{118}{220}$

Mixed number

Number composed of a whole number and a fraction.

When you multiply or divide with **mixed numbers,** you will need to change the mixed numbers to **improper fractions.** An improper fraction has a numerator that is greater than or equal to the denominator.

Improper fractions

Fractions whose numerators are equal to or greater than their denominators.

EXAMPLE   Write $3\frac{2}{5}$ as an improper fraction.

Step 1   Multiply the whole number by the denominator.
$3 \times 5 = 15$

Step 2   Add the numerator.
$15 + 2 = 17$

Step 3   Write the answer over the denominator. $\frac{17}{5}$

$$3\frac{2}{5} = \frac{17}{5} \quad \begin{array}{l} - \text{ New Numerator} \\ - \text{ Old Denominator} \end{array}$$

Exercise A   Rename these mixed numbers as improper fractions.

1) $2\frac{3}{4}$

2) $5\frac{1}{2}$

3) $6\frac{2}{3}$

4) $5\frac{4}{5}$

5) $6\frac{2}{7}$

6) $3\frac{2}{5}$

7) $8\frac{3}{7}$

8) $7\frac{3}{8}$

9) $11\frac{2}{3}$

10) $5\frac{6}{8}$

11) $4\frac{1}{3}$

12) $5\frac{2}{7}$

13) $9\frac{8}{9}$

14) $1\frac{2}{3}$

15) $2\frac{1}{3}$

16) $16\frac{5}{6}$

17) $13\frac{1}{3}$

18) $23\frac{2}{5}$

19) $6\frac{1}{9}$

20) $17\frac{1}{7}$

21) $2\frac{4}{5}$

22) $19\frac{1}{2}$

23) $13\frac{3}{4}$

24) $6\frac{2}{9}$

Exercise B   Rename these mixed numbers as improper fractions.

1) $7\frac{1}{6}$

2) $5\frac{2}{3}$

3) $8\frac{1}{9}$

4) $11\frac{1}{3}$

5) $10\frac{2}{5}$

6) $1\frac{1}{2}$

7) $18\frac{1}{2}$

8) $13\frac{2}{3}$

9) $25\frac{3}{4}$

10) $21\frac{2}{7}$

11) $66\frac{2}{3}$

12) $50\frac{1}{2}$

Calculator Practice

Use your calculator to help rename mixed numbers as improper fractions.

EXAMPLE   Rename $2\frac{4}{5}$ as an improper fraction. $2\frac{4}{5} = \frac{\blacksquare}{5}$

Step 1   Multiply the whole number by the denominator.
Press 2 $\times$ 5 $=$
The display reads 10.

Step 2   Add the product to the numerator.
Press $+$ 4 $=$

Step 3   Write the sum over the denominator.
$2\frac{4}{5} = \frac{14}{5}$

Calculator Exercise   Use a calculator to rename these mixed numbers as improper fractions.

1) $12\frac{2}{5}$

2) $33\frac{10}{11}$

3) $15\frac{6}{13}$

4) $22\frac{3}{4}$

5) $21\frac{5}{6}$

6) $31\frac{9}{11}$

7) $9\frac{11}{12}$

8) $12\frac{5}{13}$

9) $12\frac{7}{12}$

10) $13\frac{2}{7}$

11) $28\frac{12}{13}$

12) $18\frac{5}{21}$

When an answer to a problem is an improper fraction, you may need to rename it. To do this, divide the numerator by the denominator. Write any remainder over the divisor. Some improper fractions may equal whole numbers.

EXAMPLES   Rename $\frac{25}{4}$.   Rename $\frac{32}{8}$.

$$
\begin{array}{r}
6\frac{1}{4} \\
4\overline{)25} \\
-24 \\
\hline
1
\end{array}
\qquad
\begin{array}{r}
4 \\
8\overline{)32} \\
-32 \\
\hline
0
\end{array}
$$

Exercise A   Rename each improper fraction. Simplify when needed.

1) $\frac{18}{5}$ 8) $\frac{32}{6}$ 15) $\frac{61}{4}$ 22) $\frac{125}{5}$

2) $\frac{16}{6}$ 9) $\frac{48}{7}$ 16) $\frac{51}{8}$ 23) $\frac{128}{7}$

3) $\frac{17}{4}$ 10) $\frac{56}{6}$ 17) $\frac{102}{10}$ 24) $\frac{231}{9}$

4) $\frac{18}{2}$ 11) $\frac{47}{7}$ 18) $\frac{121}{11}$ 25) $\frac{162}{3}$

5) $\frac{19}{2}$ 12) $\frac{43}{6}$ 19) $\frac{99}{11}$ 26) $\frac{121}{20}$

6) $\frac{23}{4}$ 13) $\frac{21}{2}$ 20) $\frac{89}{2}$ 27) $\frac{235}{4}$

7) $\frac{42}{9}$ 14) $\frac{38}{2}$ 21) $\frac{79}{5}$

Exercise B   Rename these improper fractions as mixed numbers.

1) $\frac{18}{5}$ 4) $\frac{42}{3}$ 7) $\frac{32}{7}$ 10) $\frac{155}{10}$

2) $\frac{19}{2}$ 5) $\frac{38}{2}$ 8) $\frac{77}{10}$ 11) $\frac{75}{5}$

3) $\frac{23}{10}$ 6) $\frac{56}{12}$ 9) $\frac{81}{8}$ 12) $\frac{140}{80}$

Writing Mixed Numbers in Simplest Form

Often, the answers to fraction problems will be mixed numbers that are not in their simplest form. You will need to rename these mixed numbers in their simplest form, a whole number and a reduced proper fraction.

EXAMPLES $3\frac{2}{4} = 3 + \frac{2}{4} = 3 + \frac{1}{2} = 3\frac{1}{2}$

$5\frac{16}{8} = 5 + \frac{16}{8} = 5 + 2 = 7$

$4\frac{7}{6} = 4 + \frac{7}{6} = 4 + 1\frac{1}{6} = 5\frac{1}{6}$

$6\frac{12}{10} = 6 + \frac{12}{10} = 6 + 1\frac{2}{10} = 6 + 1\frac{1}{5} = 7\frac{1}{5}$

Exercise A Write these mixed numbers in their simplest form.

1) $6\frac{5}{15}$

2) $7\frac{6}{3}$

3) $8\frac{7}{14}$

4) $6\frac{15}{24}$

5) $9\frac{8}{6}$

6) $6\frac{4}{3}$

7) $11\frac{11}{22}$

8) $12\frac{16}{18}$

9) $17\frac{13}{10}$

10) $12\frac{8}{24}$

11) $23\frac{16}{48}$

12) $21\frac{24}{20}$

13) $19\frac{11}{33}$

14) $32\frac{5}{3}$

15) $42\frac{9}{7}$

16) $30\frac{24}{48}$

17) $52\frac{17}{51}$

18) $17\frac{18}{54}$

19) $44\frac{12}{72}$

20) $31\frac{36}{29}$

21) $19\frac{42}{7}$

22) $7\frac{36}{9}$

23) $10\frac{25}{6}$

24) $53\frac{17}{16}$

25) $36\frac{24}{96}$

26) $51\frac{12}{60}$

27) $33\frac{22}{26}$

28) $35\frac{17}{5}$

29) $41\frac{13}{13}$

30) $42\frac{26}{13}$

31) $10\frac{250}{1,000}$

32) $29\frac{45}{405}$

Exercise B Rename each mixed number in its simplest form.

1) $3\frac{7}{21}$

2) $6\frac{9}{8}$

3) $4\frac{4}{8}$

4) $8\frac{2}{6}$

5) $9\frac{7}{21}$

6) $6\frac{12}{4}$

7) $14\frac{15}{13}$

8) $13\frac{18}{38}$

9) $42\frac{18}{5}$

10) $12\frac{14}{10}$

11) $18\frac{20}{6}$

12) $14\frac{27}{12}$

Multiplying Fractions

You multiply fractions by multiplying the numerators together and then multiplying the denominators together.

EXAMPLES $\frac{2}{7} \times \frac{4}{5} = \blacksquare$

$\frac{2}{7} \times \frac{4}{5} = \frac{2 \times 4}{7 \times 5} = \frac{8}{35}$

$6 \times \frac{4}{7} = \blacksquare$

$6 \times \frac{4}{7} = \frac{6}{1} \times \frac{4}{7} = \frac{6 \times 4}{1 \times 7} = \frac{24}{7} = 3\frac{3}{7}$

Exercise A   Multiply. Write your answers in simplest form.

1) $\frac{2}{3} \times \frac{4}{5}$

2) $\frac{4}{7} \times \frac{3}{6}$

3) $\frac{2}{9} \times \frac{1}{2}$

4) $\frac{4}{7} \times \frac{2}{3}$

5) $\frac{6}{7} \times \frac{2}{5}$

6) $\frac{5}{9} \times \frac{1}{4}$

7) $\frac{5}{11} \times \frac{2}{3}$

8) $\frac{4}{5} \times \frac{7}{9}$

9) $\frac{5}{11} \times \frac{4}{6}$

10) $\frac{4}{13} \times \frac{2}{3}$

11) $\frac{6}{8} \times \frac{7}{8}$

12) $\frac{5}{16} \times \frac{8}{9}$

13) $\frac{1}{6} \times \frac{11}{12}$

14) $\frac{5}{11} \times 2$

15) $\frac{6}{13} \times 26$

16) $6 \times \frac{3}{5}$

17) $\frac{15}{16} \times \frac{6}{7}$

18) $\frac{11}{13} \times \frac{26}{33}$

19) $\frac{6}{7} \times 3$

20) $\frac{1}{3} \times 8$

21) $\frac{5}{18} \times \frac{9}{13}$

22) $\frac{7}{15} \times \frac{30}{42}$

23) $\frac{6}{7} \times \frac{5}{12}$

24) $9 \times \frac{7}{12}$

Often, you can simplify the problem before multiplying. See if numerators and the denominators have any common factors. If they do, divide both the numerator and the denominator by their common factor before you multiply.

EXAMPLE

$$\frac{9}{10} \times \frac{14}{15} = \blacksquare$$

Step 1 9 and 15 have a common factor, 3.
Divide 9 and 15 by 3.

$$\frac{\overset{3}{\cancel{9}}}{10} \times \frac{14}{\underset{5}{\cancel{15}}}$$

Step 2 10 and 14 have a common factor, 2.
Divide 10 and 14 by 2.

$$\frac{\overset{3}{\cancel{9}}}{\underset{5}{\cancel{10}}} \times \frac{\overset{7}{\cancel{14}}}{\underset{5}{\cancel{15}}}$$

Step 3 Multiply the numerators.
Multiply the denominators.

$$\frac{3 \times 7}{5 \times 5} = \frac{21}{25}$$

Sometimes the multiplication sign, $\times$, is replaced by the word *of*. Think of the word *of* as meaning "times." For example, one half of one half of a pizza is one-fourth pizza.

Exercise B Find the answers. Simplify the problem before multiplying, if you can.

1) $\frac{3}{5}$ of $\frac{7}{8}$

2) $\frac{5}{7}$ of $\frac{2}{7}$

3) $\frac{6}{7}$ of $\frac{5}{6}$

4) $\frac{5}{9}$ of $\frac{7}{8}$

5) $\frac{4}{15}$ of $\frac{5}{12}$

6) $\frac{4}{9}$ of $\frac{7}{12}$

7) $\frac{11}{12}$ of $\frac{4}{11}$

8) $\frac{6}{13}$ of $\frac{5}{12}$

9) $\frac{4}{13}$ of $\frac{5}{11}$

10) $\frac{6}{12}$ of $\frac{2}{12}$

11) $\frac{3}{7}$ of $\frac{1}{2}$

12) $\frac{3}{7}$ of $\frac{14}{15}$

13) $\frac{6}{18}$ of $\frac{36}{55}$

14) $\frac{3}{16}$ of $\frac{8}{9}$

15) $\frac{7}{10}$ of $\frac{5}{28}$

Before you multiply mixed numbers, change them to improper fractions. Then, multiply the numerators and the denominators. Next, write your answers in simplest form.

EXAMPLES

$$2\frac{3}{4} \times 1\frac{2}{3} = \blacksquare$$

$$2\frac{3}{4} \times 1\frac{2}{3} = \frac{11}{4} \times \frac{5}{3}$$

$$= \frac{55}{12} = 4\frac{7}{12}$$

$$3 \times 1\frac{5}{6} = \blacksquare$$

$$3 \times 1\frac{5}{6} = \frac{3}{1} \times \frac{11}{6}$$

$$= \frac{\overset{1}{\cancel{3}}}{1} \times \frac{11}{\underset{2}{\cancel{6}}}$$

$$= \frac{11}{2} = 5\frac{1}{2}$$

Exercise A Multiply. Write your answers in simplest form.

1) $1\frac{1}{2} \times 2\frac{3}{5}$

2) $2\frac{1}{6} \times \frac{2}{3}$

3) $4\frac{1}{3} \times \frac{1}{6}$

4) $4\frac{2}{7} \times 14$

5) $5\frac{1}{3} \times 2\frac{1}{2}$

6) $3\frac{2}{3} \times 5$

7) $\frac{15}{16} \times 2\frac{2}{5}$

8) $2\frac{1}{7} \times \frac{19}{30}$

9) $3\frac{5}{6} \times \frac{3}{8}$

10) $7\frac{2}{3} \times \frac{3}{4}$

11) $6\frac{3}{5} \times 2\frac{2}{9}$

12) $4\frac{9}{10} \times 1\frac{3}{7}$

13) $1\frac{1}{2} \times 1\frac{1}{3}$

14) $4\frac{3}{8} \times 2\frac{3}{7}$

15) $\frac{5}{6} \times 2\frac{3}{10}$

16) $\frac{1}{2} \times 3\frac{3}{7}$

17) $\frac{7}{8} \times 1\frac{3}{7}$

18) $5\frac{1}{5} \times 3\frac{1}{8}$

Exercise B   Find the answers. Write them in simplest form.

1) $\frac{5}{6}$ of $1\frac{1}{2}$

2) $\frac{4}{7}$ of $1\frac{1}{1}$

3) $3\frac{2}{3} \times 1\frac{1}{2}$

4) $\frac{3}{8}$ of $2\frac{1}{3}$

5) $\frac{3}{4}$ of $2\frac{1}{6}$

6) $2\frac{1}{3}$ of 5

7) $6 \times 1\frac{1}{3}$

8) $\frac{3}{5}$ of 9

9) $2\frac{3}{8} \times \frac{12}{19}$

10) $5\frac{2}{7} \times 1\frac{5}{37}$

11) $\frac{7}{8}$ of $3\frac{2}{7}$

12) $\frac{9}{19}$ of $4\frac{2}{9}$

13) $\frac{6}{19}$ of $6\frac{1}{3}$

14) $5\frac{4}{5} \times \frac{25}{29}$

PROBLEM SOLVING

Exercise C   Solve these word problems.

1) Jason wants to build 5 shelves, each measuring $3\frac{3}{4}$ feet long. How many feet of shelving board will he need?

2) If it takes $2\frac{1}{4}$ cups of flour to make a cake, then how much flour will you need to make $\frac{1}{2}$ of the recipe?

3) Shateel weighs 112 pounds. His sister, Alma, weighs $\frac{3}{4}$ as much. How much does Alma weigh?

4) Omar wants to fence his property. Each side of his square lot is $14\frac{1}{2}$ feet long. How much fencing does Omar need?

The easiest way to divide fractions is to invert the divisor and then multiply.

EXAMPLES $\dfrac{5}{7} \div \dfrac{4}{5} = \blacksquare$

The divisor is $\dfrac{4}{5}$. When you invert $\dfrac{4}{5}$, it becomes $\dfrac{5}{4}$.

$$\dfrac{5}{7} \div \dfrac{4}{5} = \dfrac{5}{7} \times \dfrac{5}{4}$$

$$= \dfrac{5 \times 5}{7 \times 4}$$

$$= \dfrac{25}{28}$$

$$\dfrac{3}{8} \div \dfrac{3}{5} = \blacksquare$$

$$\dfrac{3}{8} \div \dfrac{3}{5} = \dfrac{3}{8} \times \dfrac{5}{3}$$

$$= \dfrac{\overset{1}{\cancel{3}}}{8} \times \dfrac{5}{\underset{1}{\cancel{3}}}$$

$$= \dfrac{1 \times 5}{8 \times 1}$$

$$= \dfrac{5}{8}$$

Exercise A   Divide. Write your answers in simplest form.

1) $\dfrac{2}{7} \div \dfrac{5}{6}$

2) $\dfrac{3}{8} \div \dfrac{3}{4}$

3) $\dfrac{4}{7} \div \dfrac{5}{7}$

4) $\dfrac{2}{3} \div \dfrac{5}{6}$

5) $5 \div \dfrac{1}{6}$

6) $\dfrac{5}{6} \div \dfrac{5}{6}$

7) $\dfrac{5}{8} \div \dfrac{5}{6}$

8) $\dfrac{4}{7} \div \dfrac{2}{3}$

9) $\dfrac{5}{11} \div \dfrac{15}{22}$

10) $\dfrac{3}{13} \div \dfrac{7}{39}$

11) $\dfrac{8}{9} \div 4$

12) $\dfrac{6}{13} \div \dfrac{1}{26}$

13) $\dfrac{7}{8} \div \dfrac{3}{8}$

14) $\dfrac{3}{13} \div \dfrac{5}{6}$

15) $\dfrac{7}{15} \div \dfrac{14}{25}$

Exercise B   Find the answers. Write them in simplest form.

1) $\dfrac{6}{7} \div \dfrac{8}{9}$

2) $\dfrac{3}{5} \div \dfrac{5}{8}$

3) $\dfrac{7}{8} \div 4$

4) $\dfrac{7}{12} \div 7$

5) $6 \div \dfrac{5}{7}$

6) $12 \div \dfrac{6}{13}$

7) $9 \div \dfrac{9}{10}$

8) $\dfrac{4}{5} \div \dfrac{3}{5}$

9) $\dfrac{6}{11} \div \dfrac{3}{5}$

10) $\dfrac{7}{13} \div \dfrac{5}{13}$

11) $\dfrac{8}{9} \div \dfrac{4}{9}$

12) $\dfrac{4}{9} \div \dfrac{8}{9}$

13) $\dfrac{12}{14} \div \dfrac{24}{28}$

14) $\dfrac{5}{9} \div \dfrac{3}{7}$

15) $\dfrac{4}{7} \div \dfrac{2}{11}$

16) $\dfrac{5}{6} \div \dfrac{3}{13}$

17) $\dfrac{7}{9} \div \dfrac{1}{3}$

18) $\dfrac{4}{13} \div \dfrac{3}{26}$

19) $\dfrac{5}{12} \div \dfrac{25}{36}$

20) $\dfrac{9}{10} \div \dfrac{4}{5}$

21) $\dfrac{2}{3} \div \dfrac{2}{5}$

22) $\dfrac{2}{5} \div \dfrac{1}{5}$

23) $\dfrac{6}{11} \div \dfrac{5}{8}$

24) $\dfrac{5}{13} \div \dfrac{5}{16}$

25) $\dfrac{3}{11} \div \dfrac{9}{22}$

26) $\dfrac{3}{8} \div \dfrac{8}{3}$

27) $\dfrac{8}{12} \div \dfrac{8}{11}$

  PROBLEM SOLVING

Exercise C   Solve these word problems.

1) A group of home economics students needs to divide $\dfrac{3}{4}$ pound of sugar 4 ways. What fraction of a pound will each student get?

2) How many pieces of pipe can be cut from a 12-foot piece of pipe if each is to be $\dfrac{2}{3}$ of a foot long?

3) Gina can walk a mile in $\dfrac{1}{4}$ hour. At this rate, how far can she walk in 4 hours?

Lesson 10 Dividing Mixed Numbers

Invert
Change positions.

To divide mixed numbers, you first change the mixed numbers to improper fractions. Then, you **invert** the divisor and multiply.

EXAMPLE $3\frac{1}{2} \div 2\frac{1}{2} = \blacksquare$

$$3\frac{1}{2} \div 2\frac{1}{2} = \frac{7}{2} \div \frac{5}{2}$$

$$= \frac{7}{2} \times \frac{2}{5}$$

$$= \frac{7}{\cancel{2}} \times \frac{\cancel{2}}{5} = \frac{7 \times 1}{1 \times 5} = \frac{7}{5} = 1\frac{2}{5}$$

Exercise A Find the quotients. Write them in simplest form.

1) $2\frac{3}{4} \div \frac{5}{6}$

2) $1\frac{1}{3} \div \frac{1}{4}$

3) $\frac{2}{5} \div 1\frac{2}{5}$

4) $\frac{5}{7} \div 3\frac{1}{5}$

5) $2\frac{2}{7} \div 2\frac{2}{7}$

6) $4\frac{1}{5} \div 2\frac{3}{5}$

7) $7\frac{1}{2} \div 6\frac{2}{3}$

8) $6\frac{1}{2} \div \frac{1}{2}$

9) $1\frac{1}{5} \div 1\frac{2}{5}$

10) $1\frac{2}{3} \div 5$

11) $6 \div 1\frac{1}{5}$

12) $5\frac{2}{5} \div 1\frac{1}{5}$

PROBLEM SOLVING

Exercise B Solve these word problems.

1) Kim buys $3\frac{1}{3}$ pounds of potato salad for her birthday party. There are to be 20 people at the party. How much potato salad does each person get?

2) A mathematics class makes a giant turkey sandwich that measures $7\frac{1}{2}$ feet long. If 15 students share the sandwich equally, how long is each student's serving?

3) Jim loses $12\frac{1}{2}$ pounds over a 5-week period. What is his average weekly weight loss?

4) Anna needs $1\frac{2}{3}$ yards of fabric to make a dress. If she has $6\frac{2}{3}$ yards of fabric, then how many dresses can she make?

Like denominators

Having the same denominators.

Adding fractions and mixed numbers with **like denominators** is much like adding whole numbers. You add the whole numbers, add the numerators, and keep the same denominator.

EXAMPLES

$$1\frac{2}{7}$$
$$+2\frac{3}{7}$$
$$\overline{3\frac{5}{7}}$$

$$2\frac{4}{5}$$
$$+6\frac{3}{5}$$
$$\overline{8\frac{7}{5}} = 9\frac{2}{5}$$

Exercise A   Add. Write your answers in simplest form.

1) $2\frac{5}{8}$ $+1\frac{3}{8}$

6) $\frac{5}{18}$ $+\frac{7}{18}$

11) $\frac{7}{19}$ $+\frac{14}{19}$

16) $4\frac{17}{20}$ $+\frac{3}{20}$

2) $2\frac{5}{11}$ $+3\frac{4}{11}$

7) $\frac{9}{17}$ $+2\frac{8}{17}$

12) $\frac{7}{25}$ $+\frac{16}{25}$

17) $\frac{23}{40}$ $+\frac{7}{40}$

3) $2\frac{5}{16}$ $+5\frac{1}{16}$

8) $3\frac{9}{10}$ $+1\frac{3}{10}$

13) $\frac{13}{15}$ $+\frac{8}{15}$

18) $\frac{5}{6}$ $+\frac{5}{6}$

4) $3\frac{2}{19}$ $+4\frac{3}{19}$

9) $\frac{11}{16}$ $+\frac{3}{16}$

14) $\frac{9}{11}$ $+\frac{5}{11}$

19) $\frac{7}{11}$ $+\frac{9}{11}$

5) $1\frac{6}{7}$ $+\frac{2}{7}$

10) $5\frac{13}{16}$ $+6\frac{1}{16}$

15) $12\frac{11}{25}$ $+11\frac{9}{25}$

20) $6\frac{4}{15}$ $+2\frac{14}{15}$

Exercise B   Add. Write your answers in simplest form.

1) $3\frac{6}{13}$
    $+\ 4\frac{6}{13}$
    _____

2) $\frac{5}{12}$
    $+\ \frac{1}{12}$
    _____

3) $4\frac{7}{25}$
    $+\ \frac{21}{25}$
    _____

4) $\frac{7}{20}$
    $+\ \frac{13}{20}$
    _____

5) $2\frac{17}{21}$
    $+\ 6\frac{5}{21}$
    _____

6) $8\frac{15}{22}$
    $+\ \frac{3}{22}$
    _____

7) $\frac{11}{12}$
    $+\ \frac{5}{12}$
    _____

8) $4\frac{5}{17}$
    $+\ 9\frac{12}{17}$
    _____

9) $\frac{7}{15}$
    $+\ \frac{11}{15}$
    _____

10) $\frac{9}{17}$
     $+\ \frac{3}{17}$
     _____

11) $7\frac{14}{45}$
     $+\ \frac{7}{45}$
     _____

12) $\frac{5}{42}$
     $+\ \frac{11}{42}$
     _____

Exercise C   Add. Write your answers in simplest form.

1) $2\frac{13}{34} + \frac{9}{34}$

2) $\frac{23}{24} + \frac{5}{24}$

3) $\frac{5}{31} + \frac{2}{31}$

4) $2\frac{3}{5} + 1\frac{2}{5}$

5) $\frac{7}{12} + \frac{9}{12} + \frac{6}{12}$

6) $2\frac{1}{15} + 4\frac{11}{15} + 7\frac{8}{15}$

PROBLEM SOLVING

Exercise D   Solve these word problems.

1) Leon, a plumber, joins two pieces of pipe. They measure $7\frac{3}{16}''$ and $4\frac{7}{16}''$. How long is the new piece of pipe?

2) Justin works part-time after school. One week he works $3\frac{1}{4}$ hours on Monday, $2\frac{3}{4}$ hours on Wednesday, and $1\frac{1}{4}$ hours on Friday. How many hours does he work that week?

Common denominators

Common multiples of two or more denominators.

Before you can add fractions, they must have **common denominators**, or denominators that are alike. If the denominators are not alike, you will need to raise the fractions to higher terms so that the denominators are the same. This new denominator is called the **least common denominator** (**LCD**).

EXAMPLE Add $\frac{1}{6}$ and $\frac{3}{4}$.

Least common denominator (LCD)

Smallest denominator that is a multiple of two denominators.

Step 1 Find the least common multiple of the denominators.
The least common multiple of 6 and 4 is 12.

Step 2 Use 12 as a new denominator.
12 is the least common denominator or LCD.

$$\frac{1}{6} = \frac{\blacksquare}{12}$$

$$+\frac{3}{4} = \frac{\blacksquare}{12}$$

Step 3 Raise the fractions to higher terms.

$$\frac{1}{6} = \frac{2}{12}$$

$$+\frac{3}{4} = \frac{9}{12}$$

Step 4 Add the fractions.

$$\frac{2}{12}$$
$$+\frac{9}{12}$$
$$\overline{\frac{11}{12}}$$

Exercise A   Add these fractions. Write your answers in simplest form.

1) $\dfrac{2}{7}$ 2) $\dfrac{3}{8}$ 3) $\dfrac{2}{9}$ 4) $\dfrac{1}{8}$ 5) $\dfrac{5}{12}$ 6) $\dfrac{9}{16}$ 7) $2\dfrac{3}{5}$ 8) $13\dfrac{1}{5}$

$+\dfrac{3}{4}$ $+\dfrac{2}{3}$ $+\dfrac{2}{3}$ $+\dfrac{2}{5}$ $+\dfrac{2}{3}$ $+\dfrac{3}{8}$ $+3\dfrac{2}{9}$ $+2\dfrac{3}{10}$

Exercise B   Find the answers. Write them in simplest form.

1) $\dfrac{3}{4}+\dfrac{5}{6}$

2) $\dfrac{1}{8}+\dfrac{1}{5}$

3) $\dfrac{3}{7}+\dfrac{5}{21}$

4) $\dfrac{5}{11}+\dfrac{5}{22}$

5) $\dfrac{3}{8}+\dfrac{2}{11}$

6) $5\dfrac{1}{3}+4\dfrac{1}{6}$

7) $6\dfrac{3}{7}+3\dfrac{1}{3}$

8) $5\dfrac{1}{6}+2\dfrac{3}{5}$

9) $5\dfrac{1}{6}+4\dfrac{4}{9}$

10) $7\dfrac{1}{11}+2\dfrac{2}{33}$

11) $5\dfrac{3}{8}+2\dfrac{1}{6}+\dfrac{1}{4}$

12) $12\dfrac{1}{8}+3\dfrac{1}{6}+2\dfrac{1}{3}$

13) $5\dfrac{5}{6}+3\dfrac{1}{7}$

14) $4\dfrac{5}{8}+3\dfrac{1}{4}$

15) $6\dfrac{7}{10}+3\dfrac{2}{5}$

16) $2\dfrac{3}{8}+6\dfrac{3}{10}$

17) $7\dfrac{1}{9}+2\dfrac{1}{6}$

18) $11\dfrac{5}{8}+13$

PROBLEM SOLVING

Exercise C   Solve these word problems.

1) Guido buys $2\dfrac{1}{4}$ pounds of tomatoes and $3\dfrac{2}{3}$ pounds of lettuce. How many pounds of vegetables does he buy?

2) Miss Watts is building a bookshelf. She needs a piece of wood measuring $3\dfrac{1}{2}$ feet long and a piece of wood $5\dfrac{1}{4}$ feet long. What is the total length of the wood she needs?

3) Paolo needs to replace three sections of damaged pipe. They measure $2\dfrac{1}{2}$ feet, $4\dfrac{3}{4}$ feet, and $3\dfrac{1}{8}$ feet. What length of pipe must he buy to cut these three pieces from it?

You need like denominators to subtract fractions or mixed numbers. If the denominators are alike, then you subtract the whole numbers and the numerators. You keep the same common denominator for your answer. You may need to rename your answer in simplest form.

EXAMPLES			
	$\frac{7}{11}$	$13\frac{11}{12}$	$12\frac{8}{9}$
	$-\frac{3}{11}$	$-\frac{5}{12}$	$-5\frac{5}{9}$
	$\frac{4}{11}$	$13\frac{6}{12} = 13\frac{1}{2}$	$7\frac{3}{9} = 7\frac{1}{3}$

Exercise A Subtract these fractions. Write your answers in simplest form.

1) $9\frac{7}{8}$

$-2\frac{3}{8}$

5) $8\frac{11}{12}$

$-\frac{1}{12}$

9) $\frac{19}{20}$

$-\frac{11}{20}$

13) $18\frac{19}{21}$

$-7\frac{1}{21}$

2) $25\frac{4}{5}$

$-6\frac{3}{5}$

6) $10\frac{3}{4}$

$-2\frac{1}{4}$

10) $46\frac{2}{9}$

$-6\frac{1}{9}$

14) $13\frac{3}{13}$

$-5\frac{2}{13}$

3) $29\frac{5}{12}$

$-3\frac{1}{12}$

7) $19\frac{19}{21}$

$-5\frac{5}{21}$

11) $11\frac{7}{9}$

$-7\frac{4}{9}$

15) $26\frac{7}{10}$

$-18\frac{7}{10}$

4) $57\frac{7}{8}$

-48

8) $\frac{15}{16}$

$-\frac{3}{16}$

12) $12\frac{10}{11}$

$-5\frac{5}{11}$

16) $39\frac{15}{16}$

$-8\frac{5}{16}$

Exercise B Subtract. Write your answers in simplest form.

1) $12\frac{6}{7} - 3\frac{4}{7}$

2) $13\frac{7}{8} - 10\frac{3}{8}$

3) $15\frac{9}{10} - \frac{3}{10}$

4) $19\frac{7}{8} - 11$

5) $\frac{11}{13} - \frac{9}{13}$

6) $15\frac{7}{10} - 8\frac{7}{10}$

7) $28\frac{5}{12} - 19$

8) $32\frac{8}{9} - 3\frac{1}{9}$

9) $23\frac{4}{5} - 22\frac{4}{5}$

10) $19\frac{13}{21} - 15\frac{10}{21}$

11) $105\frac{3}{4} - 42$

12) $18\frac{7}{8} - 9\frac{7}{8}$

13) $8\frac{11}{12} - 6\frac{5}{12}$

14) $92\frac{5}{9} - 48\frac{1}{9}$

15) $109\frac{4}{5} - 86\frac{3}{5}$

16) Take $18\frac{7}{19}$ from $20\frac{12}{19}$

17) From $35\frac{12}{35}$ take $\frac{9}{35}$

18) Subtract $2\frac{5}{13}$ from $5\frac{12}{13}$

19) Subtract $42\frac{1}{8}$ from $42\frac{7}{8}$

20) Take $\frac{7}{18}$ from $\frac{11}{18}$

21) Subtract $27\frac{7}{8}$ from $27\frac{7}{8}$

22) Subtract $32\frac{5}{12}$ from $38\frac{11}{12}$

23) Take $\frac{8}{21}$ from $53\frac{11}{21}$

24) From $32\frac{15}{16}$ subtract $8\frac{7}{16}$

25) Subtract $8\frac{1}{8}$ from $15\frac{3}{8}$

26) From $13\frac{8}{17}$ subtract $8\frac{6}{17}$

27) Subtract $13\frac{2}{11}$ from $16\frac{5}{11}$

28) From $18\frac{5}{16}$ take $15\frac{3}{16}$

29) From $18\frac{7}{8}$ subtract $6\frac{3}{8}$

30) Subtract $3\frac{2}{9}$ from $5\frac{7}{9}$

If the denominators in a subtraction problem are not alike, then you need to rename the fractions to higher terms, just as you did with addition problems. After you have like denominators, you subtract the whole numbers. Then subtract the numerators.

EXAMPLE

$$18\frac{5}{6}$$
$$-2\frac{3}{8}$$

$$18\frac{5}{6} = 18\frac{\blacksquare}{24}$$
$$-2\frac{3}{8} = 2\frac{\blacksquare}{24}$$

$$18\frac{5}{6} = 18\frac{20}{24}$$
$$-2\frac{3}{8} = 2\frac{9}{24}$$
$$16\frac{11}{24}$$

If you cannot find the least common denominator, use the product of the denominators for a common denominator. You will get the same answer after you reduce.

EXAMPLE

$$18\frac{5}{6}$$
$$-2\frac{3}{8}$$

$$18\frac{5}{6} = 18\frac{\blacksquare}{48}$$
$$-2\frac{3}{8} = 2\frac{\blacksquare}{48}$$

$$18\frac{5}{6} = 18\frac{40}{48}$$
$$-2\frac{3}{8} = 2\frac{18}{48}$$
$$16\frac{22}{48} = 16\frac{11}{24}$$

Exercise A   Find a common denominator for each problem. Subtract.

1) $\frac{8}{9}$
$-\frac{1}{3}$

4) $25\frac{6}{7}$
$-4\frac{2}{3}$

7) $13\frac{4}{5}$
$-2\frac{1}{3}$

10) $16\frac{7}{10}$
$-16\frac{1}{2}$

2) $\frac{2}{3}$
$-\frac{2}{5}$

5) $22\frac{7}{8}$
$-4\frac{2}{3}$

8) $\frac{7}{8}$
$-\frac{3}{4}$

11) $10\frac{9}{10}$
$-\frac{3}{20}$

3) $18\frac{15}{16}$
$-2\frac{1}{4}$

6) $13\frac{11}{13}$
$-\frac{1}{39}$

9) $19\frac{5}{6}$
$-3\frac{1}{4}$

12) $26\frac{5}{6}$
$-3\frac{5}{18}$

Exercise B Subtract. Write your answers in simplest form.

1) $27\frac{5}{9}$
    $-\ 5\frac{1}{3}$

4) $11\frac{4}{5}$
    $-\ \frac{7}{25}$

7) $72\frac{11}{12}$
    $-\ 3\frac{5}{8}$

10) $\frac{11}{36}$
     $-\ \frac{1}{6}$

2) $16\frac{4}{5}$
    $-\ 4\frac{7}{10}$

5) $12\frac{9}{10}$
    $-\ 6\frac{4}{5}$

8) $52\frac{1}{2}$
    $-\ 3\frac{1}{6}$

11) $21\frac{9}{10}$
     $-\ 4\frac{1}{2}$

3) $28\frac{7}{9}$
    $-\ 5\frac{1}{6}$

6) $19\frac{13}{16}$
    $-\ 2\frac{3}{8}$

9) $23\frac{16}{27}$
    $-\ 4\frac{1}{3}$

12) $35\frac{11}{20}$
     $-34\frac{2}{5}$

Exercise C Subtract. Write your answers in simplest form.

1) From $13\frac{8}{13}$ subtract $8\frac{3}{26}$

2) From $19\frac{2}{3}$ subtract $3\frac{4}{7}$

3) From $18\frac{5}{16}$ subtract $2\frac{1}{16}$

4) Subtract $6\frac{8}{15}$ from $12\frac{5}{6}$

5) Subtract $3\frac{6}{7}$ from $8\frac{7}{8}$

6) Subtract $2\frac{4}{11}$ from $9\frac{21}{44}$

7) From the sum of $6\frac{2}{3}$ and $5\frac{2}{5}$ subtract $2\frac{1}{15}$

8) From the product of $2\frac{1}{2}$ and $3\frac{1}{2}$ subtract $2\frac{1}{3}$

Subtracting With Renaming

You can subtract a mixed number from a whole number.
First you rename the whole number as a mixed number.
Then subtract.

EXAMPLE

$$16 = 15\frac{8}{8}$$
$$- 2\frac{3}{8} = 2\frac{3}{8}$$
$$= 13\frac{5}{8}$$

$$16 = 15 + 1$$
$$= 15 + \frac{8}{8}$$
$$= 15\frac{8}{8}$$

After you change to common denominators, you may find that
the top fraction is less than the bottom fraction. Then you will
need to rename the top mixed number before you can subtract.

EXAMPLE

$$15\frac{2}{7} = 15\frac{6}{21} = 14\frac{27}{21}$$
$$- 4\frac{8}{21} = 4\frac{8}{21} = 4\frac{8}{21}$$
$$10\frac{19}{21}$$

$$15\frac{6}{21} = 14 + 1 + \frac{6}{21}$$
$$= 14 + \frac{21}{21} + \frac{6}{21}$$
$$= 14 + \frac{27}{21}$$
$$= 14\frac{27}{21}$$

Exercise A   Subtract. You may need to rename.

1)   23
$$-14\frac{3}{7}$$

3) $18\frac{2}{9}$
$$- 4\frac{3}{9}$$

5) $6\frac{2}{11}$
$$-4\frac{5}{11}$$

7) $8\frac{2}{7}$
$$-4\frac{2}{3}$$

2)   25
$$- 4\frac{2}{11}$$

4) $27\frac{4}{5}$
$$- 2\frac{5}{6}$$

6) $4\frac{2}{9}$
$$-1\frac{5}{6}$$

8)   15
$$- 2\frac{11}{15}$$

Exercise B Subtract. Write your answers in simplest form.

1) $12\frac{2}{9}$ 3) $8\frac{1}{8}$ 5) $12\frac{5}{8}$ 7) 98 9) $25\frac{5}{7}$ 11) $7\frac{5}{12}$
$-\ 6\frac{3}{8}$ $-\ 2\frac{7}{8}$ $-\ 5\frac{3}{4}$ $-\ 7\frac{11}{16}$ $-\ 2\frac{4}{5}$ $-\ 3\frac{7}{8}$

2) $5\frac{3}{14}$ 4) $5\frac{2}{13}$ 6) 16 8) $22\frac{7}{8}$ 10) $31\frac{1}{10}$ 12) $4\frac{7}{24}$
$-\ 3\frac{6}{7}$ $-\ 3\frac{5}{26}$ $-\ 1\frac{7}{8}$ $-\ 9\frac{5}{6}$ $-\ 3\frac{9}{20}$ $-\ 2\frac{5}{6}$

Exercise C Subtract. Write your answers in simplest form.

1) $15\frac{1}{3} - 6\frac{7}{11}$

2) $19 - 5\frac{9}{13}$

3) $15\frac{1}{3} - 5\frac{7}{8}$

4) $13\frac{1}{6} - 3\frac{9}{10}$

5) Subtract $5\frac{2}{9}$ from 20

6) Subtract $3\frac{7}{18}$ from $6\frac{1}{9}$

7) From $8\frac{1}{12}$ subtract $6\frac{5}{8}$

8) From $4\frac{1}{2}$ subtract $2\frac{7}{10}$

PROBLEM SOLVING

Exercise D Solve these word problems.

1) Brandon uses $7\frac{3}{4}$ yards of material from a bolt of cloth that is 18 yards long. How many yards of material are left on the bolt?

2) Julio opens a 10-pound bag of sugar. He uses $\frac{5}{8}$ of a pound for cookies. How much sugar is left?

3) If $2\frac{3}{8}$ yards of fabric on a bolt are irregular and the bolt contains $6\frac{1}{3}$ yards of fabric, then how much regular fabric remains?

4) If Renée and Geraldo combine their wood scraps, then they can try to make another doghouse. Renée has $1\frac{1}{5}$ feet of scrap and Geraldo has $9\frac{2}{7}$ feet of scrap. Do they have enough scrap to build another doghouse, if it requires $12\frac{1}{2}$ feet?

Exercise E   Practice working with fractions. Solve these word problems.

1) Jodhi opens a $6\frac{1}{2}$-pound bag of nuts. She uses $\frac{7}{8}$ pound for cookies. How many pounds of nuts does she have left?

2) Tina purchases $2\frac{3}{4}$ yards of material. She uses $\frac{2}{3}$ of the material to make a blouse. How many yards of material are left?

3) Leroy's woodpile contains $1\frac{7}{8}$ cords of wood when he buys $1\frac{1}{2}$ cords more. How many cords of wood does he have now?

4) Miranda buys $3\frac{1}{2}$ pounds of flour. She uses $2\frac{1}{8}$ pounds to bake cakes. How many pounds of flour does she have left?

5) Jim rides $15\frac{7}{10}$ miles on his bike over a two-day period. If he rides $8\frac{2}{5}$ miles the first day, how far does he ride the second day?

6) Brian lives $\frac{4}{5}$ mile from school. He jogs $\frac{1}{2}$ of this distance daily. How far does he jog every day?

7) A recipe calls for $\frac{3}{4}$ cup sugar. How much sugar is needed if you make only $\frac{1}{2}$ of the recipe?

8) Bhaktir lost $\frac{6}{7}$ pound during the first week of his diet. During the second week, he lost $\frac{2}{3}$ of what he lost the first week. How much did he lose the second week?

Compare the fractions in each pair. Write < or >.

1) $\dfrac{4}{5}$ $\dfrac{6}{7}$

2) $\dfrac{5}{6}$ $\dfrac{3}{4}$

3) $\dfrac{2}{11}$ $\dfrac{5}{12}$

Write these in simplest form.

4) $\dfrac{9}{21}$

5) $15\dfrac{8}{12}$

6) $\dfrac{50}{125}$

7) $\dfrac{11}{88}$

Rename these mixed numbers as improper fractions.

8) $3\dfrac{6}{7}$

9) $1\dfrac{1}{3}$

10) $5\dfrac{3}{8}$

Rename these improper fractions as whole numbers or mixed numbers.

11) $\dfrac{26}{7}$

12) $\dfrac{12}{3}$

13) $\dfrac{38}{6}$

Find the answers. Write them in simplest form.

14) $\frac{2}{3} \times \frac{4}{5}$

15) $1\frac{1}{3} \div 3\frac{2}{3}$

16) $1\frac{1}{2} \times 2\frac{3}{4}$

17) $2\frac{8}{11} + 3\frac{2}{11}$

18) $\frac{2}{3} \div \frac{7}{8}$

19) $15 - 4\frac{7}{8}$

20) $\begin{array}{r} 3\frac{8}{9} \\ + 2\frac{1}{9} \\ \hline \end{array}$ **21)** $\begin{array}{r} 5\frac{3}{7} \\ + 2\frac{7}{8} \\ \hline \end{array}$

22) $\begin{array}{r} 19\frac{5}{6} \\ - 3\frac{1}{4} \\ \hline \end{array}$ **23)** $\begin{array}{r} 6\frac{5}{8} \\ + 2\frac{7}{8} \\ \hline \end{array}$

24) $\begin{array}{r} 20\frac{3}{4} \\ - 4\frac{7}{8} \\ \hline \end{array}$ **25)** $\begin{array}{r} 14\frac{1}{3} \\ - 5\frac{3}{5} \\ \hline \end{array}$

Test Taking Tip   When taking a mathematics test, complete the answers that you know before tackling more difficult problems.

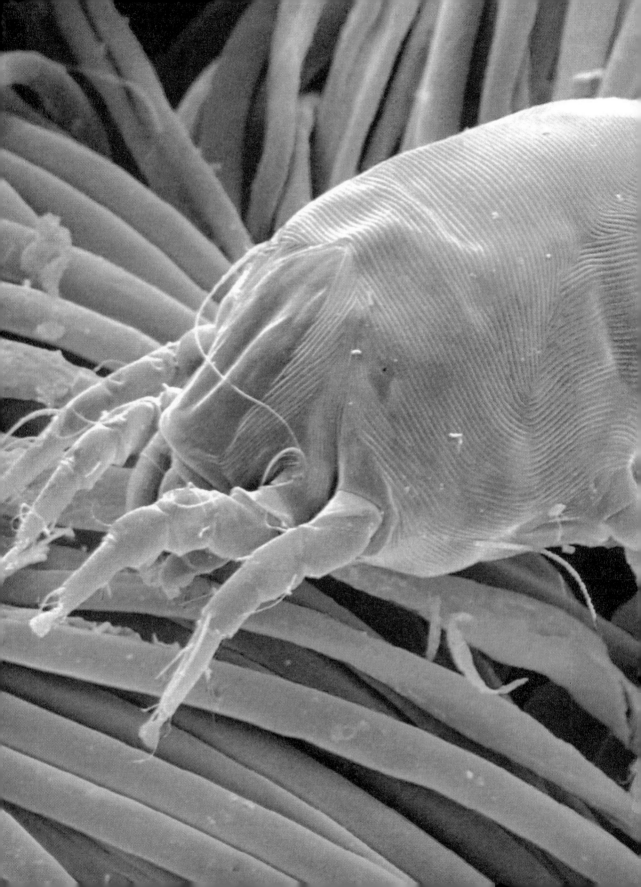

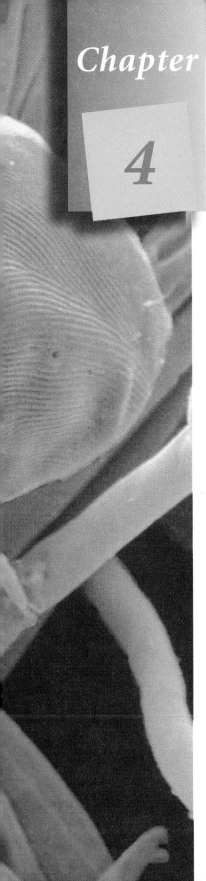

Chapter

4

Decimals

Numbers can be very large, such as a national budget in the trillions. One trillion is written as 1,000,000,000,000. Numbers can also be very small. A house dust mite is about .0001 meter, but it can be magnified to more than 2,500 times its size, as shown. Both of these numbers tell you something about the dust mite. Mathematics allows us to write numbers in more than one way. These other ways are helpful when we solve problems with very large or very small numbers.

In Chapter 4, you will learn about place value and scientific notation, which help us make sense out of numbers.

Goals for Learning

▶ To write numbers in word form and in standard notation

▶ To order numbers

▶ To round numbers

▶ To compute with decimals and whole numbers

▶ To express fractions as decimals

▶ To express numbers in scientific notation

The planet Jupiter makes one trip around the sun every 11.8613 years. We read this numeral as "eleven and eight thousand six hundred thirteen ten-thousandths." The concept of place value helps us to understand the meaning of long numbers like this one.

Ten-thousands	Thousands	Hundreds	Tens	Ones		Tenths	Hundredths	Thousandths	Ten-thousandths
			1	1	.	8	6	1	3

Exercise A Write the name of the place for each underlined digit.

1) 867.4<u>3</u>
2) 6.239<u>5</u>
3) 1<u>4</u>8.37
4) 6<u>6</u>.875
5) 9.37<u>6</u>5

6) <u>1</u>42.876
7) 0.875<u>6</u>
8) 1<u>2</u>84
9) 9<u>2</u>.8
10) 6857.<u>3</u>

11) 72.8<u>5</u>97
12) 0.47<u>6</u>
13) <u>7</u>8.94
14) 6.3<u>7</u>892
15) <u>6</u>789.03

Exercise B Write the name of the place for the last digit in each numeral.

1) 0.38
2) 427.389
3) 0.4678

4) 92.386
5) 76.8436
6) 16.0004

7) 200.307
8) 392.05
9) 867.384

Exercise C Copy each number. Underline the digit that is in the place name in italics.

1) 46.3826   *hundredths*
2) 35.0038   *ten-thousandths*
3) 148.296   *tenths*
4) 6758.23   *hundreds*
5) 91.4082   *thousandths*
6) 204.37   *tens*
7) 14.0079   *ones*
8) 208.097   *hundredths*
9) 5.23981   *thousandths*
10) 502.967   *tenths*

11) 587.029   *ones*
12) 0.298   *hundredths*
13) 329.768   *tens*
14) 52.694   *thousandths*
15) 498.276   *tenths*
16) 0.5296   *ten-thousandths*
17) 468.539   *hundreds*
18) 324.06   *tenths*
19) 567.8   *ones*
20) 1.023   *hundredths*

Place value helps us to read decimal numerals. To read a decimal numeral, use the following steps. If there is a zero or no number to the left of the decimal point, then skip Steps 1 and 2.

Step 1	Read the digits to the left of the decimal point as a whole number.
Step 2	Say "and" for the decimal point.
Step 3	Read the digits to the right of the decimal point as a whole number. These are the **decimal places**.
Step 4	Say the place name of the last digit.

Decimal places

Positions to the right of a decimal point.

EXAMPLES

16.382

Step 1	sixteen
Step 2	and
Step 3	three hundred eighty-two
Step 4	thousandths Say, "Sixteen and three hundred eighty-two thousandths."

.83

	No number
Step 3	eighty-three
Step 4	hundredths Say, "Eighty-three hundredths."

Exercise A   Read the words. Then write the numeral that means the same as the words.

1) Sixteen and twelve-hundredths	16.012	16.12	16.0012	
2) Nine-hundredths	0.0009	900	0.09	
3) One hundred and six-thousandths	0.106	100.06	100.006	
4) Seventy and eight-hundredths	70.08	70.008	0.78	
5) Seventy-nine thousandths	70.009	0.079	0.79	
6) Twenty-eight and six-tenths	28.06	0.286	28.6	
7) One thousand and six-thousandths	1006	1000.006	0.1006	
8) Forty-eight ten-thousandths	0.0048	0.048	40.008	

PROBLEM SOLVING

Exercise B   Write the numeral that means the same as the bold words.

1) Large hailstones can weigh **thirty-five hundredths** of a pound.

2) The average annual rainfall is **one hundred twenty-three and thirty-seven hundredths** inches.

3) The rainfall in one minute is **three and twelve-hundredths** inches.

4) Barnard's Star is **four ten-thousandths** times as bright as our sun.

5) The star Sirius B is **seventeen ten-thousandths** times as bright as our sun.

6) Lydia weighs **ninety-two and eight-tenths** pounds.

7) Normal body temperature is **ninety-eight and six-tenths** degrees Fahrenheit.

8) Jupiter weighs **three hundred eighteen and three-tenths** times as much as the Earth.

9) Jupiter is only **twenty-four hundredths** times as dense as the Earth.

10) Paul weighs **one hundred forty and twenty-five hundredths** pounds.

11) Lydia weighs **forty-seven and forty-five hundredths** pounds less than Paul.

Comparing and Rounding Decimals

You can tell which of two decimals is larger if you add zeros to one of them. You can easily compare them when both have the same number of decimal places to the right of the decimal point.

> EXAMPLE   Compare 19.368 and 19.37
> 19.368   19.370
> 19.370 is larger.
> 19.368 < 19.37

Exercise A   Compare these pairs of decimals. Write > or < in the space between each pair to show whether the first decimal is larger or smaller than the second.

1)	16.837	16.9	**18)**	6.205	6.25
2)	3.6	3.486	**19)**	5.304	5.403
3)	15.487	15.7	**20)**	7.62	7.6203
4)	.43	0.3	**21)**	8.34	8.304
5)	12.377	12.41	**22)**	9.36	9.036
6)	70.396	68.9	**23)**	17.228	17.28
7)	8.446	8.45	**24)**	3.62	3.598
8)	6.39	6.392	**25)**	2.25	0.225
9)	5.7	5.4	**26)**	8.00	.0800
10)	0.5	0.49	**27)**	2.01	0.398
11)	0.946	1.712	**28)**	0.023	0.00981
12)	4.68	4.71	**29)**	1.11	0.112
13)	12.348	12.2	**30)**	89.1	88.9
14)	4.72	4.724	**31)**	12.23	13
15)	3.537	3.536	**32)**	4.01	10.1
16)	2.04	2.40	**33)**	101.10	98.0231
17)	17.003	17.03	**34)**	2.2201	4

Exercise B Tell which numeral in each set is largest.

1) 5.332	5.359	5.317	**9)** 3.056	3.56	3.506
2) 2.076	2.07	2.077	**10)** 8.009	8.1	8.079
3) .392	.39	.4	**11)** 2.708	2.69	2.7
4) 1.404	1.44	1.441	**12)** 11.398	11.2	11.36
5) 3.9	3.178	3.79	**13)** 4.228	4.2	4.293
6) 14.04	14.198	14.2	**14)** 9.308	9.3	9.299
7) 11.361	11.35	11.3	**15)** 26.3	26.198	26.228
8) 72.8	72.29	71.96	**16)** 7.9	7.902	7.829

Exercise C Write each set of numerals in order from smallest to largest.

1) 3.06	3.219	3.058	**13)** 5.82	5.2	5.8
2) 12	11.98	12.006	**14)** 3.09	4	3.1
3) .9	.872	.903	**15)** 7.086	7.2	7.15
4) 4.08	4.19	4.079	**16)** .903	.95	.921
5) 2.209	2.229	2.902	**17)** 8	7.09	8.2
6) 11.36	11	11.209	**18)** 5.31	5.031	5.1
7) 4.368	4.3	4.319	**19)** 6.08	6.8	6.76
8) 14.508	14.39	14.47	**20)** 3.2	32	.32
9) 8.902	8.9	8.91	**21)** 5.091	5.19	5.6
10) 72.008	72.01	72.0	**22)** 3.08	3.1	3.092
11) 6.128	6.2	6.0091	**23)** 7.06	7.6	7.612
12) 3.876	3.869	3.87	**24)** 6.534	6.5	6.098

Sometimes you may want to round a decimal numeral so that you have a shorter number.

EXAMPLE   Round 2.346 to hundredths.

Step 1   Find the place that you are rounding to.
2.346 (hundredths)

Step 2   If the digit to the right is 5 or more, then add 1 to the place that you are rounding to. If it is less than 5, then do not add anything.
2.346 (five or more: add one)

Step 3   Drop all of the digits to the right of the place that you are rounding to.
2.35_ (digit dropped)
Therefore, 2.346 ≐ 2.35. (The symbol, ≐ , means "is about equal to.")

Exercise D   Round these decimals to the nearest tenth.
1) 2.34
2) 42.25
3) 14.6458

Exercise E   Write the choice that is the decimal correctly rounded to the nearest tenth.

1) 2.34 :	2.3	2.4	2	**6)** 2.98 :	2.9	3.0	2.99
2) 4.16 :	4.6	4	4.2	**7)** 5.06 :	5	5.11	5.1
3) 6.05 :	6	6.1	6.06	**8)** 1.18 :	1.19	1.1	1.2
4) .829 :	.83	.9	.8	**9)** .08 :	.1	.0	0
5) .03 :	.1	.04	.0	**10)** 2.07 :	2.7	2.0	2.1

Exercise F   Write the choice that is the decimal correctly rounded to the nearest hundredth.

1) 5.823 :	5.82	5.8	5.83
2) 5.095 :	5.10	5.096	5
3) 2.1239 :	2.12	2.124	2.2
4) .065 :	.06	.07	.066
5) .499 :	.5	.489	.50

Exercise G Round these decimals to the nearest:

Tenth	Hundredth	Thousandth
1) 2.36	**6)** 14.023	**11)** 5.0618
2) 4.23	**7)** .067	**12)** 8.8397
3) 2.06	**8)** 1.089	**13)** 8.0552
4) 4.109	**9)** .4209	**14)** 5.0168
5) .072	**10)** 73.9029	**15)** 78.0999

Exercise H Complete the chart by rounding to the placed named.

		Tenth	Hundredth	Thousandth
1)	2.8354	2.8		
2)	4.6215			
3)	.2918			.292
4)	.2065			
5)	.1853		.19	
6)	5.6356			
7)	2.1523			
8)	4.6652			

PROBLEM SOLVING

Exercise I Follow the directions for rounding in each problem.

1) The average lap speed in the Oceanside 500 auto race is 352.627 km/h. Round to the nearest tenth.

2) Sound travels about .336 km/s. Round this to the nearest hundredth.

3) Light travels about 2.997925×10^8 m/s. Round 2.997925 to the nearest thousandth.

4) A centimeter is about .3937 inches. Round this to the nearest hundredth.

When you add decimals, it is important to keep the places in the same column, so that you will not add tenths to hundredths. You can do this easily if you line up the decimal points. You may also want to include zeros to avoid confusion.

EXAMPLE 2.3 + 5 + .68

2.3	2.30
5.	5.00
+.68	+0.68
7.98	7.98

Exercise A Find the sums.

1)
4.57
3.9
26.
+ 3.298

5)
17.
.352
6.7
+42.06

9)
.663
48.
.43
+37.

2)
.304
42.8
3.08
+ .007

6)
8.
35.
.837
+ .6684

10)
3.207
52.
.868
+48.02

3)
7.
.346
12.8
+ 4.036

7)
5.025
64.4
.62
+ 1.013

11)
7.08
36.341
.2034
+52.

4)
.007
5.03
38.
+ .963

8)
.304
8.9
34.447
+ .003

12)
5.058
.7
9.006
+ .49

Exercise B Write these addition problems in vertical form and then add.

1) 2.35 + 6 + .42
2) 4.83 + 7.6 + 2.41
3) 5.2 + .62 + 2.5
4) 56 + 2.5 + .93
5) 4.6 + 2 + .05
6) 5 + 6.3 + .413

7) 5.1 + .12 + .53 + .116
8) 4 + 1.5 + .023 + 1
9) 2.5 + 6.25 + .63 + 1
10) .03 + .5 + .006 + 2
11) 9 + 1.2 + .26 + .711
12) 4 + 51.1 + .23 + .026

Exercise C Find the sums.

1) 2.5, 6.25, 8.31, and 6
2) 3.6, 2, .53, and .06
3) 5, .23, 2.8, and .06
4) 5.2, 4.35, .83, and 2.1
5) 61, .27, 2.3, and 2
6) 4.3, .52, .6, and .203

7) 5.5, .23, 4.16, and 2
8) .201, .6, 2, and 1.1
9) 5.9, 2.35, and .004
10) 3.2, 9.42, and .002
11) 25, 2.5, 5.02, and 5
12) .602, .35, .4, and 5

PROBLEM SOLVING

Exercise D Solve these addition problems.

1) Juan delivers newspapers after school. He walks 2.3 miles on Monday, 2.45 miles on Tuesday, and 5 miles on Wednesday. What is the total distance that Juan walks in these three days?

2) One rainy week, it rains 2.5 inches on Monday, 1.63 inches on Tuesday, and 3 inches on Wednesday. What is the total rainfall for these three days?

3) Laura goes to the store and buys apples costing $1.52, tomatoes for $.95, and candy for $2.50. How much does Laura spend at the store?

4) Corey's dog, Max, has three puppies. Their weights are 8.2 ounces, 5.12 ounces, and 6 ounces. What is the total weight?

Exercise E Add the following:

1) $2.56 + $10.03 + $4.60
2) $1.55 + $4.67 + $15
3) 2.574 + 4.3 + 2.23

4) 4.3 + 5 + 6.2 + 7.35
5) 7 + 8.7 + 2.03 + .08
6) .34 + .2 + .007 + .1

You must also line up the decimal points when you subtract decimals. It is important to include zeros to help you subtract. Remember to rewrite the problem in vertical form and line up the decimals.

EXAMPLES

$14.3 - .26 =$ ■ $46 - 2.31 =$ ■

$$\begin{array}{r} 14.30 \\ - \ \ .26 \\ \hline 14.04 \end{array} \qquad \begin{array}{r} 46.00 \\ - \ 2.31 \\ \hline 43.69 \end{array}$$

Exercise A   Rewrite these subtraction problems in vertical form and then subtract. Remember to include the zeros.

1) $12.5 - 4.2$ **16)** $2 - .16$

2) $15.6 - 2.34$ **17)** $5 - .16$

3) $5.8 - 2.14$ **18)** $4.6 - 4.14$

4) $12.6 - .42$ **19)** $13.2 - 1.1$

5) $4.7 - .62$ **20)** $14.6 - 12$

6) $.54 - .23$

7) $.43 - .023$

8) $5.2 - .423$

9) $6.2 - 4.31$

10) $14.6 - .25$

11) $5.04 - 1.2$

12) $23.1 - .9$

13) $.8 - .088$

14) $.1 - .035$

15) $5.6 - .6$

Exercise B   Find the answers to these problems.

1) From 3.5 subtract .52

2) From 3.83 subtract .83

3) From 23 subtract 4.3

4) From 3 take away 2.8

5) From 2.3 take away .34

6) From 13 take away .83

7) Take away 2.3 from 8

8) Take away .08 from 2.3

9) Subtract 5 from 16.5

10) Subtract .35 from 13.7

11) Take away 3 from 15.3

12) From .93 take away .834

PROBLEM SOLVING

Exercise C   Solve these word problems.

1) Marco weighs 135 pounds before he goes on his candy-free diet. He loses 5.6 pounds. How much does he weigh after his diet?

2) Marnie purchases a pair of skates for $68.23, including tax. She gives the salesperson $70. How much change does she receive?

3) Frank wants to have a party at the end of the school year. He buys sodas, candy, and chips for a total of $16.95. How much change does he receive from the $20 he gives the clerk?

4) Kim Lee buys potatoes for $2.98, tomatoes for $1.53, steak for $5.65, and a peach pie for $2.50. What is her change from $20.00?

5) Michael earns $15 on Saturday cutting grass. His expenses are: $1.50, bus fare; $2.75, laundry; and $7.00, lunches. How much money does Michael have left after he pays all of his expenses?

Multiplying Decimals

When multiplying decimals, count the number of decimal places in the problem to determine where to put the decimal point in the answer.

EXAMPLES   2.31 × 4.2 = ■   .85 × 4.22 = ■

$$
\begin{array}{rl}
2.31 & \text{2 places} \\
\times\ 4.2 & \text{1 place} \\
\hline
462 & \\
+9\ 24 & \\
\hline
9.702 & \text{3 places}
\end{array}
\qquad
\begin{array}{rl}
4.22 & \text{2 places} \\
\times\ .85 & \text{2 places} \\
\hline
2110 & \\
+3\ 376 & \\
\hline
3.5870 & \text{4 places}
\end{array}
$$

Exercise A   Put the decimal point in the proper place.

1) $\begin{array}{r} 2.35 \\ \times\ \ 4.2 \\ \hline 9870 \end{array}$
4) $\begin{array}{r} 7.23 \\ \times\ \ 4.22 \\ \hline 305106 \end{array}$
7) $\begin{array}{r} .45 \\ \times\ .58 \\ \hline 2610 \end{array}$
10) $\begin{array}{r} 781 \\ \times\ \ .23 \\ \hline 17963 \end{array}$

2) $\begin{array}{r} 5.34 \\ \times\ \ .56 \\ \hline 29904 \end{array}$
5) $\begin{array}{r} .23 \\ \times\ .85 \\ \hline 1955 \end{array}$
8) $\begin{array}{r} 4.73 \\ \times\ \ .123 \\ \hline 58179 \end{array}$
11) $\begin{array}{r} 2.61 \\ \times\ \ 31.2 \\ \hline 81432 \end{array}$

3) $\begin{array}{r} 7.07 \\ \times\ \ 1.12 \\ \hline 79184 \end{array}$
6) $\begin{array}{r} 6.1 \\ \times\ .72 \\ \hline 4392 \end{array}$
9) $\begin{array}{r} 7.8 \\ \times\ .02 \\ \hline 156 \end{array}$
12) $\begin{array}{r} .48 \\ \times\ .68 \\ \hline 3264 \end{array}$

Exercise B   Multiply to find the products.

1) $\begin{array}{r} 2.3 \\ \times 4.6 \\ \hline \end{array}$
3) $\begin{array}{r} .43 \\ \times 1.7 \\ \hline \end{array}$

2) $\begin{array}{r} 2.96 \\ \times\ .17 \\ \hline \end{array}$
4) $\begin{array}{r} 5.62 \\ \times\ .17 \\ \hline \end{array}$

Exercise C Rewrite these multiplication problems in vertical form. Multiply to find the products. Count the decimal places in each problem before you place the decimal point.

1) 2.3 × 4.5

2) 3.34 × 2.1

3) 4.61 × .35

4) .423 × 2.1

5) .62 × 2.3

6) 8.71 × 2.6

7) 11.3 × .27

8) 26.7 × .04

9) 9.37 × .07

10) 4.63 × 4.02

11) .961 × .35

12) .023 × 12

13) 23.45 × 1.8

14) 14.6 × 4.21

15) 37.15 × 4.35

16) 3.51 × 4.35

17) 355 × 2.78

18) 14.6 × .03

Exercise D Solve these problems.

1) 6 pounds potatoes, 89¢ per pound, cost $_____.

2) 1.2 pounds nuts, $4.75 per pound, cost $_____.

3) 7 dozen eggs, $.98 per dozen, cost $_____.

4) 3.4 mph for 6.2 hours = _____ miles.

5) 13.2 mph for 4.6 hours = _____ miles.

6) 2.3 hours, 45.2 mph = _____ miles.

7) 3.2 times 6.2

8) .73 times 2.8

9) 12.3 times .1

10) The product of 18.3 and .64 is _____.

Sometimes, your answer will not have enough digits for the number of decimal places that you need. Then you must add some zeros to your answer.

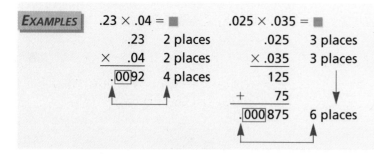

EXAMPLES

.23 × .04 = ■

	.23	2 places
×	.04	2 places
	.0092	4 places

.025 × .035 = ■

	.025	3 places
×	.035	3 places
	125	
+	75	
	.000875	6 places

Exercise E Put the decimal point in the proper place. You may need to include zeros.

1)   .23
    × .03
    ‾‾‾‾‾
      69

2)   .006
    × .023
    ‾‾‾‾‾
      138

3)   4.3
    × .07
    ‾‾‾‾‾
      301

4)   1.035
    × .002
    ‾‾‾‾‾
      2070

5)   .025
    × .07
    ‾‾‾‾‾
      175

6)   .012
    × 1.1
    ‾‾‾‾‾
      132

7)   .62
    × .09
    ‾‾‾‾‾
      558

8)   .62
    × .45
    ‾‾‾‾‾
      2790

ç

Exercise F Multiply to find the products.

1)   .483
    × .026
    ‾‾‾‾‾

2)   5.6
    × .98
    ‾‾‾‾‾

3)   .403
    × .063
    ‾‾‾‾‾

4)   2.73
    × .069
    ‾‾‾‾‾

Exercise G Rewrite these multiplication problems in vertical form and then find the products.

1) 4.3 × .06
2) .03 × .02
3) .183 × .44
4) .027 × .31
5) .034 × .06
6) 1.83 × .09

7) 1.05 × .004
8) 2.31 × .08
9) .006 × .02
10) .31 × .07
11) .09 × .09
12) .006 × .023

13) 32 × .004
14) .015 ×.012
15) 2.6 × .002
16) .024 × 1.02
17) 26 × .021
18) .036 × 1.2

PROBLEM SOLVING

Exercise H Solve these word problems.

1) What is the total length of 6 pieces of ribbon each .012 foot long?

2) If the deli scale shows that .36 pound of hummus is packaged at $2.63 per pound, then what is the cost of the package?

3) What is the total cost of 12 washers at $.03 each?

4) What is the total length of 7 pieces of pipe each .04 foot long?

5) What is the total distance traveled at 1.3 mph for .6 hour?

6) What is the cost of .6 pound of grapes at $.93 per pound?

Scientific notation

A number between one and ten, including one, multiplied by a power of ten.

A number is rewritten in **scientific notation** if it is a number between one and ten (including one) multiplied by a **power of ten**, written with an exponent.

EXAMPLE

$$2\ 84{,}000{,} = 2.84 \times 10^5$$

5 4 3 2 1

a number between one and ten   a power of ten

exponent

Power of ten

A product of multiplying ten by itself one or more times.

Exercise A   Write these numbers in scientific notation.

1) 26,000

2) 425,000

3) 630,000

4) 2,000,000

5) 21,000

6) 231,000

7) 43,000,000

8) 2,612,000

9) 500,000,000

10) 32,300

11) 52,000

12) 10,000,000

13) 21,000,000,000

14) 2,300,000,000

Negative exponent

Shows the opposite of a power of a number; used to express smaller numbers.

Decimals can also be rewritten in scientific notation. Move the decimal point to the *right*. The exponent is negative. It is called a **negative exponent**.

EXAMPLES

$$.0234 = 2.34 \times 10^{-2}$$

1 2

a number between one and ten   a power of ten

negative exponent

$$.0000321 = 3.21 \times 10^{-5}$$

a number between one and ten   a power of ten

negative exponent

Exercise B   Write these decimals in scientific notation. Remember, if you move the decimal point to the left, then you find the exponent. If you move the decimal point to the right, then you find the negative exponent.

1) .0037

2) .0000286

3) .471

4) .058

5) 40.8

6) 2.34

7) 14.8

8) .00000000057

9) .0000000671

10) .00000834

11) .0000056

12) .000128

13) .0063

14) .00309

15) 0.0012

16) 416.8

Exercise C   Express these numbers in scientific notation. Remember, if you move the decimal point to the left, then you find the exponent. If you move the decimal point to the right, then you find the negative exponent.

1) .345

2) .000051

3) 482,000

4) .00026

5) .000000377

6) .65

7) .00279

8) .0530

9) .00000007

10) 1,720,000

11) .000000250

12) .0820

13) .00305

14) .206

15) 41,200

16) .00018

17) .023

18) .0000841

19) 602,000,000

20) 51,000,000

21) 351,000

22) .0000064

Exercise D   Copy each problem and fill in the correct exponent.

1) $.0026 = 2.6 \times 10—$

2) $.000045 = 4.5 \times 10—$

3) $.0006 = 6 \times 10—$

4) $.092 = 9.2 \times 10—$

5) $.6 = 6 \times 10—$

6) $.7 = 7 \times 10—$

7) $.0069 = 6.9 \times 10—$

8) $.002 = 2 \times 10—$

9) $.000000031 = 3.1 \times 10—$

10) $.00000001 = 1 \times 10—$

11) $.00000351 = 3.51 \times 10—$

12) $.00915 = 9.15 \times 10—$

13) $.0000000851 = 8.51 \times 10—$

14) $.637 = 6.37 \times 10—$

15) $.00000000007 = 7 \times 10—$

16) $.000081 = 8.1 \times 10—$

When you divide a decimal by a whole number, you divide as though you were dividing whole numbers. After you find the quotient, then you bring the decimal point straight up into the quotient.

EXAMPLES

$$\begin{array}{r} 5.3 \\ 7\overline{)37.1} \\ -35 \\ \hline 2\,1 \\ -2\,1 \\ \hline 0 \end{array}$$

$$\begin{array}{r} 4.7 \\ 6\overline{)28.2} \\ -24 \\ \hline 4\,2 \\ -4\,2 \\ \hline 0 \end{array}$$

$$\begin{array}{r} .25 \\ 21\overline{)5.25} \\ -4\,2 \\ \hline 1\,05 \\ -1\,05 \\ \hline 0 \end{array}$$

$$\begin{array}{r} .012 \\ 14\overline{).168} \\ -14 \\ \hline 28 \\ -28 \\ \hline 0 \end{array}$$

Exercise A   Find the quotients.

1) $5\overline{)1.40}$

2) $8\overline{)1.52}$

3) $9\overline{)2.439}$

4) $7\overline{)4.69}$

5) $6\overline{)34.2}$

6) $5\overline{)11.15}$

7) $21\overline{)13.083}$

8) $35\overline{)143.15}$

9) $9\overline{)19.26}$

10) $4\overline{).304}$

11) $13\overline{).546}$

12) $12\overline{)14.424}$

13) $36\overline{)37.584}$

14) $16\overline{).912}$

15) $18\overline{).2016}$

16) $17\overline{).204}$

17) $19\overline{).2033}$

18) $23\overline{)1.012}$

Exercise B Copy each problem. Put a decimal point in the proper place in the quotient.

1) $9\,\overline{)\,74.25}$ quotient 825

6) $19\,\overline{)\,788.5}$ quotient 415

2) $8\,\overline{)\,1.888}$ quotient 236

7) $4\,\overline{)\,209.2}$ quotient 523

3) $18\,\overline{)\,.8100}$ quotient 450

8) $15\,\overline{)\,58.65}$ quotient 391

4) $6\,\overline{)\,37.38}$ quotient 623

9) $23\,\overline{)\,11,523}$ quotient 501

5) $9\,\overline{)\,.6507}$ quotient 0723

10) $11\,\overline{)\,35.75}$ quotient 325

Exercise C Find the quotients.

1) $8\,\overline{)\,21.04}$

4) $32\,\overline{)\,66.24}$

2) $28\,\overline{)\,141.4}$

5) $16\,\overline{)\,4.656}$

3) $11\,\overline{)\,584.1}$

6) $25\,\overline{)\,15.575}$

PROBLEM SOLVING

Exercise D Solve these word problems.

1) Behram earns $235.15 a week delivering newspapers. If he works 5 mornings a week, then what are his daily earnings?

2) Mrs. Brennan wants to pay her bill of $162.75 to the local food market over a 7-week period. How much will she pay each week?

3) Ray has to cut a 2.3-foot-long pipe into 4 equal pieces. How long is each piece?

4) Ronald buys some ground beef for $17.43. How much does the ground beef cost per pound if he buys 7 pounds?

5) If three dozen pencils cost $6.48, then what does one pencil cost?

If the divisor is a decimal, then follow these steps:

Step 1   Move the decimal point in the divisor to the right of the number to make it a whole number.

Step 2   Move the decimal point in the dividend the same number of places.

Step 3   Divide and then bring the decimal point straight up into the quotient.

EXAMPLES

$$
\begin{array}{r}
12.6 \\
.6\,\overline{)7.56} \\
-6 \\
\hline
1\,5 \\
-1\,2 \\
\hline
36 \\
-36 \\
\hline
0
\end{array}
\qquad
\begin{array}{r}
.018 \\
.6\,\overline{).0108} \\
-6 \\
\hline
48 \\
-48 \\
\hline
0
\end{array}
$$

1) $.5\,\overline{)6.85}$

2) $.6\,\overline{)9.36}$

3) $.7\,\overline{)8.26}$

4) $.8\,\overline{)21.28}$

5) $.9\,\overline{)13.95}$

6) $.12\,\overline{)1.416}$

7) $2.6\,\overline{)3.12}$

8) $1.6\,\overline{)5.76}$

9) $1.7\,\overline{)7.65}$

10) $2.3\,\overline{)9.453}$

11) $4.1\,\overline{)21.73}$

12) $5.2\,\overline{)5.824}$

13) $.18\,\overline{).0828}$

14) $.16\,\overline{).3696}$

15) $.21\,\overline{).01323}$

16) $.32\,\overline{)1.152}$

17) $.47\,\overline{).4794}$

18) $.39\,\overline{)1.5717}$

19) $.06\,\overline{).1896}$

20) $.07\,\overline{).1435}$

21) $.08\,\overline{).3216}$

22) $.09\,\overline{).1053}$

23) $.08\,\overline{).1688}$

24) $.07\,\overline{).2205}$

Exercise F Copy each problem. Put a decimal point in the proper place in the quotient.

1) $\dfrac{337}{.6 \,)\, 2.022}$

6) $\dfrac{391}{.09 \,)\, 3.519}$

2) $\dfrac{63}{.7 \,)\, .0441}$

7) $\dfrac{35}{.09 \,)\, .0315}$

3) $\dfrac{116}{7.8 \,)\, 90.48}$

8) $\dfrac{313}{2.9 \,)\, 9.077}$

4) $\dfrac{597}{8 \,)\, 47.76}$

9) $\dfrac{7}{.6 \,)\, .0042}$

5) $\dfrac{52}{1.8 \,)\, 93.6}$

10) $\dfrac{85}{3.3 \,)\, 28.05}$

Exercise G Find the quotients.

1) $.06 \,)\, \overline{.798}$

4) $.19 \,)\, \overline{40.85}$

2) $.002 \,)\, \overline{.1624}$

5) $8.6 \,)\, \overline{215.86}$

3) $.13 \,)\, \overline{.728}$

6) $.008 \,)\, \overline{.2832}$

  PROBLEM SOLVING

Exercise H Solve these word problems.

1) Melinda's part-time job pays her $118.65. How many hours does she work if she earns $5.65 per hour?

2) Nina pays Randy $55.25 for cleaning her basement. If the job takes Randy 8.5 hours, then what are his hourly wages?

3) John buys steaks for $45.14. If he buys 7.4 pounds of steaks, what is the price per pound?

4) At $.33 per pound, how many pounds of potatoes can you buy for $2.64?

5) Larry drives 261.56 miles in 5.2 hours. What is his average speed?

You may need to include one or more zeros after the decimal point in the dividend so that the division will work out evenly. If there is no decimal point in the dividend, then put a decimal point and the zeros to the right of the dividend.

EXAMPLES

4 divided by 8

$$
\begin{array}{r}
.5 \\
8\overline{)4.0} \\
-4\,0 \\
\hline
0
\end{array}
$$

4 divided by .5

$$
\begin{array}{r}
8. \\
.5\overline{)4.0} \\
-4\,0 \\
\hline
0
\end{array}
$$

$.06 \div .5$

$$
\begin{array}{r}
.12 \\
.5\overline{).060} \\
-5 \\
\hline
10 \\
-10 \\
\hline
0
\end{array}
$$

$.18 \div 3.6$

$$
\begin{array}{r}
.05 \\
3.6\overline{).180} \\
-180 \\
\hline
0
\end{array}
$$

Exercise I Find the quotients.

1) $5\overline{)1}$
2) $4\overline{)6}$
3) $8\overline{)6}$
4) $.5\overline{)2}$
5) $.4\overline{)36}$
6) $.12\overline{)7.2}$
7) $.19\overline{)3.8}$

8) $.18\overline{)7.2}$
9) $.12\overline{).156}$
10) $1.4\overline{)112}$
11) $.15\overline{)4.545}$
12) $4.3\overline{)473}$
13) $.63\overline{)6.93}$
14) $.025\overline{).0525}$

15) $2.3\overline{).0276}$
16) $.014\overline{).00532}$
17) $.021\overline{).0882}$
18) $.015\overline{).0825}$
19) $.026\overline{)1.3}$
20) $.016\overline{)6.56}$
21) $.063\overline{)7.56}$

Exercise J Copy each problem. Put a decimal point in the proper place in the quotient.

1)
$$
\begin{array}{r}
55 \\
.32\overline{)17.6}
\end{array}
$$

2)
$$
\begin{array}{r}
125 \\
.4\overline{)5}
\end{array}
$$

3)
$$
\begin{array}{r}
31 \\
15\overline{).465}
\end{array}
$$

4)
$$
\begin{array}{r}
96 \\
4.5\overline{)432}
\end{array}
$$

5)
$$
\begin{array}{r}
225 \\
.004\overline{).09}
\end{array}
$$

6)
$$
\begin{array}{r}
47 \\
.005\overline{).235}
\end{array}
$$

7)
$$
\begin{array}{r}
125 \\
.08\overline{)1}
\end{array}
$$

8)
$$
\begin{array}{r}
31 \\
.11\overline{)34.1}
\end{array}
$$

9)
$$
\begin{array}{r}
48 \\
.06\overline{)28.8}
\end{array}
$$

Exercise K   Find the quotients. Round answers to the nearest hundredth.

1) $.17\overline{)34}$

2) $1.03\overline{)2.7}$

3) $.28\overline{)45}$

4) $.016\overline{)4.3}$

5) $.18\overline{)5.9}$

6) $1.8\overline{).37}$

7) $.7\overline{)6.2}$

8) $.18\overline{)36}$

9) $.005\overline{).65}$

10) $.23\overline{)195.5}$

PROBLEM SOLVING

Exercise L   Solve these word problems.

1) Pat and Susan drive a distance of 885 miles on their vacation. Their total driving time is 20 hours. What is their average driving speed to the nearest hundredth?

2) Jeffrey buys some picture frame wire for $3.30. If the wire costs 60¢ per foot, then how many feet of wire does he buy?

3) Carla buys a 7.4-pound roast for $22.57. What is the cost of the roast per pound?

4) A DC-10 flies 858.2 miles in 2.8 hours. What is the plane's average speed?

5) A plane flies 958.2 miles in 3 hours. What is the plane's average speed?

6) A machinist measures four blocks of metal and gets these readings: 1.96 inches, 1.93 inches, 2.01 inches, and 1.94 inches. What is the average reading?

7) Gary rides his bike for 8.4 hours. In this time, he travels 50.4 miles. What is Gary's average speed?

8) Mr. Ota drives 310.8 miles and uses 8.4 gallons of gas. How many miles does he get per gallon of gas?

9) Ozzie drives 273 miles and uses 7.5 gallons of gas. How many miles does Ozzie travel per gallon of gas?

Exercise M   Solve these problems.

1) Divide the sum of 8.5 and 5.3 by 2.

2) Divide 76.02 by 3 and add 4.374 to the answer.

3) Divide the difference of 14.3 and 9.28 by 4.

4) Divide the sum of 8.4 and 7.47 by 2.3.

5) Divide the product of .21 and 2.5 by 3.5.

Calculator Practice

Dividing decimals can be easy with your calculator. Use the decimal point and the division key. Check each entry to make sure the decimal point is correct.

> **EXAMPLE**   72.3 ÷ 81.78
> Press 72.3 ÷ 81.78 =
> The display reads 0.8840792.
> Round to the nearest thousandth.
> 72.3 ÷ 81.78 = .884

Calculator Exercise   Use a calculator to find these quotients. Round these answers to the neatest thousandth.

1) 61.5 ÷ 72.85

2) 8.36 ÷ 9.453

3) 72.4 ÷ 83.59

4) 5.8 ÷ 63.32

5) 702.7 ÷ 835.29

6) 906 ÷ 1,740.2

7) 85.349 ÷ 263.7

8) 19.4 ÷ 46.328

9) 35.92 ÷ 758.1

10) 23.9 ÷ 49.27

11) 83.5 ÷ 85.3

12) 6.8 ÷ 17.7

13) 13.9 ÷ 42.2

14) 79.98 ÷ 96.1

15) 39.6 ÷ 40.6

A decimal numeral may be renamed as a common fraction by using the digits in the numeral for the numerator. The denominator is the value of the last place name at the right of the numeral. You may need to simplify the fraction.

EXAMPLES $.012 = \blacksquare$ $.65 = \blacksquare$

$.012 = \dfrac{12}{1,000} = \dfrac{3}{250}$ $.65 = \dfrac{65}{100} = \dfrac{13}{20}$

Exercise A   Rename each decimal as a fraction or a mixed number. Give your answers in simplest form.

1) .82	**16)** .36	**31)** .0198	**46)** .00004
2) .5	**17)** .705	**32)** .00002	**47)** .1425
3) .208	**18)** .1	**33)** .55	**48)** .625
4) .75	**19)** .505	**34)** .006	**49)** .40
5) .888	**20)** .068	**35)** .3275	**50)** .488
6) .7	**21)** .0008	**36)** 16.375	**51)** 8.75
7) .240	**22)** .48	**37)** 50.05	**52)** .0384
8) .19	**23)** .00075	**38)** .000002	**53)** 3.84
9) .3425	**24)** .386	**39)** .0296	**54)** .0800
10) .45	**25)** .182	**40)** .101	**55)** .0075
11) .128	**26)** 4.8	**41)** .33	**56)** .3279
12) .60	**27)** .9000	**42)** .0015	**57)** .0099
13) .06	**28)** .298	**43)** 5.84	**58)** .39
14) .875	**29)** .345	**44)** .009	**59)** .0045
15) .0004	**30)** .63	**45)** .57	**60)** .365

Some fractions may be renamed as decimals by changing the denominator to a power of ten — like 10, 100, or 1,000.

EXAMPLES

$$\frac{14}{25} = \frac{14 \times 4}{25 \times 4} = \frac{56}{100} = .56$$

$$\frac{3}{40} = \frac{3 \times 25}{40 \times 25} = \frac{75}{1,000} = .075$$

Exercise A   Rename each fraction as a decimal.

1) $\frac{3}{10}$ 8) $\frac{2}{5}$ 15) $\frac{1}{2}$ 22) $\frac{72}{125}$

2) $\frac{17}{100}$ 9) $\frac{5}{8}$ 16) $\frac{19}{200}$ 23) $\frac{9}{100}$

3) $\frac{125}{1,000}$ 10) $\frac{15}{16}$ 17) $\frac{117}{10,000}$ 24) $\frac{3}{16}$

4) $\frac{7}{10}$ 11) $\frac{377}{2,000}$ 18) $\frac{18}{250}$ 25) $\frac{27}{500}$

5) $\frac{16}{25}$ 12) $\frac{7}{80}$ 19) $\frac{13}{16}$ 26) $\frac{43}{80}$

6) $\frac{17}{1,000}$ 13) $\frac{17}{20}$ 20) $\frac{13}{25}$ 27) $\frac{3}{40}$

7) $\frac{3}{50}$ 14) $\frac{23}{40}$ 21) $\frac{9}{16}$ 28) $\frac{139}{400}$

PROBLEM SOLVING

Exercise B   The Earth is the densest of all of the planets in our solar system. Change the fraction in each of these problems to a decimal by first changing the denominator to a power of ten.

1) Mercury is $\frac{239}{250}$ as dense as the Earth.

2) Mars is $\frac{359}{500}$ as dense as our Earth.

3) Pluto is only $\frac{1}{4}$ as dense as our planet.

4) Venus, our closest neighbor, is $\frac{119}{125}$ as dense as the Earth.

5) Saturn is $\frac{1}{8}$ as dense as our planet.

6) Neptune is $\frac{19}{50}$ as dense as Earth.

7) The largest planet, Jupiter, is $\frac{121}{500}$ as dense as Earth.

8) Uranus is $\frac{29}{100}$ as dense as the Earth.

9) Which planet is the least dense?

10) Except for Earth, which planet is the densest?

Repeating decimal

A decimal where the same series of digits repeats.

Some fractions cannot be changed to a decimal by raising the fraction to higher terms. They can be changed to a decimal only by dividing. Continue placing zeros in the dividend until the digits in the quotient begin repeating. Draw a bar over the digits to show which digits repeat. This is a **repeating decimal**.

EXAMPLE

$$\frac{7}{11} = 11\overline{)7.0000} \quad \begin{array}{r} .6363 = .\overline{63} \\ \end{array}$$

$$\begin{array}{r}
.6363 = .\overline{63} \\
11\overline{)7.0000} \\
-66 \\
\hline
40 \\
-33 \\
\hline
70 \\
-66 \\
\hline
40 \\
-33 \\
\hline
7
\end{array}$$

Exercise A Change these fractions to repeating decimals.

1) $\frac{3}{11}$ 4) $\frac{19}{22}$ 7) $\frac{2}{33}$ 10) $\frac{5}{6}$

2) $\frac{4}{9}$ 5) $\frac{7}{15}$ 8) $\frac{1}{3}$ 11) $\frac{1}{9}$

3) $\frac{7}{12}$ 6) $\frac{10}{11}$ 9) $\frac{2}{3}$ 12) $\frac{5}{7}$

Another way to express a fraction as a decimal is to round the decimal if it does not divide evenly.

EXAMPLES

$$\frac{5}{7} = 7\overline{)5.000} \quad \begin{array}{r} .714 \doteq .71 \end{array}$$

$$\begin{array}{r}
.714 \doteq .71 \\
7\overline{)5.000} \\
-49 \\
\hline
10 \\
-7 \\
\hline
30 \\
-28 \\
\hline
2
\end{array}
\qquad
\begin{array}{r}
.166 \doteq .17 \\
6\overline{)1.000} \\
-6 \\
\hline
40 \\
-36 \\
\hline
40 \\
-36 \\
\hline
4
\end{array}$$

$\frac{1}{6} = 6\overline{)1.000}$

Exercise B Change these fractions to decimals. Divide to three places and then round to two places.

1) $\frac{8}{13}$ 4) $\frac{2}{3}$ 7) $\frac{7}{9}$ 10) $\frac{7}{8}$

2) $\frac{3}{7}$ 5) $\frac{9}{11}$ 8) $\frac{5}{6}$ 11) $\frac{10}{21}$

3) $\frac{5}{8}$ 6) $\frac{8}{21}$ 9) $\frac{1}{12}$ 12) $\frac{7}{12}$

Write these numerals in words:

1) 162.057

2) 37.1008

Write a numeral for each:

3) Nine and forty-two hundredths

4) One hundred three and ninety-six thousandths

Arrange each set in order from smallest to largest:

5) .3156   .309   315

6) .0235   .1   .0209

Round each numeral:

7) 17.429 to the nearest tenth

8) 53.0819 to the nearest thousandth

Find the answers:

9) $25 + .7 + .29 + 3$

10) $5 + .92 + 13.2 + .6$

11) 5.8×36

12) $.329 \times .003$

13) $1.7 - .236$

14) $12 - .981$

Divide:

15) $1.012 \div 23$

16) $1.152 \div .32$

17) $6.56 \div .016$

Express each fraction as a decimal rounded to 3 places:

18) $\dfrac{1}{6}$

19) $\dfrac{6}{7}$

20) $\dfrac{7}{9}$

21) $\dfrac{5}{11}$

Express these numerals in scientific notation:

22) .000835

23) .0000051

24) .0000009315

25) .000851

Test Taking Tip | When you read decimal numbers, get in the habit of reading them as mathematical language. For example, read .61 as "sixty-one hundredths" instead of "point 61."

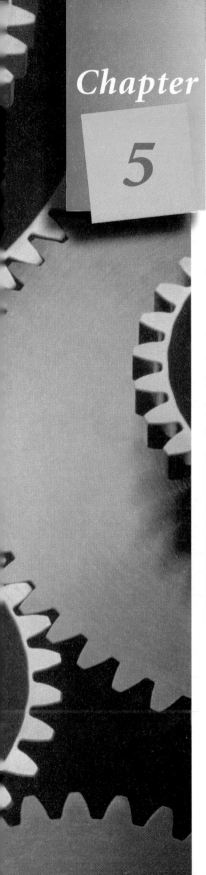

Chapter 5

Ratio and Proportion

Whether you ride a bicycle, repair the gears in a large machine, or prepare recipes, you use ratio and proportion to help you. Ratio and proportion can help you solve problems throughout your lifetime. You'll find yourself using the skills you learn in this chapter when you read maps, buy gasoline, or rearrange your bedroom.

In Chapter 5, you will learn some of the ways to use division and algebra to help you solve problems.

Goals for Learning

▶ To write a ratio as a fraction in simplest form

▶ To compare amounts, using a ratio

▶ To identify ratios that form a proportion

▶ To find the missing term in a proportion

▶ To solve word problems, using ratios and proportions

Ratio

Comparison of two numbers using division.

A **ratio** is a **comparison** of two numbers that uses division. This division is usually written as a fraction.

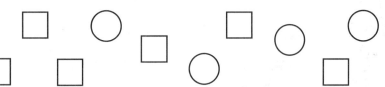

Comparison

Examining two numbers to see which is larger.

There are four circles and six squares. The ratio of the number of circles to the number of squares is *four to six*. Three ways to write this ratio are:

$$4 \text{ to } 6 \qquad 4:6 \qquad \frac{4}{6}$$

The ratio of squares to circles is *six to four*. This ratio can also be written in three ways:

$$6 \text{ to } 4 \qquad 6:4 \qquad \frac{6}{4}$$

Fractional form

Expressed as a fraction.

You can simplify a ratio by writing it as a fraction and then dividing both terms by their greatest common factor. Leave the ratio in **fractional form** even if you can change the fraction to a whole number or a mixed number.

EXAMPLES   9 to 12   20 to 15

$$\frac{9}{12} = \frac{9 \div 3}{12 \div 3} \qquad\qquad \frac{20}{15} = \frac{20 \div 5}{15 \div 5}$$

$$= \frac{3}{4} \qquad\qquad\qquad\qquad = \frac{4}{3}$$

Exercise A   Write each ratio as a fraction in simplest form.

1) 12 to 20   **6)** 14 to 21   **11)** 8 to 2

2) 18 to 21   **7)** 21 to 14   **12)** 9 to 12

3) 12 to 8   **8)** 8 to 36   **13)** 20 to 24

4) 4 to 6   **9)** 15 to 19   **14)** 16 to 12

5) 12 to 15   **10)** 6 to 15   **15)** 8 to 19

A ratio may compare two amounts or two sets of objects. It may describe a rate. Use like units whenever possible.

EXAMPLES

4 pounds for $1.20 $\frac{4}{120} = \frac{1}{30}$

□□□ to ○○
□□□   ○○ $\frac{6 \text{ shapes}}{4 \text{ shapes}} = \frac{3}{2}$

15 minutes to 1 hour $\frac{15 \text{ minutes}}{60 \text{ minutes}} = \frac{1}{4}$

Exercise B   Write a ratio to compare each of the following. Express it in simplest form.

1) 150 miles to 4 hours

2) 1 quarter to 1 nickel

3) 4 cans of soup for 85¢

4) 150 miles on 8 gallons

5) $4.35 per hour

6) 1 fifty-cent piece to 1 dime

7) 4 hits for 6 times at bat

8) 12 oranges for $1.00

9) 25 minutes to 2 hours

10) 4 days to 2 weeks

11) 1 nickel and 1 penny to 2 dimes

12) 1 year to 8 months

13) 3 hamburgers to 2 people

14) 140 miles to 8 gallons

Proportion

Two equal ratios.

When two ratios are equal, we say that they form a **proportion.** You can tell if two ratios are equal by comparing the cross products.

EXAMPLES

Do $\frac{5}{8}$ and $\frac{12}{16}$ form a proportion?

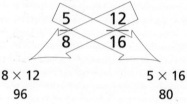

8×12 5×16

96   80

The cross products are 96 and 80. The cross products are not equal. Therefore, the ratios do not form a proportion. This inequality can be shown with a symbol, ≠, which means "is not equal to."

$$\frac{5}{8} \neq \frac{12}{16}$$

Do $\frac{1\frac{1}{2}}{4}$ and $\frac{3}{8}$ form a proportion?

$$\frac{1\frac{1}{2}}{4} = \frac{3}{8}$$

4×3 $1\frac{1}{2} \times 8 = \frac{3}{2} \times \frac{8}{1} = \frac{24}{2}$

12   12

The cross products are 12 and 12. The cross products are equal. Therefore, the ratios do form a proportion.

$$\frac{1\frac{1}{2}}{4} = \frac{3}{8}$$

Exercise A Use cross products to see if the ratios are equal. Write an equal sign to show which ratios form a proportion. Write an inequality symbol (≠) to show which ratios do not form a proportion.

1) $\frac{10}{16}$ $\frac{5}{8}$ 4) $\frac{12}{20}$ $\frac{3}{5}$ 7) $\frac{10}{12}$ $\frac{2}{3}$

2) $\frac{4}{8}$ $\frac{2}{3}$ 5) $\frac{10}{12}$ $\frac{15}{18}$ 8) $\frac{5}{9}$ $\frac{15}{27}$

3) $\frac{6}{8}$ $\frac{9}{12}$ 6) $\frac{\frac{2}{3}}{6}$ $\frac{3}{2}$ 9) $\frac{1\frac{1}{2}}{3}$ $\frac{3}{6}$

Calculator Practice

Use your calculator to find cross products. If the cross products are equal, the ratios form a proportion.

> **EXAMPLES** $\frac{2}{3}$ and $\frac{4}{6}$
>
> Press 3 ✕ 4 = The display reads *12*.
> Press 2 ✕ 6 = The display reads *12*.
>
> 12 = 12 Therefore the ratios are equal and form a proportion.
>
>
> $\frac{5}{6}$ and $\frac{7}{8}$
>
> Press 6 ✕ 7 = The display reads *42*.
> Press 5 ✕ 8 = The display reads *40*.
>
> 40 ≠ 42 Therefore the ratios do not form a proportion.

Calculator Exercise   Use a calculator to find the cross products. Compare the cross products and determine if the ratios form a proportion.

1) $\frac{3}{12}$ and $\frac{10}{30}$

2) $\frac{7}{16}$ and $\frac{42}{66}$

3) $\frac{13}{70}$ and $\frac{39}{200}$

4) $\frac{16}{34}$ and $\frac{80}{170}$

5) $\frac{11}{12}$ and $\frac{66}{72}$

6) $\frac{14}{17}$ and $\frac{112}{134}$

7) $\frac{2}{3}$ and $\frac{120}{190}$

8) $\frac{23}{99}$ and $\frac{115}{495}$

Solving Proportions

Unknown term

The missing number in a proportion.

You can use cross products to find an **unknown term** in a proportion. The letter *n* stands for the missing number.

n

A letter used to stand for an unknown number.

EXAMPLES

$$\frac{8}{n} = \frac{4}{6}$$

$$4 \times n = 8 \times 6$$

$$4n = 48$$

$$\frac{4n}{4} = \frac{48}{4}$$

$$n = 12$$

$$\frac{2\frac{1}{2}}{5} = \frac{n}{6}$$

$$5 \times n = 2\frac{1}{2} \times 6$$

$$5n = 15$$

$$\frac{5n}{5} = \frac{15}{5}$$

$$n = 3$$

Exercise A Solve for the missing number.

1) $\frac{12}{n} = \frac{20}{25}$

2) $\frac{5}{8} = \frac{n}{24}$

3) $\frac{2}{3} = \frac{16}{n}$

4) $\frac{12}{14} = \frac{n}{21}$

5) $\frac{n}{10} = \frac{6}{15}$

6) $\frac{12}{3} = \frac{10}{n}$

7) $\frac{\frac{1}{2}}{4} = \frac{n}{20}$

8) $\frac{5}{n} = \frac{10}{16}$

9) $\frac{12}{8} = \frac{4\frac{1}{2}}{n}$

10) $\frac{30}{20} = \frac{n}{15}$

11) $\frac{3}{n} = \frac{51}{17}$

12) $\frac{1\frac{1}{2}}{3} = \frac{n}{8}$

13) $\frac{9}{n} = \frac{27}{33}$

14) $\frac{8}{10} = \frac{n}{25}$

15) $\frac{6}{8} = \frac{7}{n}$

16) $\frac{3}{7} = \frac{n}{25}$

17) $\frac{4}{n} = \frac{12}{15}$

18) $\frac{n}{10} = \frac{8}{11}$

Mixtures	Proportions can be used to solve problems involving **mixtures**. You must be careful that the two ratios are written in the same order.
Combinations of two or more items.	

EXAMPLE | Sunburst Gold paint is made by mixing 2 parts yellow to 1 part red. How many pints of red paint should be mixed with 3 pints of yellow paint?

$$\frac{\text{Yellow}}{\text{Red}} \qquad \frac{2}{1} = \frac{3}{n} \qquad 3 = 2n$$

$$\frac{3}{2} = \frac{2n}{2}$$

$$1\frac{1}{2} = n$$

You should use $1\frac{1}{2}$ pints of red paint.

PROBLEM SOLVING

Exercise A   Use proportions to help you solve these word problems.

1) Apple Green paint is made by mixing 7 parts yellow to 3 parts blue. How much yellow should be mixed with 9 pints of blue?

2) Gorp is 5 parts peanuts and 2 parts raisins. How many pounds of peanuts should be mixed with one-half pound of raisins?

3) Peach paint is 1 part yellow to 3 parts red. How much yellow should be mixed with 4 quarts of red?

4) Mix 3 quarts of water with 2 lemons to make lemonade. How many quarts of water are mixed with 1 lemon?

5) Mix 6 parts cornstarch to 1 part water to make Glop. How much water should be used with 2 cups cornstarch?

6) Purple paint is 5 parts blue to 1 part red. How much red should be mixed with 2 quarts of blue?

7) Mix 4 parts yellow to 2 parts red to get orange. How much red and yellow should be mixed to get 2 gallons of orange?

A five-speed bicycle has a chain that is attached to a pedal **sprocket** in the front and to five gears in the back. The ratio of pedal turns to rear wheel turns for each gear is:

$$\frac{\text{Pedal Turns}}{\text{Rear Wheel Turns}}$$

1st gear	2d gear	3d gear	4th gear	5th gear
$\dfrac{9}{14}$	$\dfrac{4}{7}$	$\dfrac{1}{2}$	$\dfrac{3}{7}$	$\dfrac{5}{14}$

Sprocket
A wheel with teeth that pulls a chain.

You can use a proportion to help you find the number of times that the rear wheel turns for a given number of pedal turns.

EXAMPLE In second gear, the pedal turned 16 times. How many times did the rear wheel turn?

$$\frac{\text{Pedal Turns}}{\text{Rear Wheel Turns}} \qquad \frac{4}{7} = \frac{16}{n}$$

$$112 = 4n$$
$$28 = n$$

The rear wheel turned 28 times.

You can also find the number of times that you must turn the pedal for a given number of rear wheel turns.

EXAMPLE In fourth gear, the rear wheel turned 28 times. How many pedal turns were there?

$$\frac{\text{Pedal Turns}}{\text{Rear Wheel Turns}} \qquad \frac{3}{7} = \frac{n}{28}$$

$$7n = 84$$
$$n = 12$$

The pedal turned 12 times.

Exercise B Use a proportion to help you find the missing numbers in this chart.

	Gear	Pedal Turns	Rear Wheel Turns
1)	1st	270	
2)	2d	270	
3)	3d	270	
4)	4th	270	
5)	5th	270	
6)	1st		42
7)	2d		42
8)	3d		42
9)	4th		42
10)	5th		42

EXAMPLE With one rear wheel turn, a 26-inch bicycle moves 82 inches along the ground. If someone makes 270 pedal turns in first gear, then how many feet does the bike travel?

Step 1 Solve a proportion for pedal turns to rear wheel turns in first gear.

$$\frac{9 \text{ Pedal turns}}{14 \text{ Rear wheel turns}} = \frac{270 \text{ Pedal turns}}{n \text{ Rear wheel turns}}$$

$n = 420$. There are 420 rear wheel turns in 270 pedal turns.

Step 2 Calculate how many inches are in 420 rear wheel turns.

$$\frac{1 \text{ Rear wheel turn}}{82 \text{ Inches}} = \frac{420 \text{ Rear wheel turns}}{n \text{ Inches}}$$

$n = 34{,}440$. The bike will have traveled 34,440 inches with 420 pedal turns in first gear.

PROBLEM SOLVING

Exercise C Use the ratios on page 122 to solve the following word problems.

1) Shana makes 24 pedal turns in second gear with her 26-inch bicycle. About how many inches has her bicycle traveled?

2) A 24-inch bicycle travels about 75 inches with one rear wheel turn. How many inches will the bike go with 270 rear wheel turns in fifth gear?

Proportions may be used to make **conversions** between the **currencies** of different countries.

Conversions

Changes from one unit of measure to a different one.

Country	Currency	U.S. Dollar =
Barbados	Barbados dollar = 100 cents	1.96 BBD
Cayman Islands	Cayman Islands dollar = 100 cents	.85 CID
Haiti	Gourde = 100 centimes	5.00 GOU
West Indies	East Carib dollar = 100 cents	1.85 ECD

Currency

Money.

Exercise D Use a proportion to make these currency conversions. Refer to the chart above. Round your answers to the nearest cent.

EXAMPLES Change 40 U.S. dollars to Barbados currency.

$$\frac{USD}{BBD} \qquad \frac{1}{1.96} = \frac{40}{n}$$

78.40 = 1n
78 dollars and 40 cents

Change 32 Barbados dollars to U.S. currency.

$$\frac{USD}{BBD} \qquad \frac{1}{1.96} = \frac{n}{32}$$

1.96n = 32
n = 16.326
16 dollars and 33 cents

1) Change 50 U.S. dollars to Haitian currency.

2) Change 74 East Carib dollars to U.S. currency.

3) Change 60 U.S. dollars to Barbados currency.

4) Change 40 gourdes to U.S. currency.

5) Change 45 U.S. dollars to Cayman Islands currency.

6) Change 80 Barbados dollars to U.S. currency.

Exercise E   Use a proportion to help you solve each word problem.

1) A car travels 240 miles on 15 gallons of gas. How far can the car travel on 20 gallons of gas?

2) Three gallons of paint will cover 825 square feet of wall space. How many square feet will 4 gallons cover?

3) Mario can drive 250 miles in 4 hours. How far can he drive in 6 hours?

4) At Smythe College, there are 5 females for every 4 males. If there are 372 males, then how many females are there?

5) If 2 pounds of hamburger will serve 3 people, then how many pounds of hamburger will serve 7 people?

6) Kim Lu can mow 2 lawns in $1\frac{1}{2}$ hours. How long will it take him to mow 6 lawns?

7) At Camp Runabout, there are 2 counselors for every 15 campers. If 165 campers are at the camp, then how many counselors are there?

8) On a map, 1 inch equals 15 miles. How many miles apart are two towns that are 6.4 in. apart on the map?

9) A deluxe dollhouse is built to a 1:40 scale. If the dollhouse is 20 inches high, then how high is the actual house?

10) Oranges are selling at the rate of 12 oranges for a dollar. How much will 27 oranges cost?

11) Kevin's car gets 32 miles to one gallon of gas. How much gas will he use on a 475-mile trip?

Write each ratio as a fraction in simplest form:

1) 18 to 24

2) 48 to 32

3) 27 to 32

Write a ratio to compare these amounts:

4) 35 minutes to 1 hour

5) 15¢ to 25¢

Tell whether or not each pair of ratios forms a proportion.
Use = or ≠ .

6) $\dfrac{12}{15}$ $\qquad$ $\dfrac{8}{10}$

7) $\dfrac{12}{8}$ $\qquad$ $\dfrac{4}{3}$

8) $\dfrac{6}{8}$ $\qquad$ $\dfrac{9}{12}$

Solve for the missing number:

9) $\dfrac{n}{8} = \dfrac{6}{12}$

10) $\dfrac{4}{10} = \dfrac{n}{15}$

11) $\dfrac{7}{9} = \dfrac{5}{n}$

12) $\dfrac{\frac{2}{3}}{n} = \dfrac{7}{21}$

13) $\dfrac{4}{3} = \dfrac{n}{9}$

14) $\dfrac{378}{5.4} = \dfrac{n}{3.1}$

Solve these word problems:

15) Sunset Gold paint is made by mixing 3 parts yellow to 1 part red. How much red is to be mixed with 2 quarts of yellow?

16) Twelve oranges cost $1.00. How much do 9 oranges cost?

17) John's car gets 36 miles to one gallon of gas. How much gas will he use to travel 81 miles?

18) The scale on a map is 1 inch to 20 miles. How many miles apart are two towns that are $8\frac{2}{5}$ inches apart on the map?

19) Paula drives 252 miles and uses 8 gallons of gas. How far does she drive on one gallon of gas?

20) If one dollar equals 85¢ in Cayman Islands currency, then what would $10.71 in Cayman Islands currency be in U.S. currency?

Test Taking Tip   Learn from your mistakes. Review corrected homework and identify your errors.

Sale

50%OFF

Or More On Original Prices

Priced as Marked

Chapter 6

Percent

L ist the places where you have seen percents used to communicate an idea to people. Does your list include baseball statistics on trading cards, grades on reports, projects, and tests? How about money off at sales? Tips for good service are usually based on a percent. Even pay for selling goods is sometimes calculated with percents. When you think about it and look around you, you see that we use percent many ways in our daily lives.

In Chapter 6, you will learn about the mathematics involved in working with percents. Next time you and your friends go out to eat, you can be the one who calculates the tip!

Goals for Learning

▶ To rename a percent as a decimal and a fraction in simplest form

▶ To rename a decimal and a fraction as a percent

▶ To find the missing terms in a percent sentence

▶ To use a proportion to find the missing term in a percent sentence

▶ To solve word problems involving percents and tax, commissions, interest, and tips

▶ To calculate monthly payments on an installment plan

Percent, %
Part per one hundred.

The symbol "%" is read as "percent." **Percent** means "per hundred" or "out of one hundred." Therefore, 82% means 82 per hundred, or 82 out of one hundred. In the example below, 82 squares out of the 100 squares are shaded. We say that 82% of the figure is shaded.

EXAMPLE

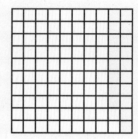

Exercise A Tell what percent of each figure is shaded.

1)
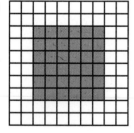

3)
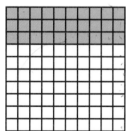

5)
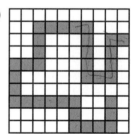

2)
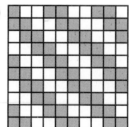

4)
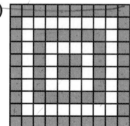

6)
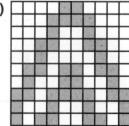

Twenty-seven percent means 27 per hundred or 27 hundredths. We can write 27 hundredths as .27 or as $\frac{27}{100}$. By writing the percent as hundredths, we can write a percent as a decimal or a fraction. You may need to simplify the fraction to lowest terms.

EXAMPLES   Write 24% as a decimal and as a fraction.
$24\% = .24$

$24\% = \frac{24}{100} = \frac{6}{25}$

Write 6% as a decimal and as a fraction.
$6\% = .06$

$6\% = \frac{6}{100} = \frac{3}{50}$

Exercise A   Write each percent as a decimal and as a fraction.

1) 13%

2) 7%

3) 68%

4) 20%

5) 45%

6) 8%

7) 1%

8) 10%

9) 3%

10) 97%

11) 36%

12) 40%

13) 50%

14) 75%

15) 120%

You may see a percent that is not a whole number. You still move the decimal point two places to the left to change to a decimal. Do not count any fractions in the two places.

Change 1.6% to a decimal.

$1.6\% = .016$

Change $4\frac{3}{4}\%$ to a decimal.

$4\frac{3}{4}\% = .04\frac{3}{4}$

Exercise B Change each percent to a decimal.

1) 46.3%

2) $8\frac{1}{3}\%$

3) .8%

4) $22\frac{1}{3}\%$

5) 3.62%

6) $4.4\frac{1}{2}\%$

7) 1.04%

8) .27%

9) $5\frac{1}{3}\%$

10) $128\frac{1}{2}\%$

11) $\frac{4}{5}\%$

12) $.007\frac{1}{2}\%$

You can easily change a percent that contains a fraction to a fraction if you think of "percent" as meaning "times one-hundredth."

Change $12\frac{1}{2}\%$ to a fraction.

$$12\frac{1}{2}\% = 12\frac{1}{2} \times \frac{1}{100}$$
$$= \frac{25}{2} \times \frac{1}{100}$$
$$= \frac{1}{8}$$

Change $6\frac{2}{3}\%$ to a fraction.

$$6\frac{2}{3}\% = 6\frac{2}{3} \times \frac{1}{100}$$
$$= \frac{20}{3} \times \frac{1}{100}$$
$$= \frac{1}{15}$$

Exercise C Change each percent to a fraction in simplest form.

1) $2\frac{1}{2}\%$

2) $17\frac{1}{2}\%$

3) $3\frac{1}{3}\%$

4) $42\frac{1}{2}\%$

5) $20\frac{1}{2}\%$

6) $2\frac{1}{5}\%$

7) $37\frac{1}{2}\%$

8) $8\frac{1}{3}\%$

9) $16\frac{2}{3}\%$

10) $22\frac{2}{9}\%$

11) $14\frac{2}{7}\%$

12) $20\frac{1}{5}\%$

You can rename a decimal as a percent by moving the decimal point two places to the right and adding the percent symbol. You would not write the decimal point if it occurs at the end of the number.

EXAMPLES   Change .184 to a percent.

.184 = 18.4%

Change .6 to a percent.

.6 = 60%

Exercise A   Rename these decimals as percents.

1) .46	**5)** .003	**9)** .253
2) .102	**6)** 1.28	**10)** .0461
3) .9	**7)** .0042	**11)** 12.3
4) .046	**8)** 3.4	**12)** .068

You can change a fraction to a percent by dividing the denominator into the numerator. Add a decimal point and two zeros to the numerator. Divide. This gives you a two-place decimal for a quotient. Rename the decimal as a percent.

EXAMPLES   Change $\frac{3}{5}$ to a percent.

$$\begin{array}{r} .60 = 60\% \\ 5\,\overline{)3.00} \end{array}$$

Change $\frac{4}{7}$ to a percent.

$$\begin{array}{r} .57\frac{1}{7} = 57\frac{1}{7}\% \\ 7\,\overline{)4.00} \end{array}$$

Exercise B   Rename these fractions as percents.

1) $\frac{3}{4}$	**4)** $\frac{5}{9}$	**7)** $\frac{1}{15}$	**10)** $\frac{3}{16}$
2) $\frac{1}{20}$	**5)** $\frac{7}{13}$	**8)** $\frac{2}{3}$	**11)** $\frac{7}{8}$
3) $\frac{5}{8}$	**6)** $\frac{3}{50}$	**9)** $\frac{17}{20}$	**12)** $\frac{20}{13}$

You may not want a fractional percent for an answer. Then you would round to the nearest whole percent. This is done by dividing to three places instead of two. Round the three-place decimal to a two-place decimal and then change this decimal to a percent.

EXAMPLE   Rename $\frac{5}{7}$ as a percent.

$$.714 \doteq .71 = 71\%$$
$$7\,\overline{)5.000}$$

Exercise C   Rename each fraction as a percent. Round to the nearest whole percent, if necessary.

1) $\frac{7}{8}$

2) $\frac{4}{5}$

3) $\frac{6}{7}$

4) $\frac{5}{11}$

5) $\frac{8}{9}$

6) $\frac{7}{10}$

7) $\frac{8}{12}$

8) $\frac{12}{24}$

9) $\frac{33}{40}$

10) $\frac{4}{10}$

11) $\frac{6}{8}$

12) $\frac{4}{9}$

13) $\frac{8}{10}$

14) $\frac{14}{20}$

15) $\frac{14}{16}$

16) $\frac{9}{12}$

17) $\frac{8}{22}$

18) $\frac{16}{20}$

19) $\frac{8}{14}$

20) $\frac{2}{7}$

21) $\frac{3}{8}$

22) $\frac{5}{8}$

23) $\frac{6}{9}$

24) $\frac{2}{3}$

25) $\frac{3}{4}$

26) $\frac{3}{12}$

27) $\frac{3}{24}$

28) $\frac{52}{100}$

29) $\frac{6}{12}$

30) $\frac{22}{25}$

31) $\frac{6}{20}$

32) $\frac{18}{48}$

33) $\frac{16}{48}$

34) $\frac{13}{20}$

35) $\frac{11}{15}$

36) $\frac{35}{40}$

37) $\frac{42}{50}$

38) $\frac{78}{100}$

39) $\frac{38}{50}$

40) $\frac{32}{64}$

Exercise D Rename the fractions described in these word problems as percents. Round any remainders.

1) Manuel receives $\frac{7}{8}$ of the votes cast. What percent of the votes does he receive?

2) Jason correctly answers 32 problems out of 35 problems on a test. What percent of the problems does he get correct?

3) An advertisement claims that seven out of ten doctors recommend Brand A aspirin. What percent of the doctors recommend the aspirin?

4) Kennedy Middle School wins 12 of their 20 football games. What percent of their games do they win? What percent of their games do they lose?

5) The ninth-grade class sells 16 tickets on Monday, 17 tickets on Tuesday, and 19 tickets on Wednesday. What percent of 135 tickets have they sold?

6) Suki can make 18 out of 25 shots from the foul line. What percent of the shots can she make?

7) Two-thirds of a neighborhood attend a meeting. What percent of the neighborhood attends the meeting?

8) Four members of the class are absent. What percent of the class of 35 is absent?

9) The Stateliners win 5 out of their 12 games. What percent of their games do they win?

10) Katie gets 38 of 45 problems correct. What percent of the problems does she get correct?

Exercise E   Fill in this chart.

	Fraction	Decimal	Percent
1)	$\frac{3}{8}$		
2)			84%
3)		.48	
4)			9%
5)		$.26\frac{2}{3}$	
6)	$\frac{3}{40}$		
7)			$6\frac{2}{3}\%$
8)		.8	

PROBLEM SOLVING

Exercise F   Make the conversions asked for in these word problems.

1) "55% cotton." What fraction is cotton?

2) The Bluebirds win .625 of their games. What percent do they win?

3) 48% are girls. What fraction are girls?

4) 87% pass the test. What fraction passes?

5) "$\frac{1}{4}$ off all prices." What is the percent off?

6) Joe is batting .408. What percent is this?

7) "22% down on a car." What fraction is this?

8) Sales are up 6.4%. What is this as a decimal?

9) "16% unemployed." What fraction are unemployed?

10) "4 out of 5 doctors recommend…" What percent is this?

Calculator Practice

Use your calculator to rename fractions as decimals and then you can change decimals to percents. Round decimals to two places.

EXAMPLE   Express $\frac{6}{13}$ as a percent.

Press 6 ÷ 13 =

The display reads 0.4615385.

Round the decimal to two places, then move the decimal point two places to the right and add the percent symbol.

The answer is 46%.

Calculator Exercise   Use a calculator to rename these fractions as percents.

1) $\frac{5}{13}$

2) $\frac{6}{17}$

3) $\frac{8}{22}$

4) $\frac{5}{17}$

5) $\frac{6}{19}$

6) $\frac{5}{11}$

7) $\frac{9}{11}$

8) $\frac{15}{21}$

9) $\frac{34}{50}$

10) $\frac{8}{13}$

11) $\frac{45}{49}$

12) $\frac{9}{13}$

Rate

Percent.

Base

The amount you are taking a part or percent of.

Percentage

Result obtained by multiplying a number by a percent.

Three elements are in any percent sentence—the rate, the base, and the percentage. The **rate** is the percent in the problem. The **base** is the whole amount, the number from which you are taking a percentage. The **percentage** is the part, the number that you get when you take the percent of the base.

EXAMPLE   20% of 80 is 16

Rate   Base   Percentage

Exercise A   In the problems below, identify the rate, the base, and the percentage. If one of these elements is not given, write *n* for that unknown element. It is not necessary to work any of the problems.

1) 35% of 40 is 14

2) 4.5 is 18% of 25

3) *x*% of 82 is 6

4) What is 29% of 103?

5) 18 is what percent of 82?

6) 9% of what number is 14?

7) What percent of 82 is 36?

8) 12% of 106 is what number?

9) 35 is 72% of what number?

10) 20% of 82

11) She got 82% of the 50 questions correct.

12) 4 out of 5 dentists recommend Brand A toothbrushes.

13) 25% off the regular price of $52.00

14) The 15% tip amounts to $1.75

15) 8% of the 52,000 parts are defective.

You can find the percentage, or part, in a percent problem by expressing the rate as a decimal and multiplying it by the base.

EXAMPLES   28% of 62 is what number?
$$.28 \times 62 = n$$
$$17.36 = n$$

3% of 45 is what number?
$$.03 \times 45 = n$$
$$1.35 = n$$

Exercise A   Find the percentage in each of these percent sentences.

1) 22% of 36 is ___.
2) 52% of 50 is ___.
3) 7% of 48 is ___.
4) 2% of 16 is ___.
5) 29% of 3 is ___.
6) 45% of 23 is ___.
7) 3.2% of 42 is ___.

8) 43% of 3.2 is ___.
9) 39% of .7 is ___.
10) .3% of .6 is ___.
11) 86% of 72 is ___.
12) 9.2% of 15 is ___.
13) 2% of 18 is ___.
14) 16% of 19 is ___.

15) 35% of 15 is ___.
16) 3.2% of 25 is ___.
17) 9% of 23 is ___.
18) 26% of 23 is ___.
19) .5% of 100 is ___.
20) 82% of 200 is ___.
21) 36% of 36 is ___.

Exercise B   Solve for the percentage.

1) What number is 23% of 8?
2) What number is 15% of 30?
3) What number is 28% of 8?
4) What number is 19% of .6?
5) What number is 10% of 16?
6) What number is 2% of .7?
7) What number is .8% of .3?
8) What number is 1.9% of 2?
9) n is .02% of 1.7
10) n is 1.6% of 100
11) n is 25% of 50
12) n is 75% of 80
13) 82% of 50.2 is n
14) n is 92% of 92

15) n is 6.5% of 23
16) 0.8% of 50 is n
17) n is 6.5% of 60
18) 0.1% of 100 is n
19) n is .3% of 24
20) n is 2.2% of 10
21) 23% of 51 is n
22) n is 31% of 2.1
23) 0.9% of 34 is n
24) 25% of 72 is n
25) n is 39% of 10
26) 10% of 10 is n
27) 18% of 200 is n
28) n is 75% of 250

| EXAMPLE | Andre earns $250. He spends 60%. How much does he spend? |

60% of $250 is what number?

$$.60 \times \$250 = n$$
$$\$150.00 = n$$

PROBLEM SOLVING

Exercise C   Solve these word problems. Write a percent sentence first.

1) A test has 50 questions. Al gets 90% correct. How many questions does he get correct?

2) The team plays 60 games. They win 30%. How many do they win?

3) 35 students are in class. 60% are girls. How many are girls? How many are boys?

4) 25 students are tested. 20% do very well. How many do very well?

5) There are 960 tenth-grade students. 85% participate in extracurricular activities. How may students participate?

6) Raoul weighs 130 pounds. He loses 10% on a diet. How many pounds does he lose?

7) Cassie earns $150 per week. She receives a 20% raise. How much money is the raise?

8) Selena finds $32,000. There is a 15% reward. How much is the reward?

You can find the base in a percent problem by dividing the percentage by the rate. Rename the rate as a decimal first.

EXAMPLES   25% of what number is 12?

$.25 \times n = 12$

$n = 12 \div .25$

$n = 48$

1.3% of what number is .104?

$0.013 \times n = 0.104$

$n = 0.104 \div 0.013$

$n = 8$

Exercise A   Find the base in each of these percent sentences.

1) 22% of ___ is 17.6

2) 45% of ___ is 80.55

3) 60% of ___ is 120

4) 75% of ___ is 42.6

5) 80% of ___ is 32

6) 30% of ___ is 18

7) 20% of ___ is 18

8) 10% of ___ is 8

9) 20% of ___ is 6.4

10) 12% of ___ is 7.2

11) 45% of ___ is 27

12) 60% of ___ is 42

13) 24% of ___ is 36

14) 15% of ___ is 60

15) 84% of ___ is 63

16) 48% of ___ is 78

17) 20% of ___ is 37

18) 5% of ___ is 92

19) 16% of ___ is 32

20) 19% of ___ is 57

Exercise B Solve for the base.

1) 5.75 is 23% of what number?
2) 35 is 35% of what number?
3) 45 is 25% of what number?
4) 64 is 32% of what number?
5) 21.6 is 48% of what number?
6) 6.5 is 13% of what number?
7) 12.6 is 28% of what number?
8) 190 is 95% of what number?
9) 2.2 is 40% of n
10) 1.62 is 60% of n
11) 22% of n is 21.56
12) 27 is 30% of n
13) 40% of n is 22
14) 57 is 95% of n

15) 21 is 35% of n
16) 26% of n is 13
17) 4.2 is 12% of n
18) 85% of n is 56.1
19) 20% of n is 1.7
20) 7.2 is 8% of n
21) 0.21 is 6% of n
22) 18% of n is 36
23) 30 is 60% of n
24) 10% of n is 0.55
25) 4.5 is 25% of n
26) 18% of n is 9
27) 85% of n is 680
28) 14.4 is 90% of n

EXAMPLE

20% of the class are girls. 6 girls are in the class. How many students are in the class?

20% of what number is 6?

$.20 \times n = 6$

$n = 6 \div .20$

$n = 30$

PROBLEM SOLVING

Exercise C Solve these word problems. Write a percent sentence first.

1) 75% of the buses have arrived. 48 have arrived. How many buses are there in all?

2) 80% of the students vote. 48 students vote. How many students are there in all?

3) Marit loses 32% of her beads. Marit loses 24 beads. How many beads did she have to begin with?

4) 8 students did not go on a trip. 16% did not go on the trip. How many students are there in all?

5) John saves 20% of his salary. He saves $16 per week. What is his weekly salary?

6) Susan spends 80% of her earnings. She spends $40. How much does she earn?

7) The team won 55% of their games. 33 games were won. How many games were played?

8) Ana receives a 20% reward for finding money. The reward is $48. How much money did she find?

You can find the rate by dividing the percentage by the base. Remember that the rate is a percent. This means that the answer that you get is the rate times 100. One way to ensure that you get the correct answer is to mark off two decimal places in the base before dividing.

EXAMPLES   What percent of 17 is 1.02?

$$n\% \times 17 = 1.02 \qquad\qquad n \times 17 = 1.02$$
$$n \times .17 = 1.02 \qquad\qquad n = \frac{1.02}{17}$$
$$n = 1.02 \div .17 \qquad\qquad n = .06 = 6\%$$
$$n = 6\%$$

What percent of 35 is 21?

$$n\% \times 35 = 21 \qquad\qquad n \times 35 = 21$$
$$n \times .35 = 21 \qquad\qquad n = \frac{21}{35}$$
$$n = 21 \div .35 \qquad\qquad n = .6 = 60\%$$
$$n = 60\%$$

Exercise A   Find the rate in each of these percent sentences.

1) ___% of 18 is 2.7

2) ___% of 45 is 9

3) ___% of 200 is 120

4) ___% of 50 is 17.5

5) ___% of 80 is 65.6

6) ___% of 70 is 10.5

7) ___% of 48 is 24.48

8) ___% of 40 is .8

9) ___% of 70 is 2.45

10) ___% of 57 is 5.13

11) ___% of 50 is 11.5

12) ___% of 70 is 64.4

13) ___% of 80 is 3.6

14) ___% of 62 is 12.4

15) ___% of 35 is 34.3

16) ___% of 35 is 14.7

17) ___% of 96 is 35.52

18) ___% of 20 is 8.4

19) ___% of 2.6 is .221

20) ___% of 3.2 is 1.344

Exercise B   Solve for the rate.

1) 6.5 is what percent of 50?

2) 1 is what percent of 20?

3) 6.8 is what percent of 85?

4) 1.5 is what percent of 75?

5) 19.8 is what percent of 60?

6) 450 is what percent of 500?

7) 117 is what percent of 90?

8) 42 is what percent of 56?

9) 24 is $n\%$ of 30

10) 0.11 is $n\%$ of 2.5

11) $n\%$ of 53 is 12.19

12) 18.2 is $n\%$ of 35

13) $n\%$ of 600 is 150

14) 8.1 is $n\%$ of 45

15) 1 is $n\%$ of 40

16) $n\%$ of 60 is 3

17) 3.2 is $n\%$ of 80

18) $n\%$ of 70 is 8.4

19) $n\%$ of 90 is 5.4

20) 40 is $n\%$ of 50

21) $n\%$ of 500 is 375

22) 15.6 is $n\%$ of 130

23) $n\%$ of 67 is 6.7

24) 54 is $n\%$ of 180

25) $n\%$ of 70 is 63

26) 2 is $n\%$ of 80

27) $n\%$ of 50 is 4

28) 43.2 is $n\%$ of 270

29) 110.4 is $n\%$ of 920

30) $n\%$ of 143 is 24.31

Ted has $150 to spend. He spends $12 on clothes. What percent does he spend on clothes?

What percent of $150 is $12?

n% of 150 is 12

$n \times 1.50 = 12$ $n \times 150 = 12$

$n = 12 \div 1.50$ $n = \dfrac{12}{150}$

$n = 8\%$ $n = .08 = 8\%$

PROBLEM SOLVING

Exercise C Solve these word problems. Write a percent sentence first.

1) 40 students are in the class. 18 students go on the field trip. What percent go on the field trip?

2) The total distance is 52 miles. Sue drives 13 miles. What percent of the distance does she drive?

3) Gary attempts 84 shots. He makes 63. What percent of the shots does he make?

4) Joe's allowance is $12. He spends $7.80. What percent does he spend?

5) 1,200 sandwiches are made for the picnic. 1,140 sandwiches are eaten. What percent are eaten?

6) The team plays 50 games. They win 35 games. What percent do they win?

7) 620 automobiles have to be inspected. 527 pass inspection. What percent do *not* pass?

8) There are 450 students. 90 are at home with the flu. What percent are absent?

All three types of percent problems can also be solved by using a proportion. The three major elements of a percent sentence are the rate, the base, and the percentage. Enter two of these elements in the proportion and solve for the third.

$$\frac{\text{RATE}}{100} = \frac{\text{PERCENTAGE}}{\text{BASE}}$$

EXAMPLES   60% of 35 is __   __% of 40 is 8   35% of __ is 14

$$\frac{60}{100} = \frac{n}{35} \qquad \frac{n}{100} = \frac{8}{40} \qquad \frac{35}{100} = \frac{14}{n}$$

$$100n = 2{,}100 \qquad 800 = 40n \qquad 1{,}400 = 35n$$

$$\frac{100n}{100} = \frac{2{,}100}{100} \qquad \frac{800}{40} = \frac{40n}{40} \qquad \frac{1{,}400}{35} = \frac{35n}{35}$$

$$n = 21 \qquad 20 = n \qquad 40 = n$$

You can write the correct proportion by following these steps:

Step 1   Write this: $\dfrac{\overline{}}{100} = \dfrac{\overline{}}{}$

Step 2   Write the percent over the 100.

Step 3   Find the phrase "percent of." The number after "percent of" goes on the bottom.

Step 4   The third number goes on the top.

Exercise A   Use a proportion to help you find the missing number.

1) __% of 30 is 6

2) 32% of 450 is __

3) __ is 40% of 9

4) 28% of __ is 14

5) 16 is 8% of __

6) 12 is 80% of __

7) 6% of 15 is __

8) __% of 9 is 2

9) __ is 45% of 200

10) 18 is __% of 48

11) $4\frac{1}{2}$% of $3\frac{1}{3}$ is __

12) 3.5% of __ is 14

PROBLEM SOLVING

Exercise B   Use a proportion to solve each of these percent problems.

1) Sampson gets 12 hits for 15 times at bat. What percent of the time does Sampson get a hit?

2) Sixty percent of the people sampled in a school survey prefer vanilla yogurt. If 84 of the people prefer vanilla, then how many people were surveyed?

3) If 70% is a passing grade, then how many questions do you need to answer correctly on a 40-question test to pass?

4) The fluid in your car's cooling system should be 40% antifreeze. If the cooling system holds 15 quarts of fluid, then how many quarts of antifreeze will you need?

5) Robin makes 85% of her shots from the foul line. How many foul shots will she make out of 60 attempts?

6) A tiger weighs 298 pounds. It has a 5% weight loss. How many pounds does the tiger lose?

7) 18 boys and 27 girls are in a class. What percent of the class are boys?

8) If iron ore is 15% iron, then how many tons of ore are needed to get 30 tons of iron?

9) Bagels used to sell for 30¢. Now they sell for 35¢. What is the percent of increase in the price of bagels?

10) Sharina buys a used car for $3,060. She pays $765 as a down payment. What percent of the total cost is her down payment?

Discount
A reduction made from the regular price.

Discount rate
Percent that the price is reduced.

List price
Regular price.

Sale price
Reduced price of an item.

Stores frequently offer items for sale at a reduced cost. The usual price of an item is called the **list price**. The reduced cost is called the **sale price**. The **discount** is the amount that you save. The **discount rate** is the percent off the regular price. You can work discount problems if you remember these formulas:

> Discount = List Price × Discount Rate
> Sale Price = List Price − Discount
> Discount Rate = Discount ÷ List Price

EXAMPLES Find the sale price of a watch that lists for $25.50, if the discount rate is 20%.

Step 1 Identify formula
Sale price = List price − Discount

Step 2 Find discount
$ 25.50 List Price
× .20 Discount Rate
$5.1000 Discount

Step 3 Apply formula for sale price
$25.50 List Price
− 5.10 Discount
$20.40 Sale Price

Find the discount rate if an item that sells for $34.20 is on sale for $29.07.

$ 34.20 List Price   .15 = 15% Discount Rate
− 29.07 Sale Price   34.20) 5.1300
$ 5.13 Discount   − 3 420
                             1 7100
                           − 1 7100

Find the sale price of a book that usually sells for $5.98, if the discount rate is 15%. Round to the nearest cent.

$ 5.98 List Price $5.98 List Price
× .15 Discount Rate   − .90 Discount
$.8970 Discount $5.08 Sale Price

Exercise A Solve these discount problems.

1) $150 list price
   20% discount rate
   Discount _____
   Sale Price _____

2) Shirt usually costs $25
   30% discount rate
   Discount _____
   Sale Price _____

3) Radio costing $65.50
   45% discount rate
   Discount _____
   Sale Price _____

4) Shoes costing $45.50
   Discount rate is 20%
   Discount _____
   Sale Price _____

5) Television costs $450
   You pay only $360
   Discount _____
   Discount Rate _____

6) Radio usually costs $19.50
   You pay only $15.60
   Discount _____
   Discount Rate _____

7) Calculator costs $9.95
   10% discount rate
   Discount _____
   Sale Price _____

8) Computer game costs $46.50
   15% discount rate
   Discount _____
   Sale Price _____

9) Car costs $6,295
   10% discount rate
   Discount _____
   Sale Price _____

10) Bike costs $175
    On sale for $122.50
    Discount _____
    Discount Rate _____

PROBLEM SOLVING

Exercise B Solve these discount problems.

1) A pen usually sells for $5.75. It is on sale for 15% off. What is the sale price?

2) A stereo usually sells for $125.20. It is on sale for $100.16. Find the discount rate.

3) A dress shirt lists for $17.89. You can save 20% while it is on sale. Find the sale price.

Sales tax

Money paid as tax when you buy an item.

Most states charge a **sales tax** on items a consumer buys. The consumer pays this tax. The **tax rate** is a percent of the price to be added to the price. With sales tax, you round any part of a cent up instead of to the nearest cent.

Tax rate

The percent charged as tax.

EXAMPLES Find the cost of a video game selling for $15.72 if the state sales tax is 5%.

Step 1
$15.72	Price
× .05	Tax Rate
$.7860	Tax

Step 2
$15.72	Price
+ .79	Tax rounded up
$16.51	Price with tax

Find the cost of a calculator selling for $18.35 if the state sales tax is 6%.

Step 1
$ 18.35	Price
× .06	Tax Rate
$1.1010	Tax

Step 2
$18.35	Price
+ 1.11	Tax rounded up
$19.46	Price with tax

Exercise A Solve these tax problems. Remember to round up.

1) A poster costs $10.90. Tax rate 5%.
Tax _____
Price with tax _____

2) Tickets cost $15.00. Tax rate 6%.
Tax _____
Price with tax _____

3) A used car costs $4,000. Tax rate 8%.
Tax _____
Price with tax _____

4) A clock costs $7.50. Tax rate 3%.
Tax _____
Price with tax _____

5) A jacket costs $75.25. Tax rate 5%.
Tax _____
Price with tax _____

When you buy an item on sale, you pay the sales tax on the sale price rather than on the list price.

> **EXAMPLE** Find the actual cost of a book that usually sells for $14.50, if you get a 10% rate of discount and the sales tax is 5%.

Step 1
$ 14.50	List Price
× .10	Discount Rate
$1.4500	Discount

Step 2
$14.50	List Price
− 1.45	Discount
$13.05	Sale Price

Step 3
$13.05	Sale Price
× .05	Tax Rate
$.6525	Tax

Step 4
$13.05	Sale Price
+ .66	Tax rounded up
$13.71	Price with tax

Exercise B   Complete the combination discount-tax table below.

	List Price	Discount Rate	Discount	Sale Price	Tax Rate	Tax	Amount Paid
1)	$14.50	10%	$1.45	$13.05	5%	$.66	$13.71
2)	$18.00	20%			5%		
3)	$23.00	20%			6%		
4)	$48.00	35%			6%		
5)	$1.95	15%			7%		
6)	$245	10%			7%		
7)	$3,268	10%			6%		
8)	$.85	20%			5%		
9)	$1,060	25%			5%		
10)	$38.95	12%			3%		

Principal

Amount borrowed or invested.

When you put money into a savings account, the bank pays you interest. You can solve interest problems if you remember this formula:

Interest = **Principal** × **Rate of Interest** × Time

Rate of interest

Percent paid or charged for the use of money.

You may need to round any parts of a cent. You would follow the usual rules for rounding to two decimal places. If the time is not given in years, it must be changed to years before working the problem.

EXAMPLES   Compute the interest on a principal of $55.00 at a rate of interest of 5% for 2 years.

$ 55.00 Principal	$2.75 1 Year's Interest
× .05 Interest Rate	× 2 2 Years
$2.7500 1 Year's Interest	$5.50 2 Years' Interest

Compute the interest on a principal of $175.00 at a rate of interest of 6% for 6 months.

$ 175.00 Principal
×   .06 Interest Rate
$10.5000 1 Year's Interest

6 months = $\frac{1}{2}$ year = .5 year

$10.50 × $\frac{1}{2}$ = $5.25 or $10.50 × .5 = $5.25

Exercise A   Compute the interest. Round to the nearest cent.

1) $70 at 5% for 2 years

2) $172 at 4% for 3 years

3) $38 at 6% for 6 months

4) $45 at 9% for 4 months

5) $345 at 6% for 5 years

6) $945 at 7% for 1 year

7) $80 at 5% for 2 years

8) $85 at 12% for 3 years

9) $102 at 9% for 8 months

10) $286 at 12.5% for 2 years

11) $86 at 16% for 4 years

12) $227 at 11% for 3 years

13) $92 at 10% for 8 months

14) $48 at 15% for 4 years

Many stores have arrangements for buying expensive items on the installment plan. This means that you pay for the item over a period of months. Some stores charge a monthly finance charge of $1\frac{1}{2}\%$ of the unpaid balance.

Previous balance

Amount owed before a payment is made.

Finance rate

Percent charged for borrowing money.

Finance charge

Cost for borrowing money.

EXAMPLE Duane buys a TV set for $250.00 on the installment plan. He agrees to make monthly payments of $25.00 until the bill for the TV is paid in full.

Step 1	$250.000	**Previous Balance**
	$\times$ .015	**Finance Rate** ($1\frac{1}{2}\%$ = .015)
	$3.75000	**Finance Charge** for first month

Step 2	$250.00	Previous Balance
	+ 3.75	Finance Charge
	$253.75	Balance Before First Payment

Step 3	$253.75	Balance Before First Payment
	− 25.00	First Month's Payment
	$228.75	New Balance

The new balance becomes the previous balance for the next month.

Exercise A Fill in this chart to show how Duane will pay for his TV set on the installment plan.

Month	Previous Balance	Finance Charge	Before Payment	Monthly Payment	New Balance
April	$250.00	$3.75	$253.75	$25.00	$228.75
May	$228.75	$3.43	_____	$25.00	_____
June	_____	_____	_____	$25.00	_____
July	_____	_____	_____	$25.00	_____
Aug.	_____	_____	_____	$25.00	_____
Sept.	_____	_____	_____	$25.00	_____
Oct.	_____	_____	_____	$25.00	_____
Nov.	_____	_____	_____	$25.00	_____
Dec.	_____	_____	_____	$25.00	_____
Jan.	_____	_____	_____	$25.00	_____
Feb.	_____	_____	_____	_____	$0.00

Commission	Salespeople are often paid a **commission** on their sales. A commission is a percent of the total amount of sales. You find the amount of the commission by multiplying the **rate of commission** by the total sales.
Percentage of total sales.	

Commission
Percentage of total sales.

Rate of commission
The percent used to compute commissions.

EXAMPLE   Mr. Sanchez sold $6,542 worth of jewelry last week. He is paid a 6% rate of commission. How much is his commission?

$$
\begin{array}{r}
\$\ 6{,}542 \\
\times\ \ \ \ .06 \\
\hline
\$392.52
\end{array}
$$
Mr. Sanchez's commission is $392.52.

PROBLEM SOLVING

Exercise A   Answer these word problems about commission.

1) Mary is paid an 11% rate of commission. What is her commission for selling $1,286 worth of merchandise?

2) A real estate agent receives 7% of the sale price of a house for commission. What is the commission for selling a house for $65,000?

3) Alberta receives an 8% rate of commission on all sales over $2,000. How much is her commission for $4,280 in sales?

4) Pedro gets a 2% rate of commission on the first $2,000 worth of sales and a 5% rate on all sales over $2,000. How much is his commission for sales totaling $13,283?

5) Li receives a different rate of commission for selling different items. Figure out his total commission for the sales in the chart below.

Item	Chains	Earrings	Tie Tacks	Rings	Pins
Total Sales	$10,428	$12,417	$6,453	$13,208	$348
Rate of Commission	4%	3%	6%	4%	2%

Tip		
An amount of money paid for service.		

It is usual to leave a **tip** for your server when you dine in a restaurant. The tip is usually 15% of the total cost of the meal.

EXAMPLE   The meal costs $12.45. The tip should be 15% of $12.45.

Tip rate
Percent left as a tip.

Step 1 $ 12.45   Meal cost
    ×   .15   **Tip rate**
    $1.8675 = $1.87   Amount of tip

Step 2 $12.45   Meal
    + 1.87   Tip
    $14.32   Total cost

Exercise A   For each check, find the cost of the meal, the amount of a 15% tip, and the total cost.

1) Candle Hearth

1 salad	$1.90
1 soup	$1.00
1 chicken dinner	$5.25
1 fish dinner	$6.75
1 pie	$1.36
1 coffee	$1.00
Meal cost	_____
Tip	_____
Total cost	_____

2) Captain Jack's

1 spaghetti dinner	$5.25
1 fish dinner	$6.75
1 sundae	$1.45
1 lemonade	$.50
1 root beer	$.50
Meal cost	_____
Tip	_____
Total cost	_____

3) Hilltop Inn Cafeteria

1 soup	$1.15
2 salads	$1.90
1 steak	$13.70
1 shrimp dinner	$6.50
1 pudding	$.68
1 coffee	$1.00
1 iced tea	$.50
Meal cost	_____
Tip	_____
Total cost	_____

4) Papa Nick's

2 salads	$2.30
1 soup	$1.20
2 chef specials	$14.50
1 fish dinner	$6.75
3 iced teas	$1.50
Meal cost	_____
Tip	_____
Total cost	_____

Rename each of the following as a decimal:

1) 8%

2) 42.6%

3) 5.2%

Rename each percent as a fraction in simplest form:

4) 45%

5) 79%

6) $12\frac{1}{2}$%

7) $5\frac{1}{3}$%

Rename each as a percent:

8) .4

9) .057

10) $\frac{3}{20}$

11) $\frac{8}{11}$

Find the missing numbers:

12) ____ is 30% of 82

13) 12 is 40% of ____

14) ____% of 32 is 8

15) 6% of 28 is ____

16) .6% of ____ is 9

17) 2.4 is ____% of 8

Find the missing numbers, using a proportion:

18) 15 is ___% of 300

19) 16% of ____ is 36

Find the answers to these word problems:

20) The bill for dinner comes to $45.30. How much is a 15% tip to the nearest cent?

21) Tracy buys a dress for $24.65, a belt for $6.85, and a scarf for $3.70. How much sales tax is due if the tax rate is 5%?

22) A coat usually sells for $48.60. It is on sale for 15% off. What is the sale price?

23) Yoshi is paid a 4% rate of commission on all sales over $600. How much commission does she get on $3,840 worth of sales?

24) How much interest is paid on $1,200 invested at 7% per year for 3 years?

25) Bill is going to buy a TV for $365. He makes a down payment of $50 and pays off the rest in 9 equal monthly payments. How much is each payment?

Chapter 7

Introduction to Geometry

Look around you. Think about the shapes you see. Notice the patterns that bricks make on the face of a building. Look closely at the angles made by the doors and windows in your room. Are these angles like those seen on the Louvre Museum in Paris? Which angles are the same and which are different? All of these are examples of geometry in your world. Geometry is a form of mathematics that helps us construct safe and beautiful buildings. It also helps us in every part of our life.

In Chapter 7, you will learn more about the mathematics involved in measuring angles and describing shapes.

Goals for Learning

▶ To identify parallel lines

▶ To identify the point of intersecting lines

▶ To measure angles

▶ To name triangles by looking at angles and sides

▶ To name solid figures by looking at faces, vertices, and edges

Angle

Two rays with the same endpoint.

Geometry

The study of points, lines, angles, surfaces, and solids.

Line segment

Part of a line.

Plane

A flat surface that extends forever in all directions.

Ray

A line that has a beginning point but no end.

Vertex

The point where two rays meet.

Geometry is the study of points, lines, angles, surfaces, and solids. To study geometry, we need to define some geometric terms.

A *point* is a location in space. It is represented by a dot. Points are usually named with a letter. We say "point A" or "point M."

A *line* is a collection of points that extend forever in the same direction. A line does not have any endpoints. A line is named with any two points. We represent line AB like this: $\overleftrightarrow{AB}$.

A **line segment** is a part of a line. It has two endpoints. We represent line segment AB like this: $\overline{AB}$.

A **ray** is a collection of points that begin at one point and extend forever in one direction. A ray has one endpoint. We represent ray AB like this: $\overrightarrow{AB}$.

When two rays have the same endpoint, they form an **angle**. We call this angle ∠ ABC or ∠ CBA. The common endpoint B is in the middle of the symbol.

The common endpoint is called the angle's **vertex**.

We usually look at lines and points that are all on the same flat surface, like a piece of paper. A flat surface that extends forever in all directions is called a **plane**. We represent a plane with a lowercase letter like p.

Exercise A   Give the best name for each drawing.

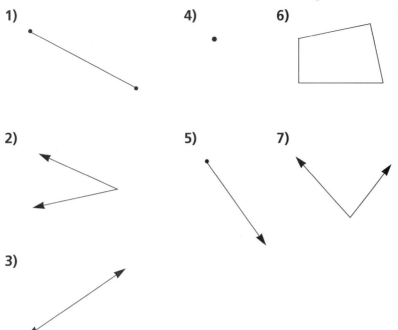

Lines in a Plane   If two lines are drawn in the same plane, then they might meet at a point or stay the same distance apart and never meet. Two lines that are always the same distance apart are called **parallel lines**. Lines that meet are called **intersecting lines**. Intersecting lines can meet in such a way that the four angles formed are all the same size. These lines are called **perpendicular lines**.

Parallel lines

Lines that are always the same distance apart.

Intersecting lines

Lines that cross in the same plane.

Perpendicular lines

Intersecting lines that cross and form four right angles.

Exercise B   Give the best name for each drawing.

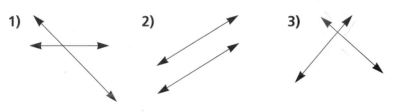

Circle

A plane figure whose points are equally distant from the center.

Degree

A measure of angles.

An angle is formed by the intersection of two rays. A ray is a line that has a beginning point but no end. Angular measure is based on the **circle**. The circle is divided into 360 equal parts, each called one **degree**.

If you divide a circle in half, then each part will contain 180 degrees. Therefore, the angular measure of a straight line, or a straight angle, is 180°. If you divide a circle into four equal parts with perpendicular lines, then each part will contain 90 degrees. Each 90° angle is called a right angle. Angles are classified by the number of degrees contained in them.

An angle can be classified as either an **acute angle**, a **right angle**, an **obtuse angle**, a **straight angle**, or a **reflex angle**. The chart shows you how the different types of angles look. Once you see them it will be easier for you to remember their names.

Kind of Angle	Description	Degrees	Example
Acute	Less than a right angle	Between 0° and 90°	
Right	Formed by 2 perpendicular rays	90°	
Obtuse	Larger than a right angle but smaller than a straight angle	Between 90° and 180°	
Straight	2 rays form a straight line	180°	
Reflex	Larger than a straight angle	Between 180° and 360°	

Exercise A   Give the correct name for each angle below.

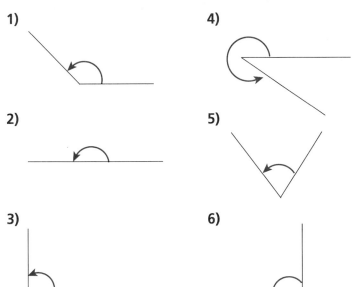

1)

2)

3)

4)

5)

6)

Exercise B   Use the diagram at right to answer these questions.

1) Which two lines are parallel?

2) What kind of angle is ∠ DEF?

3) What kind of angle is ∠ CGF?

4) What kind of lines are $\overleftrightarrow{AC}$ and $\overleftrightarrow{DG}$?

5) What kind of angle is ∠ DGF?

6) Which two lines are perpendicular?

7) What kind of angle is ∠ DCA?

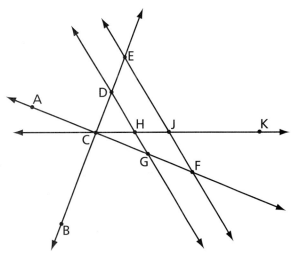

8) Two angles that together measure 180° are called supplementary angles. Name two supplementary angles.

9) Two angles that together measure 90° are complementary angles. Name two complementary angles.

Protractor

A tool used to draw or measure angles.

An angle is formed by the intersection of two rays. The rays are the sides of the angles. The point where the two rays intersect is called the vertex of the angle. The size of the angle is not affected by the length of the rays. The same number of degrees would be in the angle no matter how long you drew the rays. We use a **protractor** to measure angles. A protractor is a semicircle with the 180° marked off along its edge.

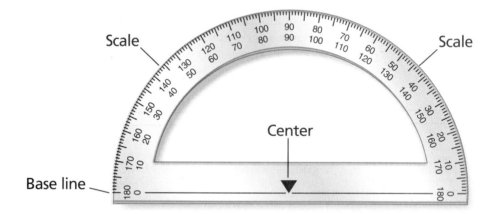

Follow these steps to measure an angle:

Step 1 Place the protractor on the angle to be measured so that the center is over the vertex of the angle and the base line is over one ray of the angle.

Step 2 Make sure that the second ray of the angle crosses the scale of the protractor. You may need to make the second ray longer.

Step 3 Read the number of degrees in the angle where the second ray of the angle crosses the scale.

If the first ray extends to the right of the vertex, then use the outside scale. If the first ray points left, then use the inside scale.

The following examples use these three steps to measure angles.

EXAMPLES Measure this acute angle.   Measure this obtuse angle.

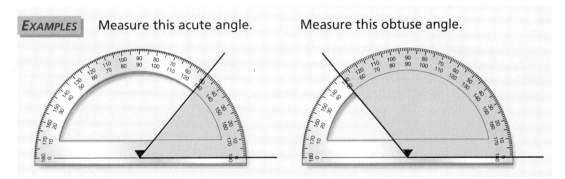

The acute angle measures 50°. One line of the angle crosses 0 on the outer scale of the protractor. The other line crosses 50. You may notice a 130 at the same point. Since we are reading the outer scale for this angle, we do not use the 130.

The obtuse angle measures 130°. The outer scale of the protractor is used to measure this angle too.

Exercise A   Measure these acute angles.

1)

3)

5)

2)

4)

6)

Exercise B   Measure these obtuse angles. All of them will be more than 90 degrees.

1)

3)

5)

2)

4)

6)

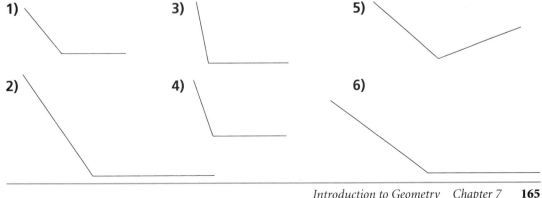

Exercise C   Use a protractor to help you measure these angles.

1)

6)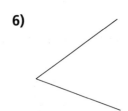

2)

7)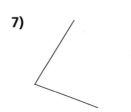

3)

8)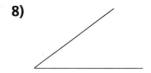

4)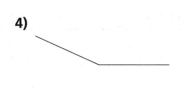

9)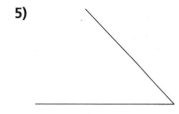

5)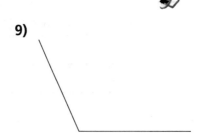

10)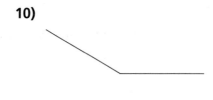

Constructing Angles   Follow these steps to construct an angle:

Step 1 Use the baseline of the protractor to draw one ray of the angle. Mark the vertex.

Step 2 Place the protractor on the ray so that the center is over the vertex of the angle to be drawn.

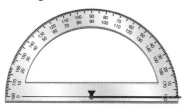

Step 3 On the scale of the protractor, find the number of degrees for the angle to be drawn. Make a mark (point) next to the number of degrees.

Step 4 Use the baseline of the protractor to connect the point and the vertex of the angle.

Step 5 Draw a ray from the vertex to the point.

Exercise D   Use a protractor to help you construct angles with the following measures:

1) 60°

2) 45°

3) 130°

4) 155°

5) 180°

6) 72°

7) 105°

8) 90°

9) 133°

10) 28°

Lesson 4 Polygons

Polygon

A closed plane figure with three or more sides.

A closed plane figure made of three or more line segments is called a **polygon**. Polygons are named according to the number of sides they have.

Number of Sides	Name of Polygon
3	triangle
4	quadrilateral
5	pentagon
6	hexagon
7	heptagon
8	octagon
9	nonagon
10	decagon
12	dodecagon

Exercise A Count the number of sides on each polygon. Write the name for each polygon. Use the table above to help you.

1)

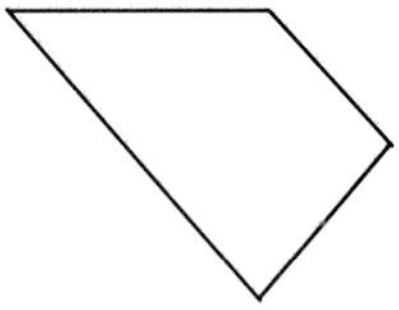

3)

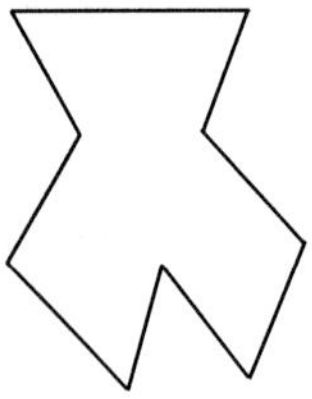

5)

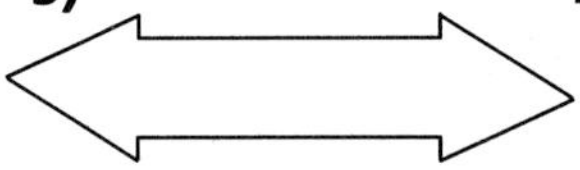

7)

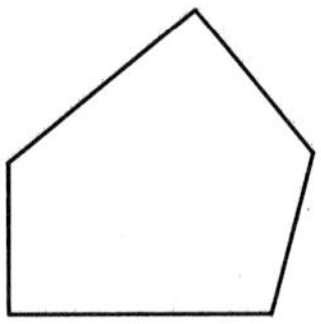

2)

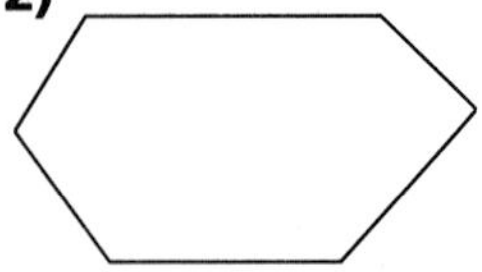

4)

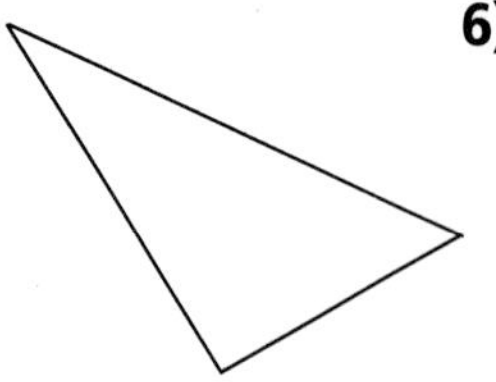

6)

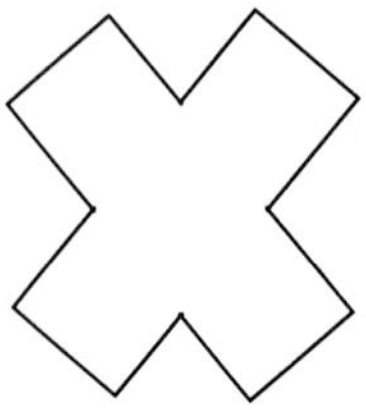

8)

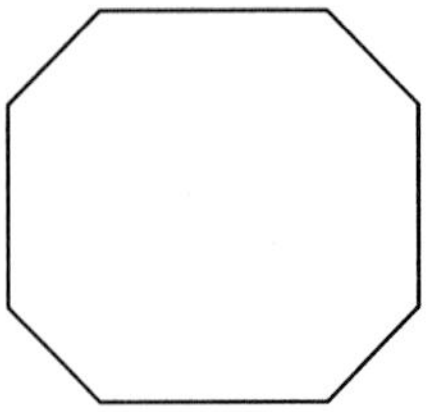

Types of Triangles

Triangles may be classified by their angles.

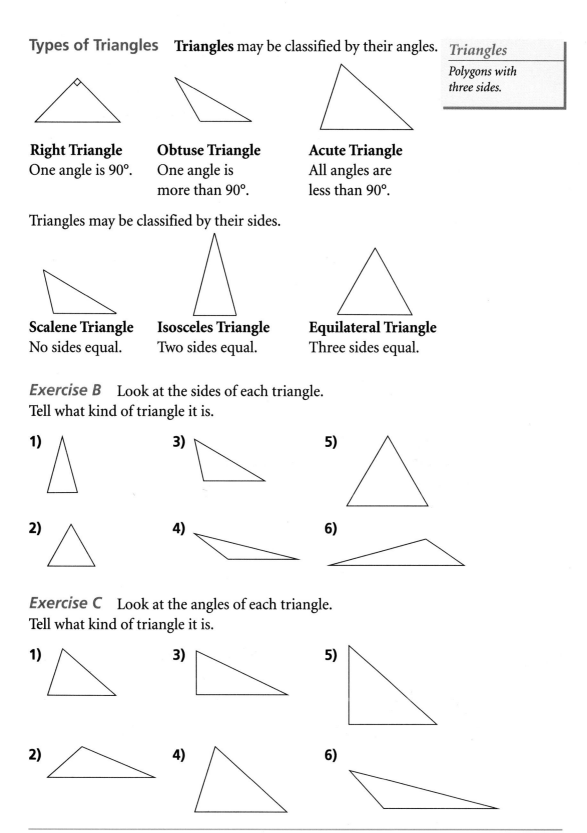

> **Triangles**
>
> *Polygons with three sides.*

Right Triangle
One angle is 90°.

Obtuse Triangle
One angle is more than 90°.

Acute Triangle
All angles are less than 90°.

Triangles may be classified by their sides.

Scalene Triangle
No sides equal.

Isosceles Triangle
Two sides equal.

Equilateral Triangle
Three sides equal.

Exercise B   Look at the sides of each triangle.
Tell what kind of triangle it is.

1)

3)

5)

2)

4)

6)

Exercise C   Look at the angles of each triangle.
Tell what kind of triangle it is.

1)

3)

5)

2)

4)

6)

Types of Quadrilaterals **Quadrilaterals** are classified by relationships of their sides and angles.

A **square** has four equal sides and four right angles.

A **rectangle** has four right angles and the opposite sides are equal.

A **rhombus** has four equal sides and the opposite angles are equal.

A **parallelogram** has two pairs of equal and parallel sides.

A **trapezoid** has one pair of parallel sides and one pair of sides that are not parallel.

Exercise D Give the best name for each quadrilateral.

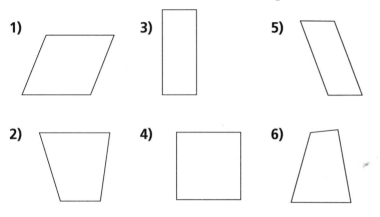

1)

2)

3)

4)

5)

6)

Measure of the Interior Angles of a Polygon

The sum of the measures of the angles in a triangle is 180°. We can show this by marking each angle of the triangle. If we arrange the angles so that they have the same vertex, then we see that the three angles form a straight angle. The measure of a straight angle is 180°.

Exercise E

1) Draw a quadrilateral. Select one vertex and draw a line segment to the opposite vertex. This line segment should divide the quadrilateral into two triangles. The sum of the angles of the quadrilateral is the same as the sum of the angles of the two triangles. How many degrees is the sum of the four angles of the quadrilateral?

2) Draw a pentagon. Select one vertex so the you can draw line segments to the other vertices without going outside of the pentagon. How many triangles are formed? What is the sum of the angles of a pentagon?

3) Draw a hexagon. Select one vertex and draw line segments to the other vertices to make triangles. How many triangles are formed? What is the sum of the angles of a hexagon?

Calculator Practice The memory key on a calculator can store a number you want to use more than once in a set of problems. The repeated number is called a constant.

EXAMPLE	Two angles in a triangle measure 70° and 80°. What is the measure of the third angle?
Step 1	Press *180* M+ . (The constant is 180°.)
Step 2	Press C to clear the display. The constant, 180°, is stored in the calculator's memory.
Step 3	Press MR . (Memory Recall) The display reads *180*.
Step 4	Press — *70* — *80* = The display reads *30*. The measure of the third angle is 30°.

Calculator Exercise Use your calculator's memory key to find the measure of the third angle in these triangles.

1) 124	48	**5)** 95	43	**9)** 85	15
2) 21	42	**6)** 45	45	**10)** 64	59
3) 18	113	**7)** 80	60	**11)** 15	145
4) 95	5	**8)** 60	60	**12)** 33	69

Prism

A solid figure with two parallel faces that are polygons of the same shape.

Many geometric figures are three dimensional. A solid figure with parallelograms for sides and two parallel faces of the same shape is called a **prism**. A prism is named for the shape of its faces. A prism with squares for sides and faces is called a **cube**.

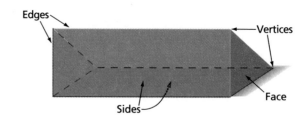

Cube

A prism with square sides and faces.

Triangular Prism
A prism with triangular faces.

Hexagonal Prism
A prism with hexagonal faces.

Rectangular Prism
A prism with rectangular faces.

Pyramid

A solid figure with a base that is a polygon and triangular sides.

A **pyramid** has triangles for sides.

Some solid figures have curved surfaces.

Cylinder
A solid figure with two equal circular bases that are parallel.

Cone
A solid figure with a circular base connected to a vertex.

Sphere
A solid figure with a curved surface in which all points on the surface are equal distance from the center.

Exercise A Write the name of each solid figure. Look at the examples on the opposite page to help you.

1)

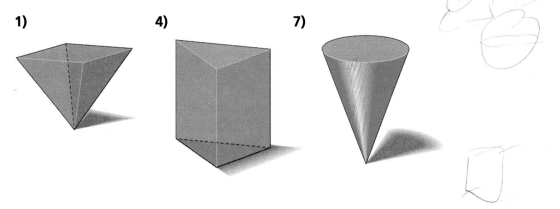

4)

7)

2)

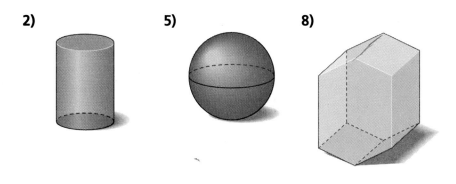

5)

8)

3)

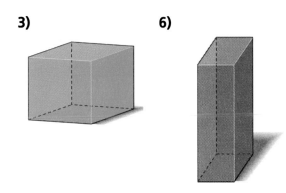

6)

Use the diagram to help you answer the questions.

1) What line is parallel to line $\overleftrightarrow{GH}$?

2) Lines $\overleftrightarrow{AB}$ and $\overleftrightarrow{GE}$ intersect at what point?

3) What kind of angle is ∠ FCB?

4) If $\overleftrightarrow{CE}$ is perpendicular to $\overleftrightarrow{BG}$, then what kind of angle is ∠ BGC?

5) If ∠ FBC is 26° and ∠ CFB is 37°, then how many degrees is ∠ FCB?

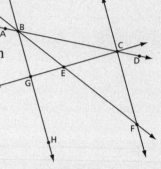

6) What triangle is formed by $\overleftrightarrow{GE}$, $\overleftrightarrow{AD}$, and $\overleftrightarrow{BF}$?

Write the name of each polygon.

7)

9)

8)

10)

11) What kind of triangle has two equal sides?

12) One angle of a triangle measures 135°. What kind of triangle is it?

Write the name of each quadrilateral.

13)

14)

15)

Write the name of each solid figure.

16) 17) 18) 19)

20) What is the name of a prism that has squares for all of its faces?

Use your protractor to help you measure these angles:

21) 22)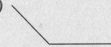

23) What kind of angle is in question 21?

24) What kind of angle is in question 22?

Use a protractor to help you construct angles with these measurements:

25) 15°

26) 125°

27) 180°

28) 70°

29) 45°

30) 90°

Test Taking Tip | When you prepare for a test that will require you to use tools such as a ruler or a protractor, practice with them before the test. Remember to bring the tools with you to the test.

Chapter 8

Metric Measurement

Many countries use the metric system as their official standard of measurement. Americans are becoming more familiar with these units of measurement. We now buy soda in liter bottles. Mechanics use metric tools to fix cars and equipment with metric measurements. In this age of worldwide communication and trade, understanding the metric system is useful.

In Chapter 8, you will learn how to make measurements, using the metric system.

Goals for Learning

▶ To measure line segments to the nearest tenth of a centimeter

▶ To estimate accurately the best unit for measuring a distance

▶ To change from one metric unit to another

▶ To find area measured in square units

▶ To find volume measured in cubic units

▶ To find volume, or capacity, measured in liters

177

In the **customary** system of measurement, conversions from one unit to another are difficult because the units are so different. There are 5,280 feet in a mile, 16 ounces in a pound, 2 cups in a pint, and 36 inches in a yard. Also, the units of measure are not easily related to each other. One gallon of water weighs about 8.345 pounds.

In the **metric system**, however, the measurement units are all powers of ten, and units are easily related to each other. One liter of water weighs one kilogram.

The **meter** is used to measure length. The **liter** is used to measure capacity. The **gram** is used to measure mass or weight. Other units are named by adding these **prefixes** to **meter**, **liter**, and **gram**.

Prefix	Value	Symbol	Example
kilo	one thousand	k	kilometer
hecto	one hundred	h	hectometer
deka	ten	da	dekagram
deci	one-tenth	d	decimeter
centi	one-hundredth	c	centigram
milli	one-thousandth	m	milliliter

Customary
Ordinary.

Gram, g
Measure of mass about equal to the weight of a paper clip.

Liter, L
Measure of capacity about equal to the capacity of a coffee can.

Meter, m
Measure of length about equal to the height of a doorknob.

Metric system
A system of measuring using the gram and the meter as basic units.

Prefix
Set of letters placed before a unit of measure.

Exercise A Give the correct name for each measurement described. Use the chart above to help you.

1) What is one-tenth of a liter called?
2) What number does the symbol *d* stand for?
3) What symbol means one thousand?
4) How many meters are in a dekameter?
5) Which prefix means one hundred?
6) What is one-thousandth of a gram called?
7) What symbol means one-hundredth?
8) How many liters are in a hectoliter?
9) How many grams are in a milligram?
10) What number does the symbol *c* stand for?

Centimeter, cm

A measure of length about equal to the width of a large paper clip.

The basic unit of length in the metric system is the meter. The distance from the floor to a doorknob is about one meter.

Some lengths are too short to measure in meters. We use the **centimeter** and **millimeter** for these shorter lengths. A centimeter is about the width of a large paper clip. A millimeter is about the thickness of the wire used to make the paper clip.

Millimeter, mm

Measure of length about equal to the width of the wire in a paper clip.

Look at this drawing of a metric ruler.

Each of the numbered spaces is one centimeter in length.
Each of the small spaces is one millimeter in length.

Often, we want to give measurements as parts of a centimeter.

EXAMPLES If an object is 7 centimeters and 3 millimeters long, then we say that it is 7.3 cm long.

7 cm + 3 mm ⟶ 7.3 cm

If a line is 5 centimeters and 8 millimeters long, then we say that it is 5.8 centimeters long.

5 cm + 8 mm ⟶ 5.8 cm

Exercise A Use a metric ruler. Measure each line segment to the nearest centimeter and to the nearest millimeter.

1) _____

2) _____

3) _____

4) ___

5) _____

Exercise B Measure the lengths of these bars to the nearest tenth of a centimeter.

1)

2)

3)

4)

5)

Exercise C How far is it from the beginning of the ruler to each arrow? Give your measurements to the nearest tenth of a centimeter. For example, the distance to the arrow marked with the letter A is 6.3 cm.

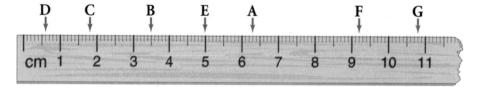

We use meters to measure things like the length of material for a dress, the length and width of your yard, and the height of a building.

Centimeters are used to measure shorter lengths like desktops and picture frames.

Millimeters are used for measuring very small things and when accurate measurements are needed. Wire sizes, nuts, bolts, and film are all measured in millimeters.

Kilometer, km

A distance of 1,000 meters, or a little more than a half mile.

Long distances are measured with the **kilometer**. A kilometer is about five city blocks long. It takes about ten minutes to walk one kilometer.

Exercise A   Choose the best measurement for each of these distances.

1) Height of a building
  396 mm   396 cm   396 m   396 km

2) Length of your classroom
  6 mm   6 cm   6 m   6 km

3) Length of a grasshopper
  63 mm   63 cm   63 m   63 km

4) Length of a piece of chalk
  6 mm   6 cm   6 m   6 km

5) Distance between two cities
  72 mm   72 cm   72 m   72 km

6) Length of your foot
  23 mm   23 cm   23 m   23 km

Conversion factor

Number you multiply by to change to another unit of measure.

To change from one metric unit to another, we multiply or divide by 10, 100, or 1,000. Since these **conversion factors** are all powers of 10, we can think of moving the decimal point to the right or left instead of actually multiplying or dividing.

1 kilometer	= 1,000 meters
1 meter	= 100 centimeters
1 centimeter	= 10 millimeters
1 meter	= 1,000 millimeters

EXAMPLES   To change meters to centimeters, multiply by 100 or move the decimal point 2 places to the right.

m _____2_____ cm _____1_____ mm

5.2 m = 520 cm

To change centimeters to meters, divide by 100 or move the decimal point 2 places to the left.

m _____2_____ cm

63 cm = .63 m

Exercise A   Use the chart to help you fill in the missing numbers.

1) 348 cm = ____ m

2) 784 m = ____ km

3) 56 cm = ____ mm

4) 82 m = ____ cm

5) 57 cm = ____ m

6) 43 mm = ____ cm

7) 6 m = ____ mm

8) 5 km = ____ m

9) 4.8 cm = ____ mm

10) 43.6 cm = ____ m

11) 5.23 km = ____ m

12) 586 mm = ____ m

13) 16.5 m = ____ km

14) 9.6 cm = ____ mm

15) 1,870 mm = ____ m

16) 4,280 cm = ____ m

17) .036 km = ____ cm

18) 5.2 m = ____ cm

When working with measurements of length, it is important to express all of the measurements in the same units. If they are not in the same units, you must change them to the same units before you can work with them.

EXAMPLE   .34 km + 63 m + 428 cm = ___ m

340 m   4.28 m

$$\begin{array}{r} 340 \\ 63 \\ +\ \ \ 4.28 \\ \hline 407.28 \text{ m} \end{array}$$

Exercise B   Find the answers to these addition problems.
1) 42 cm + 6.5 cm + 95 cm = ___ cm
2) 58 mm + 8 cm + 37 mm = ___ mm
3) 64 m + 168 cm + 12 m = ___ m
4) 43 cm + 92 mm + 87 cm = ___ cm
5) 18 km + 7 km + 4380 m = ___ km

Exercise C   Find the distance around the sides of these polygons in centimeters.

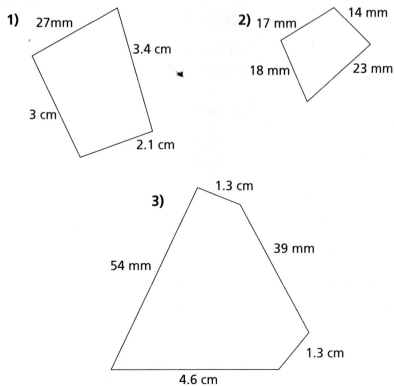

1)   27mm   3.4 cm   3 cm   2.1 cm

2) 17 mm   14 mm   18 mm   23 mm

3) 1.3 cm   54 mm   39 mm   4.6 cm   1.3 cm

Area
The amount of space inside a shape.

cm²
Square centimeter.

km²
Square kilometer.

Length, l
Distance from end to end.

m²
Square meter.

mm²
Square millimeter.

Square unit
A measure of area.

Width, w
The distance across.

The **area** of a shape is the amount of space inside the shape. Area is measured in **square units** such as square millimeters (**mm²**), square centimeters (**cm²**), square meters (**m²**), and square kilometers (**km²**). Here are the actual sizes of two of these square units.

□

1 square millimeter
1 mm²

1 square centimeter
1 cm²

The area of this rectangle is 10 cm².

You can find the area of a rectangle by multiplying the **length** by the **width**.

$$\text{Area} = \text{length} \times \text{width}$$

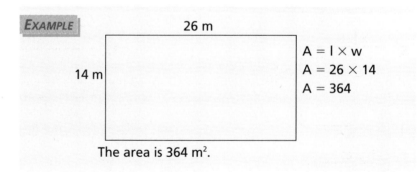

26 m

14 m

$A = l \times w$
$A = 26 \times 14$
$A = 364$

The area is 364 m².

Exercise A   Find the area of each rectangle. Remember to include the proper units in each answer.

1)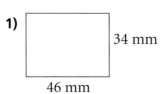
34 mm
46 mm

2)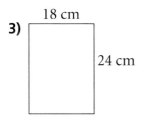
15 cm
3 cm

3)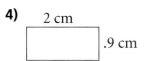
18 cm
24 cm

4)
2 cm
.9 cm

5)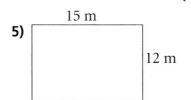
15 m
12 m

6)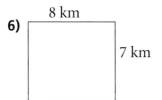
8 km
7 km

7)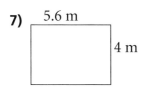
5.6 m
4 m

8)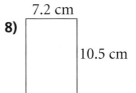
7.2 cm
10.5 cm

9)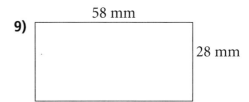
58 mm
28 mm

10)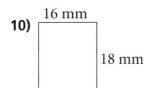
16 mm
18 mm

11)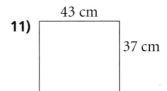
43 cm
37 cm

12)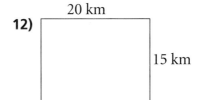
20 km
15 km

13)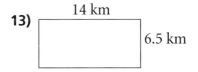
14 km
6.5 km

14)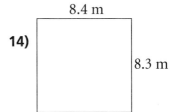
8.4 m
8.3 m

Exercise B Solve these word problems. In some of them, you must change the units so that they are all the same before you work the problem.

1) Yumi wants to fence in her yard. She measured her property and found that its sides were 27 m, 35 m, 28 m, and 39 m. How many meters of fence will she need?

2) Kaleena is buying some carpeting that costs $12.50 per m². How much will a 4 m by 5 m carpet cost?

3) Michelle measured a picture that she wants to frame. She found that the two long sides were each 82 cm. The other two sides were each 75 cm long. How many meters of framing should she buy?

4) Jesse is fencing in his pasture. It measures 180 m long and 173 m wide. How many meters of fence should Jesse buy?

5) Alonzo is carpeting three rooms. They measure 8 m by 7 m, 4 m by 5 m, and 3.5 m by 4.5 m. How many square meters of carpet does he need?

6) Juanita is training for the swimming meet. The last five days she swam 4.2 km, 520 m, 3 km, 1,280 m, and 2.8 km. How many meters did she swim altogether?

7) Enuma planned to hike 85 km in 6 days. On Monday she hiked 15 km. Tuesday she hiked 14.8 km. On Wednesday she had sore feet, so she walked only 2,400 m. Thursday and Friday Enuma hiked 16.4 km each day. How many kilometers must she hike on Saturday if she is to finish the 85 km?

8) Lucas rowed 2.4 km on Tuesday and 4,800 m on Thursday. These were the only two days he rowed this week. What is the total number of meters Lucas rowed?

cm³

Cubic centimeter.

Cubic units

Units used to measure volume.

m³

Cubic meter.

mm³

Cubic millimeter.

Volume

Number of cubic units that fill a container.

Volume is measured with **cubic units.** The most commonly used units are the cubic millimeter (**mm³**), the cubic centimeter (**cm³**), and the cubic meter (**m³**).

1 cubic millimeter

1 cubic centimeter

You can think of finding the volume of a rectangular prism as filling the inside of the box. You might wish to sketch a rectangular prism to see what you are trying to calculate. To find the volume, you would multiply the length times the width times the height. The result is measured in cubic units.

Volume = length × width × height

EXAMPLE   Find the volume of a rectangular prism having a length of 2 cm, a width of 2 cm, and a height of 3 cm.

Volume = length × width × height
V = 2 cm × 2 cm × 3 cm

The volume is 2 × 2 × 3, or 12 cm³.

Exercise A   Find the volume of each rectangular prism.

1)

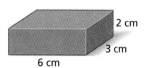

2 cm
3 cm
6 cm

7)

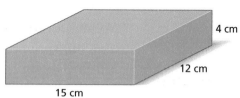

4 cm
12 cm
15 cm

2)

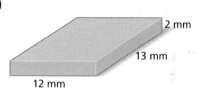

2 mm
13 mm
12 mm

8)

9 cm
8 cm
1 cm

3)

7 m
12 m
3 m

9)

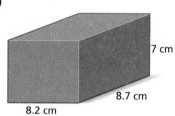

7 cm
8.7 cm
8.2 cm

4)

10 cm
11 cm
9 cm

10)

.7 m
5.2 m
4 m

5)

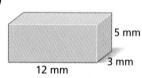

5 mm
3 mm
12 mm

11)

11 mm
11 mm
11 mm

6)

11 m
5 m
5 m

12)

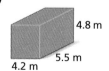

4.8 m
5.5 m
4.2 m

Exercise B Answer these questions about volume. Be sure to include the units in your answers.

1) A rectangular cake pan measures 20 cm by 15 cm by 8 cm. What is its volume?

2) An aquarium measures 60 cm by 40 cm and is 30 cm high. How many cubic centimeters of water does it hold?

3) Two guppies can live in 1,000 cm³ of water. How many guppies can live in the aquarium in problem 2?

4) A swimming pool has an average depth of 1.7 m. It is 50 m long and 30 m wide. What is its volume?

5) How many cubic meters of air are in a room that measures 4 meters by 3 meters and is 2.5 meters high?

6) How much dirt is needed to fill in a hole that measures 4 meters by 3.2 meters by 3 meters?

7) A banquet hall measures 15 meters by 12 meters and is 2.7 meters high. How many cubic meters of air does it hold?

8) Two cubic meters of air space per person are required. How many people will the hall in problem 7 hold?

9) Another banquet hall measures 18 meters by 9 meters. It is also 2.7 meters high. How many cubic meters of air does it hold?

10) Two cubic meters of air are required for each person. How many people will the hall in problem 9 hold?

Calculator Practice   Use your calculator to find the volume of a rectangular prism.

EXAMPLE   Find the volume of this rectangular prism.

length (l)   =   2.5 mm
width (w)   =   5 mm
height (h)   =   6 mm

Volume = l × w × h

Press 2.5 ⊠ 5 ⊠ 6 ⊟
The display reads 75.

Volume is measured in cubic units, so the volume
is 75 mm³.

6 mm

5 mm

2.5 mm

Calculator Exercise   Use a calculator to find the volume of
each rectangular prism. Round your answers to the nearest
whole number. Express each volume in cubic units.

1) l   =   23.5 m
    w   =   14 m
    h   =   2.3 m

2) l   =   5 m
    w   =   3 m
    h   =   2.7 m

3) l   =   5.6 m
    w   =   2 m
    h   =   3.2 m

4) l   =   8 mm
    w   =   0.3 mm
    h   =   0.5 mm

5) l   =   9.6 cm
    w   =   1.3 cm
    h   =   0.5 cm

6) l   =   26.2 m
    w   =   4.5 m
    h   =   7.23 m

7) l   =   2.3 mm
    w   =   0.5 mm
    h   =   10 mm

8) l   =   1.3 mm
    w   =   1 mm
    h   =   5 mm

9) l   =   4 cm
    w   =   1.1 cm
    h   =   3 cm

Capacity

The amount a container will hold when full.

Volume, or **capacity**, is also measured in liters (L). Both liquid and dry measurements are given in liters. Smaller amounts are measured in **milliliters** (mL). Large amounts are measured in **kiloliters** (kL).

A milliliter is equal to one cubic centimeter (cm^3). Two aspirin tablets take up about 1 mL of space. Perfume, flavor extracts, and medicine are all measured in milliliters.

Milliliter, mL

Measure of capacity about equal to that of an eye dropper.

A liter is equal to 1,000 cubic centimeters, or 1,000 mL. Two large juice boxes hold about 1 liter of liquid. A one-pound coffee can holds 1 liter of coffee. Liters are used to measure such things as paint, soda, and gasoline.

Kiloliter, kL

Measure of capacity about equal to that of a small wading pool.

A kiloliter is equal to 1 cubic meter, or 1,000 liters. A king-size water bed holds about 1 kiloliter of water. Kiloliters are used to measure large amounts. The capacity of a tank truck might be measured in kiloliters.

PROBLEM SOLVING

Exercise A   Tell whether you would use milliliters, liters, or kiloliters to measure each item.

1) A large bottle of soda
2) Oil in a delivery truck
3) A dose of medicine
4) A carton of ice cream
5) A carton of milk served with a school lunch
6) Punch in a bowl
7) Water in a tank at the National Aquarium
8) Amount of paint in a can
9) Water in a car's cooling system
10) A glass of lemonade
11) Water in an Olympic-sized pool

12) A bottle of perfume
13) Gas for a car
14) Annual orange juice production in Florida
15) Baking powder in a recipe for biscuits
16) Oil in a recipe for salad dressing
17) Milk drunk by a family in a week
18) Water in a town's reservoir
19) Vanilla extract used in making a cake
20) Amount of soda in a six-pack

Convert

Change to an equivalent measure.

The units of capacity that are most often used are milliliters, liters, and kiloliters. To convert between units of capacity, we can use a similar chart to the one we used to **convert** between meters, centimeters, millimeters, and kilometers.

$$
\begin{aligned}
1 \text{ kiloliter} &= 1{,}000 \text{ liters} \\
1 \text{ liter} &= 100 \text{ centiliters} \\
1 \text{ centiliter} &= 10 \text{ milliliters} \\
1 \text{ liter} &= 1{,}000 \text{ milliliters}
\end{aligned}
$$

EXAMPLES   To change L to kL, divide by 1,000 or move the decimal point 3 places to the left.

kL __3__ L __2__ cL __1__ mL

560 L = .56 kL

To change L to mL, multiply by 1,000 or move the decimal point 3 places to the right.

kL __3__ L __2__ cL __1__ mL

7.6L = 7,600 mL

Exercise A   Use the chart above to help you fill in the missing numbers.

1) 4,700 mL = ____ L

2) 8.2 kL = ____ L

3) 480 L = ____ kL

4) 3.2 cL = ____ mL

5) 17,000 mL = ____ kL

6) .005 kL = ____ cL

7) .0042 L = ____ mL

8) 1.36 cL = ____ L

9) 5.36 L = ____ mL

10) 6 mL = ____ L

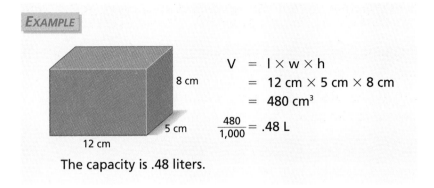

$$V = l \times w \times h$$
$$= 12 \text{ cm} \times 5 \text{ cm} \times 8 \text{ cm}$$
$$= 480 \text{ cm}^3$$

$$\frac{480}{1,000} = .48 \text{ L}$$

The capacity is .48 liters.

Exercise B   Find the capacity of these rectangular prisms in liters. Remember that 1 liter (L) = 1,000 cubic centimeters (cm³). To find the volume you must multiply length by width by height.

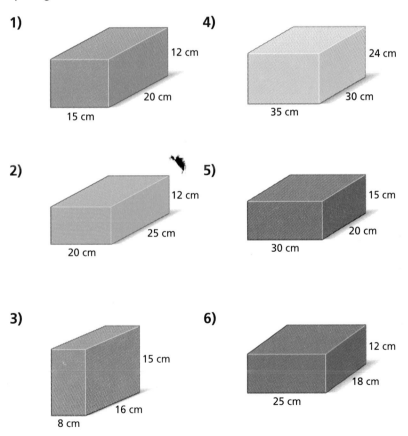

1)
12 cm
20 cm
15 cm

4)
24 cm
30 cm
35 cm

2)
12 cm
25 cm
20 cm

5)
15 cm
20 cm
30 cm

3)
15 cm
16 cm
8 cm

6)
12 cm
18 cm
25 cm

To change liters (L) to deciliters (dL), multiply by 10, or move the decimal point 1 place to the right. To change deciliters (dL) to liters (L), divide by 10, or move the decimal point 1 place to the left. To change milliliters (mL) to liters (L), divide by 1,000, or move the decimal point 3 places to the left. To change liters (L) to milliliters (mL), multiply by 1,000, or move the decimal point 3 places to the right.

1 kiloliter	= 1,000 liters
1 liter	= 100 centiliters
1 centiliter	= 10 milliliters
1 liter	= 1,000 milliliters

EXAMPLE   How much does 1.5 L of oil cost if 1,234 mL costs $1.65?

Step 1   Convert 1.5 L to mL. (In this case, you're going from a larger to smaller unit, so you multiply. You know from the chart that there are 1,000 mL in 1 liter.)

    1,000   Number of mL in 1 L
    × 1.5   Number of L
    1,500   Number of mL in 1.5 L

Step 2   Set up a proportion.

$$\frac{\$1.65}{1,234} = \frac{n}{1,500}$$

Step 3   Cross-multiply to find n.

$$\frac{\$1.65 \times 1,500}{1,234} = n \qquad \frac{\$2,475}{1,234} = n \qquad \$2.01 = n$$

PROBLEM SOLVING

Exercise C   Solve these word problems.

1) Bob wants to buy 150 dL of soda. If 7.65 L costs $9.40, then how much will he pay for 150 dL?

2) If 3.78 liters of cranberry juice costs $6.95, then how much will Niki pay for 7.56 liters?

3) If 20 mL of medicine costs $2.00 to produce, then how much does 1 L cost?

4) Siri buys 180 milliliters of hand lotion for $5.00. She wants to divide the lotion evenly among 10 smaller bottles to give as gifts. How many milliliters will be in each bottle? How many deciliters?

5) Tony is conducting a science experiment with water and oil. If he purchases 10 mL of oil at a health food store that charges $3.00 for 100 milliliters, then how much will Tony pay?

Kilograms, kg
Measure of mass about equal to the weight of four rolls of quarters.

Mass
Measure of matter.

Milligram, mg
Measure of mass about equal to $\frac{1}{10}$ of a grain of rice.

Weight
A measure of the heaviness of an object.

The **mass** of an object is the quantity of matter in the object. The **weight** of an object is the force of the earth's gravitational pull on the mass of the object. Because the mass and the weight of an object are nearly the same when you are at the earth's surface, people use the term weight when they are talking about mass.

Milligrams, grams, and **kilograms** are used to measure weight. Milligrams are used to measure small amounts of medicine and the amount of nutrients in food. An uncooked grain of rice is about 10 milligrams.

A gram is the weight of one cubic centimeter of water. A large paper clip weighs about one gram. Grams are used to measure the weight of things like the boxes of food that you buy in a grocery store. A dollar bill is about 1 gram.

A kilogram is the weight of one liter of water. Two dozen medium eggs weigh about one kilogram. Kilograms are used to measure heavier things, like a person's weight, cuts of meat, and the weight of a bag of sugar or flour. Four rolls of quarters are about 1 kilogram.

Exercise A   Choose the best measurement for each of these weights.

1) An egg
  50 mg   50 g   50 kg

2) A watermelon
  14 mg   14 g   14 kg

3) Amount of sodium in a bowl of cereal
  180 mg   180 g   180 kg

4) A box of breakfast flakes
  480 mg   480 g   480 kg

5) A plastic straw
  500 mg   500 g   500 kg

6) A high school student
  42 mg   42 g   42 kg

7) An aspirin
  235 mg   235 g   235 kg

8) A nickel
  5 mg   5 g   5 kg

9) A sack of onions
  2.3 mg   2.3 g   2.3 kg

10) A postage stamp
  14 mg   14 g   14 kg

Working With Units of Mass

The units of mass that are most often used are the milligram, the gram, and the kilogram. The centigram is almost never used.

1 kilogram	= 1,000 grams
1 gram	= 100 centigrams
1 centigram	= 10 milligrams
1 gram	= 1,000 milligrams

EXAMPLES To change from mg to g, divide by 1,000 or move the decimal point 3 places to the left.

kg —3— g —2— cg —1— mg
←————————————

52,000 mg = 52 g

To change from kg to cg, multiply by 100,000 or move the decimal point 5 places to the right.

kg —3— g —2— cg —1— mg
————————————→

.0006 kg = 60 cg

Exercise A   Fill in the missing numbers.

1) 3,000 g = ____ kg

2) .005 g = ____ mg

3) 42 mg = ____ g

4) .36 kg = ____ g

5) 12 g = ____ cg

6) .24 cg = ____ mg

7) 82 mg = ____ g

8) 1,200 g = ____ kg

9) .00007 kg = ____ mg

10) 1.08 g = ____ cg

We know that 1 liter of water weighs 1 kilogram and that
1 liter is the same as 1,000 cubic centimeters. This means that
1,000 cm³ of water weigh 1 kilogram.

EXAMPLE   Find the weight of water in kilograms that this
container will hold.

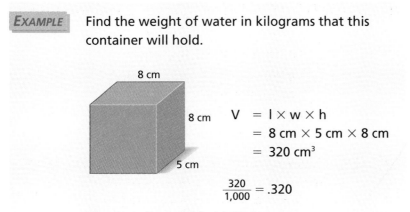

$$V = l \times w \times h$$
$$= 8 \text{ cm} \times 5 \text{ cm} \times 8 \text{ cm}$$
$$= 320 \text{ cm}^3$$

$$\frac{320}{1,000} = .320$$

The container will hold .32 kg of water.

Exercise B   Find the weight of water in kilograms that each
container will hold.

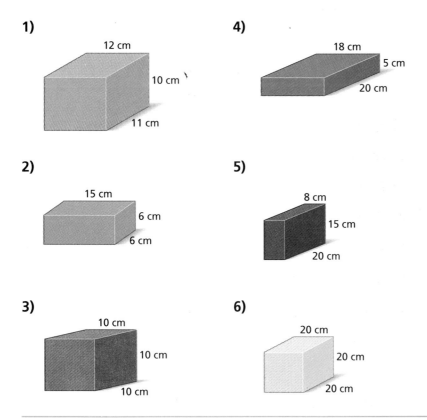

1)
12 cm
10 cm
11 cm

4)
18 cm
5 cm
20 cm

2)
15 cm
6 cm
6 cm

5)
8 cm
15 cm
20 cm

3)
10 cm
10 cm
10 cm

6)
20 cm
20 cm
20 cm

Measure these line segments to the nearest tenth of a centimeter:

1) _____

2) _____

How far is it from the beginning of the ruler to each arrow?
Give the answer to the nearest millimeter.

3)   **4)**   **5)**

Tell which is the best measurement for these distances:

6) The width of a kitchen

     4 mm   4 cm   4 m   4 km

7) The length of an adult's arm

     65 mm   65 cm   65 m   65 km

Fill in the missing numbers:

8) 37 cm = ____ mm

9) 1,200 g = ____ kg

10) 820 mL = ____ L

11) 500 mg = ____ g

12) 8.1 kL = ____ L

Find the answers to these problems:

13)   48 cm   **14)**   54 mm
         37 mm   4.6 cm
     +39 cm   2.9 cm
                                     +38 mm

Find the answers to the following questions:

15) What is the area of Yvette's yard if it measures 50 meters by 37 meters?

16) What is the volume of this rectangular prism in liters?

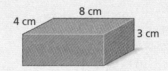

17) A swimming pool has an average depth of 1.6 m. It is 50 m long and 30 m wide. What is its volume?

18) What is the area of this rectangle?

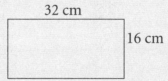

Tell whether you should use milliliters, liters, or kiloliters to measure each.

19) The amount of vanilla extract in a recipe

20) The amount of punch in a punch bowl

Tell whether you should use milligrams, grams, or kilograms to measure these weights:

21) A tenth-grade student

22) A postage stamp

23) A vitamin tablet

24) An apple

25) A truck

Chapter 9

Customary Measurement

Measuring things is a necessary everyday activity. We measure ingredients to cook, material to sew, and courts and fields to play games. Because things are measured in many ways, we use many units of measurement. Whether we find how many gallons of gas are needed to make a trip or how much lumber is needed to build a house, knowing how to measure is a valuable skill.

In Chapter 9, you will learn about customary American units for measuring capacity, weight, length, width, area, and volume.

Goals for Learning

▶ To convert units of liquid capacity

▶ To convert units of weight

▶ To use a ruler to help you measure line segments

▶ To convert units of length and distance

▶ To find the perimeter of a given shape

▶ To calculate the area within a shape

▶ To compute the volume within a prism

Fluid ounce
Unit of liquid capacity equal to $\frac{1}{16}$ of a pint.

Gallon
Unit of liquid capacity.

Pint
Measure of liquid capacity.

Quart
Measure of liquid capacity.

The most frequently used units of liquid capacity are listed below.

> 1 **pint** = 16 **fluid ounces**
> 1 **quart** = 2 pints
> 1 quart = 32 fluid ounces
> 1 **gallon** = 4 quarts

When you convert a large unit to smaller units, you *multiply*.
When you convert small units to a larger unit, you *divide*.

EXAMPLES

3 pints = _____ ounces

3 pints = __48__ ounces

$$\begin{array}{r} 16 \\ \times\ 3 \\ \hline 48 \end{array}$$

20 quarts = _____ gallons

20 quarts = __5__ gallons

$$4\overline{)20} \qquad 5$$

Exercise A   Make these conversions.

Multiply:

1) 3 quarts = ___ pints

2) 6 gallons = ___ quarts

3) 2 gallons = ___ pints

4) 5 pints = ___ ounces

5) 9 pints = ___ ounces

Divide:

6)   8 pints = ___ gallons

7)   12 pints ≠ ___ quarts

8)   16 quarts = ___ gallons

9) 144 ounces = ___ pints

10)   20 quarts = ___ gallons

Exercise B   Make these conversions. Decide whether to multiply or divide for each one.

1) 80 ounces = ___ pints

2)   8 gallons = ___ quarts

3)   3 quarts = ___ ounces

4)   6 pints = ___ quarts

5) 13 pints = ___ ounces

6)   7 quarts = ___ pints

7)   44 quarts = ___ gallons

8)   64 ounces = ___ quarts

9) 128 ounces = ___ pints

10)   6 gallons = ___ pints

Ounce

Unit of weight equal to $\frac{1}{16}$ of a pound.

The weight of various objects is measured in **ounces**, pounds, or tons.

1 pound = 16 ounces
1 ton   = 2,000 pounds

To convert a large unit to smaller units, you multiply.
To convert a small unit to larger units, you divide.

EXAMPLES

3 tons = _____ pounds
3 tons = __6,000__ pounds

$$\begin{array}{r} 2{,}000 \\ \times \quad 3 \\ \hline 6{,}000 \end{array}$$

48 ounces = ____ pounds
48 ounces = __3__ pounds

$$\begin{array}{r} 3 \\ 16\overline{)48} \end{array}$$

Exercise A   Make these conversions.

Multiply:

1) 5 tons = ____ pounds

2) 8 pounds = ____ ounces

3) 8 tons = ____ ounces

4) 12 pounds = ____ ounces

5) 18 tons = ____ pounds

Divide:

6) 144 ounces = ____ pounds

7) 18,000 pounds = ____ tons

8) 80 ounces = ____ pounds

9) 5,000 pounds = ____ tons

10) 192 ounces = ____ pounds

Exercise B   Make these conversions. Decide whether to multiply or divide for each one.

1) 32 ounces = ____ pounds

2) 3 pounds = ____ ounces

3) 5 tons = ____ pounds

4) 176 ounces = ____ pounds

5) 50,000 pounds = ____ tons

6) 20 ounces = ____ pounds

To measure with a standard ruler, you need to know what each division on the ruler means. One inch may be divided into different parts.

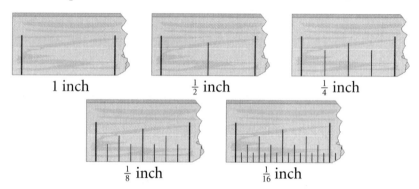

1 inch $\frac{1}{2}$ inch $\frac{1}{4}$ inch

$\frac{1}{8}$ inch $\frac{1}{16}$ inch

Notice that the denominator of the fraction is always equal to the number of parts that the inch is divided into.

Exercise A   Number your paper from 1 to 10. Use a ruler to help you measure the length of each line segment shown below.

1) ———————————————

2) —————————————————————

3) —————————

4) ——————————————————————————————

5) ————————————————————

6) ——————————————————

7) ————————————————————————

8) ——————————

9) ———————————————

10) —————————

Exercise B   Use a ruler to help you draw line segments of these lengths on another sheet of paper.

1) 4 inches

2) $2\frac{3}{4}$ inches

3) $7\frac{7}{8}$ inches

4) $2\frac{5}{8}$ inches

5) $6\frac{1}{4}$ inches

6) $3\frac{1}{2}$ inches

7) $2\frac{3}{16}$ inches

8) $5\frac{2}{4}$ inches

9) $4\frac{1}{4}$ inches

10) $1\frac{3}{8}$ inches

11) $5\frac{6}{16}$ inches

12) $\frac{3}{4}$ inch

13) $\frac{6}{8}$ inch

14) $\frac{1}{4}$ inch

15) $1\frac{3}{4}$ inches

16) $6\frac{5}{8}$ inches

Linear measurement	Measurement of length and distance is often called **linear measurement**. Linear measurement is "straight line" measurement. The most commonly used units of linear measurement are shown below. When you convert a large unit to smaller units, you *multiply*. When you convert a small unit to a larger unit, you *divide*.
The length of a line between fixed points.	

```
1 foot = 12 inches
1 yard = 36 inches
1 yard = 3 feet
1 mile = 5,280 feet
```

EXAMPLES

3 yards = _____ inches

3 yards = _108_ inches

$$\begin{array}{r} 36 \\ \times\ \ 3 \\ \hline 108 \end{array}$$

48 inches = ___ feet

48 inches = _4_ feet

$$\begin{array}{r} 4 \\ 12\overline{)48} \end{array}$$

Exercise A   Convert these units of length and distance.

Divide:

1) 60 inches = ___ feet

2) 120 inches = ___ feet

3) 31,680 feet = ___ miles

4) 48 feet = ___ yards

5) 384 inches = ___ feet

6) 15,840 feet = ___ yards

7) 600 inches = ___ feet

8) 135 feet = ___ yards

Multiply:

9) 7 feet = ___ inches

10) 8 yards = ___ feet

11) 2 miles = ___ feet

12) 33 miles = ___ feet

13) 5 feet = ___ inches

14) 27 feet = ___ inches

15) 3 yards = ___ feet

16) 4 miles = ___ feet

Operations With Linear Measurements

When you add or subtract units of measure, you line up the like units. You may need to simplify your answer. Before you can subtract, you may need to rename or borrow.

EXAMPLE   1 yard 5 inches + 2 yards 1 foot 10 inches

> 1 yard   5 inches
> + 2 yards 1 foot 10 inches
> ─────────────────────────────
> 3 yards 1 foot 15 inches = 3 yards 2 feet 3 inches

Exercise A   Rewrite in vertical form and add. Simplify your answers.

1) 3 yards 2 feet + 5 yards 3 feet
2) 6 yards 2 feet + 7 yards 1 foot
3) 8 feet 6 inches + 2 feet 5 inches
4) 12 feet 7 inches + 5 feet 6 inches
5) 13 yards 2 feet + 4 feet 3 inches

EXAMPLE   6 feet 5 inches − 2 feet 8 inches

We cannot subtract the 8 from the 5, so we borrow 1 foot, or 12 inches, and add it to the 5 inches.

>   5   17
> 6̸ feet 5̸ inches
> −2 feet 8 inches
> ─────────────────
> 3 feet 9 inches

Exercise B   Rewrite in vertical form and subtract.

1) 8 feet 5 inches − 2 feet 6 inches
2) 12 feet 6 inches − 5 feet 8 inches
3) 13 yards 2 feet − 4 yards 1 foot
4) 8 yards 1 foot − 6 yards 2 feet
5) 12 feet 4 inches − 6 feet 8 inches

Exercise C Rewrite in vertical form and add or subtract. Remember to write your answers in simplest form.

1) 6 yards 3 feet 7 inches − 3 yards 2 feet 9 inches

2) 3 yards 5 feet 5 inches + 2 yards 5 feet 4 inches

3) 5 feet 3 inches − 2 feet 8 inches

4) 7 yards 2 feet 9 inches + 4 feet 7 inches

5) 8 yards 5 feet 3 inches + 3 yards 2 feet 8 inches

6) 7 feet 4 inches − 13 inches

7) 13 yards − 2 yards 5 feet 5 inches

8) 6 feet 7 inches + 5 feet 9 inches

9) 16 yards 1 foot 5 inches + 11 yards 2 feet 4 inches

10) 10 yards 6 inches − 2 feet 8 inches

11) 3 yards 4 feet 7 inches + 1 yard 4 feet 11 inches

12) 13 feet 9 inches − 2 yards 5 feet 4 inches

13) 4 yards 3 feet 4 inches + 5 yards 2 feet 9 inches

14) 14 yards − 3 yards 2 feet 7 inches

15) 7 yards 4 inches + 4 feet 7 inches

16) 11 yards 4 inches − 3 yards 2 feet 10 inches

17) 10 yards 1 foot 3 inches + 3 yards 2 feet 5 inches

When you multiply a measurement by a number, remember to multiply each part of the measurement by the number. You may need to simplify the answer.

EXAMPLES   5 times (3 feet 2 inches) = ■

$$
\begin{array}{r}
3\text{ feet}\quad 2\text{ inches} \\
\times \qquad 5 \\
\hline
15\text{ feet } 10\text{ inches} = 5\text{ yards } 10\text{ inches}
\end{array}
$$

2 times (6 yards 8 feet 7 inches) = ■

$$
\begin{array}{r}
6\text{ yards}\quad 8\text{ feet}\quad 7\text{ inches} \\
\times \qquad\qquad 2 \\
\hline
12\text{ yards } 16\text{ feet } 14\text{ inches} = 17\text{ yards} \\
2\text{ feet} \\
2\text{ inches}
\end{array}
$$

Exercise D   Rewrite each problem in vertical form and multiply. Simplify your answers.

1) $7 \times$ (7 yards 3 feet 1 inch)
2) $3 \times$ (2 feet 5 inches)
3) $5 \times$ (1 foot 5 inches)
4) $6 \times$ (5 yards 2 feet)
5) $4 \times$ (9 yards 2 feet 2 inches)
6) $2 \times$ (4 yards 13 feet 4 inches)
7) $8 \times$ (7 feet 2 inches)
8) $5 \times$ (3 yards 2 feet 6 inches)
9) $4 \times$ (6 yards 5 feet 8 inches)
10) $12 \times$ (9 yards 4 feet 3 inches)
11) $2 \times$ (85 inches)
12) $3 \times$ (9 feet 17 inches)

When you divide a measurement by a number, remember to divide each part of the measurement by the number. You may need to simplify the answer.

EXAMPLES   (15 yards 10 feet) ÷ 5 = ■

$$\frac{15 \text{ yards } 10 \text{ feet}}{5} = 3 \text{ yards } 2 \text{ feet}$$

(24 yards 8 feet 4 inches) ÷ 4 = ■

$$\frac{24 \text{ yards } 8 \text{ feet } 4 \text{ inches}}{4} = 6 \text{ yards } 2 \text{ feet } 1 \text{ inch}$$

Exercise E   Divide. Remember to simplify your answers.

1) (15 yards 10 feet) ÷ 5
2) (16 feet 8 inches) ÷ 2
3) (18 yards 9 inches) ÷ 9
4) (21 yards 18 feet 6 inches) ÷ 3
5) (33 feet 18 inches) ÷ 3
6) (12 yards 6 feet 9 inches) ÷ 3
7) (8 feet 10 inches) ÷ 2
8) (48 yards 24 feet 12 inches) ÷ 6
9) (45 yards 27 feet 9 inches) ÷ 3
10) (15 yards 25 feet 20 inches) ÷ 5

Perimeter

Distance around.

The **perimeter** of a shape is the distance around the outside. The perimeter of a shape can be found by adding the lengths of all of the sides of the shape. Often when the opposite sides are equal, only one measurement is given for those two sides.

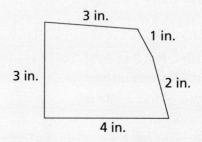

3 + 1 + 2 + 4 + 3 = 13 inches

Perimeter = 13 inches

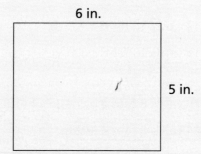

6 + 5 + 6 + 5 = 22 inches

Perimeter = 22 inches

Exercise A Find the perimeters.

1)
6 in.

7 in.

2)
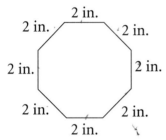
5 in.

5 in.

8 in.

3)
2 in.

2 in.   2 in.

2 in.   2 in.

2 in.   2 in.

2 in.

4)
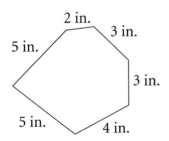
2 in.

3 in.

5 in.

3 in.

5 in.   4 in.

5)
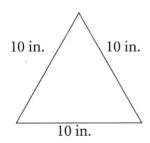
10 in.   10 in.

10 in.

6)
5 yd.

4 yd.   5 yd.

4 yd.

9 yd.

7)
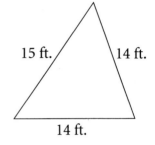
15 ft.   14 ft.

14 ft.

8)
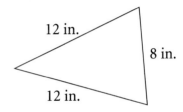
12 in.

8 in.

12 in.

9)
5 yd.

5 yd.   5 yd.

5 yd.

10)
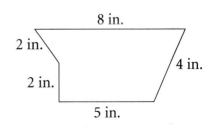
8 in.

2 in.

4 in.

2 in.

5 in.

Exercise B Find the perimeters.

1)

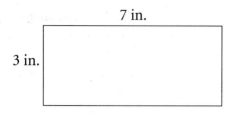

7 in.

3 in.

2)

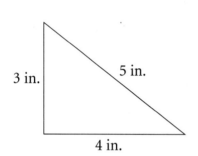

3 in.

5 in.

4 in.

3)

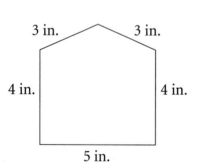

3 in.   3 in.

4 in.   4 in.

5 in.

4)

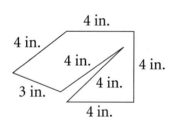

4 in.

4 in.

4 in.   4 in.

4 in.

3 in.

4 in.

5)

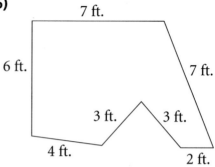

7 ft.

6 ft.   7 ft.

3 ft.   3 ft.

4 ft.   2 ft.

6)

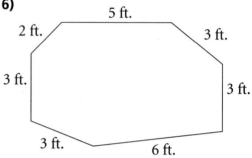

5 ft.

2 ft.   3 ft.

3 ft.   3 ft.

3 ft.   6 ft.

7)

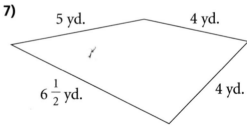

5 yd.   4 yd.

$6\frac{1}{2}$ yd.   4 yd.

8)

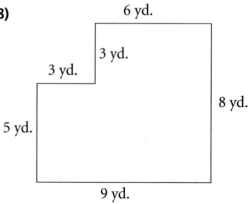

6 yd.

3 yd.

3 yd.

5 yd.   8 yd.

9 yd.

The area of a shape is the amount of space inside the shape. Area is measured in square units. The area of a rectangle can be found by multiplying the length times the width.

Area = length × width

EXAMPLE   A rectangle is 6 units long and 3 units wide. What is the area of the rectangle?

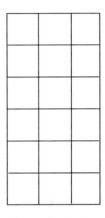

Area = length × width
     = 6 units × 3 units
     = 18 square units

The length and the width of the rectangle must be given in the same units. If the units in the example had been inches, then the area would have been 18 square inches.

Exercise A Find the area of each rectangle. Include the proper units in each answer.

1)

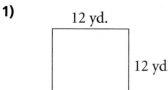

12 yd.

12 yd.

2)

24 yd.

14 yd.

3)

55 ft.

20 ft.

4)

2 in.

5 in.

5)

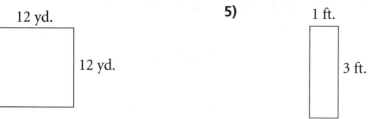

1 ft.

3 ft.

6)

5 miles

4 miles

7)

8 ft.

9 ft.

8)

27 yd.

13 yd.

Computing Perimeter and Area   These problems give you practice in finding the perimeter and area of different objects. Follow these steps in solving them:

Step 1   Read the problem and decide whether you are asked to find the perimeter or the area.

Step 2   Look at all the measurements to see if they are given in the same units. If not, make the necessary conversions.

Step 3   Perform the correct operation to find the answer.

Step 4   Include the correct unit of measurement in your answer.

PROBLEM SOLVING

Exercise B   Solve these word problems.

1) Find the area of a rectangle that has a width of 6 inches and a length of 1 foot.

2) Yumi plans to carpet her bedroom which measures 16 feet by 11 feet. How many square feet of carpeting will she need?

3) Rita decided to put a fence around her garden. The garden is rectangular in shape, measuring 25 feet by 50 feet. How many feet of fencing will she need?

4) Ezra and his dad are building a garage with a length of 40 feet and a width of 8 yards. How many square feet of floor space will they have?

5) What is the distance around the garage?

6) The roof of the garage will be two rectangles, each measuring 40 feet by 15 feet. How many square feet of shingles will Ezra and his dad need to cover the entire roof?

Base, b *One side of a polygon* *used to find area.*	The area of a triangle is found by multiplying $\frac{1}{2}$ times the **base** times the **height**. The answer is expressed in square units. $$\text{Area} = \frac{1}{2}\ \textbf{base} \times \textbf{height}$$

Height, h *Distance from bottom* *to top.*	EXAMPLE 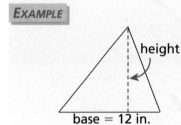

$$\begin{aligned}\text{Area} &= \tfrac{1}{2}\ bh\\ &= \tfrac{1}{2} \times 12 \times 10\\ &= 6 \times 10\\ &= 60 \text{ square inches}\end{aligned}$$

Exercise A   Find the area of each of these triangles.

1)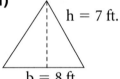

2)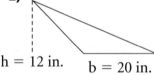

3)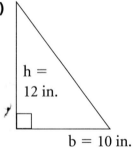

Exercise B   Find the area of each triangle described below.

1) base = 25 feet
height = 10 feet

2) base = 12 yards
height = 30 yards

3) base = 11 inches
height = 50 inches

4) base = 15 inches
height = 6 inches

5) base = 15 inches
height = 4 inches

6) base = 3 inches
height = $\frac{1}{3}$ inch

7) base = 3 feet
height = 12 inches

8) base = 12 feet
height = $\frac{2}{3}$ foot

Calculator Practice   When you use a calculator with customary measurement, sometimes you will need to rename fractions as decimals.

> EXAMPLE   Find the area of this triangle.
>
> base (b) = $2\frac{1}{2}$ feet
> height (h) = 3 feet
>
> Area = $\frac{1}{2}$ × b × h or b × h ÷ 2
>
> h = 3
> b = $2\frac{1}{2}$
>
> **Step 1**   Rename the base and height measurements as decimals.
>
> b = $2\frac{1}{2}$ feet = 2.5 feet
> h = 3 feet = 3 feet
>
> **Step 2**   Press 2.5 ✕ 3 ÷ 2 =
> The display reads 3.75.
>
> **Step 3**   Since the measurements were given as fractions, rename 3.75 as a fraction.
>
> 3.75 = $3\frac{3}{4}$
>
> Area is measured in square units, so the area is $3\frac{3}{4}$ square feet.

Calculator Exercise   Use a calculator to find the area of each triangle described below. Rename decimal answers to fractions. Express each area in square units.

1) b = 2 feet

   h = $1\frac{1}{2}$ feet

2) b = 3 yards

   h = $5\frac{1}{2}$ yards

3) b = $5\frac{3}{4}$ inches

   h = 2 inches

4) b = $18\frac{1}{2}$ feet

   h = $13\frac{1}{2}$ feet

5) b = $2\frac{1}{2}$ inches

   h = 90 inches

6) b = $2\frac{1}{4}$ yards

   h = 5 yards

The area of a parallelogram is found by multiplying the base times the height. The answer is expressed in square units.

Area = base × height

EXAMPLE

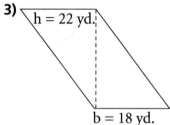

Area = bh
= 18 inches × 6 inches
= 108 square inches

Exercise A   Find the area of each of these parallelograms.

1)
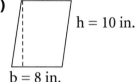
h = 10 in.

b = 8 in.

2)
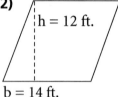
h = 12 ft.

b = 14 ft.

3)
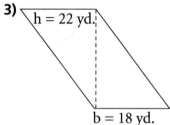
h = 22 yd.

b = 18 yd.

Exercise B   Find the area of each parallelogram described below. You may need to convert some units.

1) base = 18 feet
    height = 6 feet

2) base = 13 inches
    height = 5 inches

3) base = 36 inches
    height = 18 inches

4) base = 9 yards
    height = 5 yards

5) base = 2 feet
    height = 12 inches

6) base = 6 feet
    height = 3 yards

7) base = $\frac{2}{3}$ inch
    height = $\frac{3}{4}$ inch

8) base = 12 feet
    height = 3 yards

The volume of a prism is the measure of the space inside the prism. A prism is a solid figure with two parallel faces of the same shape. Volume is measured in cubic units. You can find the volume of a prism by multiplying the area of its base by the height of the prism.

$$\text{Volume} = \underbrace{\text{area of base}}_{\text{length} \times \text{width}} \times \text{height}$$

EXAMPLE

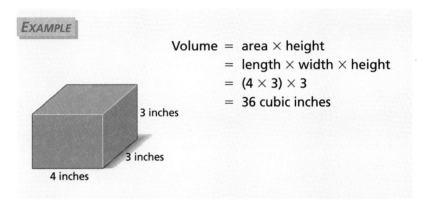

Volume = area × height
= length × width × height
= (4 × 3) × 3
= 36 cubic inches

Exercise A Find the volume of each rectangular prism.

1)
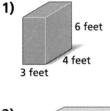
6 feet
4 feet
3 feet

4)
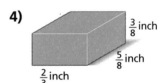
$\frac{3}{8}$ inch
$\frac{5}{8}$ inch
$\frac{2}{3}$ inch

2)
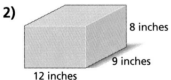
8 inches
9 inches
12 inches

5)
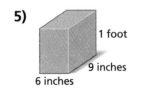
1 foot
9 inches
6 inches

3)
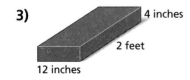
4 inches
2 feet
12 inches

6)
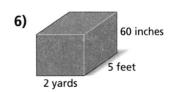
60 inches
5 feet
2 yards

Exercise B Find the volume of each rectangular prism.
Include the correct units in your answer.

1)
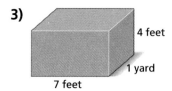
11 inches
6 inches
5 inches

6)
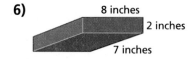
8 inches
2 inches
7 inches

2)
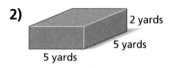
2 yards
5 yards
5 yards

7)
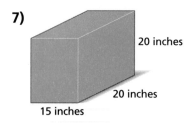
20 inches
20 inches
15 inches

3)
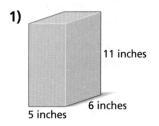
4 feet
1 yard
7 feet

8)

1 foot
1 yard
8 feet

4)
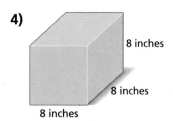
8 inches
8 inches
8 inches

9)
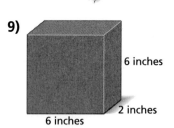
6 inches
2 inches
6 inches

5)
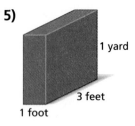
1 yard
3 feet
1 foot

10)
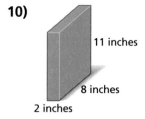
11 inches
8 inches
2 inches

The volume of a prism is found by multiplying the area of its base by the height of the prism. The volume of a triangular prism, therefore, is found by multiplying the area of the base triangle by the height of the prism. The triangle is the prism's base.

$$\textbf{Volume} = (\tfrac{1}{2} \textbf{ base} \times \textbf{height}) \textbf{ Height}$$

EXAMPLE

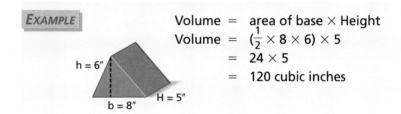

$$
\begin{aligned}
\text{Volume} &= \text{area of base} \times \text{Height} \\
\text{Volume} &= (\tfrac{1}{2} \times 8 \times 6) \times 5 \\
&= 24 \times 5 \\
&= 120 \text{ cubic inches}
\end{aligned}
$$

Exercise A Find the volume of each triangular prism. Include the correct units in your answer.

1)

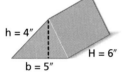

h = 4"
b = 5"
H = 6"

4)

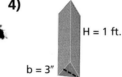

H = 1 ft.
b = 3"
h = 3"

7)

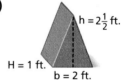

$h = 2\frac{1}{2}$ ft.
H = 1 ft.
b = 2 ft.

2)

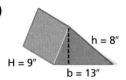

h = 8"
H = 9"
b = 13"

5)

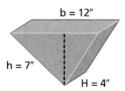

b = 12"
h = 7"
H = 4"

8)

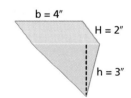

b = 4"
H = 2"
h = 3"

3)

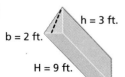

h = 3 ft.
b = 2 ft.
H = 9 ft.

6)

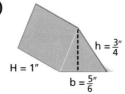

$h = \frac{3}{4}$"
H = 1"
$b = \frac{5}{6}$"

9)

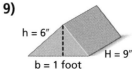

h = 6"
H = 9"
b = 1 foot

Convert these units:

1) 6 gallons = ___ pints

2) 4 quarts = ___ pints

3) 48 ounces = ___ pounds

4) 3 tons = ___ pounds

5) 72 inches = ___ feet

6) 4 yards = ___ feet

7) 9 feet = ___ yards

Find these answers. Simplify if possible.

8)
$$\begin{array}{r} 15 \text{ yards } 5 \text{ feet } 2 \text{ inches} \\ -\qquad\quad 2 \text{ feet } 5 \text{ inches} \\ \hline \end{array}$$

9) 8 times (9 yards 5 feet 2 inches)

10) (16 feet 8 inches) ÷ 2

11)
$$\begin{array}{r} 13 \text{ feet } 6 \text{ inches} \\ -\; 5 \text{ feet } 8 \text{ inches} \\ \hline \end{array}$$

12)
$$\begin{array}{r} 5 \text{ yards } 2 \text{ feet } 6 \text{ inches} \\ +\qquad\quad 2 \text{ feet } 7 \text{ inches} \\ \hline \end{array}$$

Measure these line segments to the nearest $\frac{1}{8}''$.

13) ─────────────

14) ──────────

Use a ruler to draw line segments that measure:

15) $2\frac{5}{8}$ inches

16) $3\frac{3}{4}$ inches

Solve these problems:

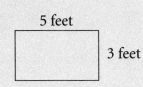

5 feet

3 feet

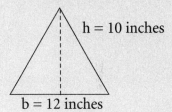

h = 10 inches

b = 12 inches

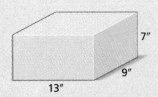

7"

9"

13"

17) What is the area of the rectangle?

18) What is the perimeter of the rectangle?

19) What is the area of the triangle?

20) What is the volume of the rectangular prism?

Test Taking Tip   When you read a question, notice what it is *not* asking for.

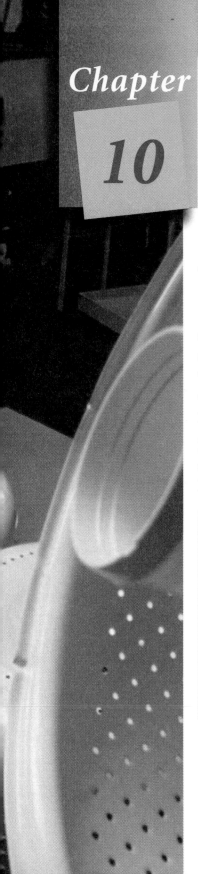

Chapter

10

Other Units of Measure

When you go shopping, you see big, square cases of soup and even larger boxes for appliances like washing machines. But if you look closer, you will see circles and cylinders. Look at the top of a soup can. It's a circle, and the can is a cylinder. And inside your rectangular washing machine is a round cylinder where you place your clothes. The soup can and the washing machine cylinders differ in the volume that they can hold.

In Chapter 10, you will learn how to measure circular shapes and how to find the volume of a cylinder. You will also learn how time is measured.

Goals for Learning

▶ To find the circumference of a circle

▶ To determine the diameter of a circle

▶ To calculate the area of a circle

▶ To compute the volume of a cylinder

▶ To add and subtract units of time

▶ To determine the elapsed time from one given time to another given time

A *circle* is a closed curved line with all points equally distant from the center.

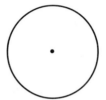

Diameter
Distance across a circle through the center.

The **diameter** of a circle is the length of a line segment through the center of the circle with its ends on the circle. A diameter divides the circle into two equal halves.

Radius
Distance from the center of a circle to the edge of a circle.

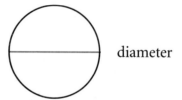

diameter

The **radius** is the length of a line segment from the center of the circle to a point on the circle. Two radii equal the diameter.

Circumference
Distance around a circle.

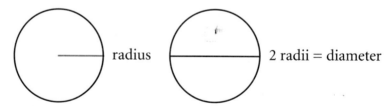

radius   2 radii = diameter

The **circumference** is the distance around the circle. The circumference of a circle is about 3.14 times as long as its diameter.

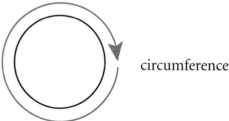

circumference

The ratio of the circumference of a circle to its diameter is about 3.14, or $\frac{22}{7}$. We call this ratio **pi** and write it with a Greek letter, π. To compute with π, use 3.14 when it is easier to use decimals. Use $\frac{22}{7}$ when it is easier to use fractions.

Pi, π

Ratio of the circumference to the diameter.

$$\frac{\text{Circumference}}{\text{Diameter}} = 3.14 = \pi$$

The formulas are:

$$\text{Circumference} = \pi \times \text{diameter}$$

$$\text{Circumference} = 2 \times \pi \times \text{radius}$$

Remember that the diameter is two times the radius.

EXAMPLES Find the circumference (C) of a circle with a diameter (d) of 8 inches.

d = 8"

$C = \pi\, d$
$C = 3.14 \times 8$
$C = 25.12$ inches

Find the circumference (C) of a circle with a radius (r) of 7 inches.

r = 7"

$C = 2\,\pi\, r$
$C = 2 \times \frac{22}{7} \times 7$
$C = 44$ inches

Exercise A Find the circumference of a circle for each diameter or radius given. Use $\frac{22}{7}$ for π in problems 3, 6, 7, 10, and 11.

1) d = 5 in.

2) d = 10 in.

3) d = 7 in.

4) d = 2 ft.

5) r = 6 ft.

6) d = $8\frac{5}{8}$ in.

7) d = 21 yd.

8) r = 3 ft.

9) d = 23 yd.

10) r = $13\frac{1}{2}$ in.

11) d = 28 ft.

12) d = 100 yd.

The formula for finding the diameter (d) of a circle is:

$$\text{Diameter} = \frac{\text{Circumference}}{\pi}$$

EXAMPLE   Find the diameter of a circle with a circumference
of 28.26 inches.

C = 28.26"

$$d = \frac{C}{\pi}$$

$$d = \frac{28.26}{3.14}$$

$$d = 9 \text{ inches}$$

Exercise B   Find the diameter of a circle for each circumference.

1) C = 21.98 in.   **7)** C = 29.83 ft.
2) C = 15.7 in.   **8)** C = 41.134 mi.
3) C = 9.42 yd.   **9)** C = 47.1 ft.
4) C = 40.82 mi.   **10)** C = 53.38 mi.
5) C = 31.4 ft.   **11)** C = 97.34 mi.
6) C = 12.56 yd.   **12)** C = 97.34 yd.

PROBLEM SOLVING

Exercise C   Answer these questions about circumference.

1) The circumference of a can of soup
is 9.42 inches. What is the diameter
of the can?

4) What is the diameter of a circular
sports arena with a circumference of
47.1 yards?

2) The distance around a circular pond
is 78.5 yards. What is the distance
across the pond at its widest point?

5) What is the diameter of a round
table with a circumference of
301.44 inches?

3) The diameter of the expressway
surrounding Northwood is 50.24
miles. What is the distance around
(circumference of) the expressway?

The area of a circle can be found by multiplying π times the radius times the radius. If you are given the diameter of the circle instead of the radius, divide the diameter by 2 to get the radius.

$$\text{Area of a Circle} = \pi \times (\text{radius})^2$$

EXAMPLES Find the area of a circle whose radius is 5 inches.

r = 5"

$A = \pi r^2$
$A = 3.14 \times 5 \times 5$
$A = 78.5$ square inches

Find the area of a circle whose diameter is 6 inches.

d = 6"

$A = \pi r^2$
$A = 3.14 \times 3 \times 3$
$A = 28.26$ square inches

Exercise A   Use the formula $A = \pi r^2$ to find the area of each of these circles.

1) r = 4 in.
2) r = 1.5 yd.
3) r = 3.5 ft.
4) r = 7 ft.
5) r = 10 yd.
6) r = 8 in.
7) r = 20 ft.
8) r = 15 in.
9) d = 10 yd.
10) r = 2.5 ft.
11) r = 9 in.
12) d = 22 in.

13) r = 2.3 mi.
14) r = 2 yd.
15) r = 1 yd.
16) r = 8.6 yd.
17) d = 2 ft.
18) d = 5 in.
19) r = 12 yd.
20) r = 1.7 yd.
21) d = 3 ft.
22) r = 5.1 ft.
23) r = 14 in.
24) d = 24 in.

Exercise B   Find the area of each circle.

1) r = 13 ft.
2) r = 5 in.
3) r = 7 yd.
4) r = 3.3 in.
5) d = 8 in.

6) r = 6 ft.
7) r = 11.6 ft.
8) d = 6 in.
9) d = 4 in.

Calculator Practice   Use your calculator to find the area of a circle.

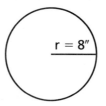

r = 8"

EXAMPLE   Find the area of a circle with a radius of 8 in.
Area = π r² or π × (r × r)

Press 3.14   M+
Since π = 3.14 in the formula, store 3.14 as a constant in the calculator's memory.

Press   C   to clear the display.

Press   MR   ×   8   ×   8   =

The display reads 200.96.

Area is measured in square units, so the area is 200.96 sq. in.

Calculator Exercise   Use a calculator to help you find the area for each of these circles.

1) r = 6 in.

2) r = 10 ft.

3) r = 4 yd.

4) r = 3 mi.

5) r = 7 in.

6) r = 8 ft.

7) r = 5 yd.

8) r = 2 mi.

The volume of a cylinder is found by multiplying the area of the face times the height of the cylinder. The volume is always measured in cubic units.

Volume of a Cylinder = π × (radius)² × Height

EXAMPLE   **Find the volume of this cylinder.**

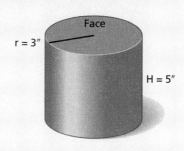

$$V = \pi r^2 H$$
$$V = 3.14 \times 3 \times 3 \times 5$$
$$V = 28.56 \times 5$$
$$V = 141.3 \text{ cubic inches}$$

Exercise A   Find the volume of each cylinder.

1) r = 2 in.
   H = 3 in.

2) r = 5 ft.
   H = 11 ft.

3) r = 5 ft.
   H = 2 ft.

4) r = 8 in.
   H = 2 in.

5) d = 8 in.
   H = 4 in.

6) d = 16 ft.
   H = 5 ft.

Exercise B   Find the volume of the cylinders described below.

1) r = 2 in.
   H = 3 in.

2) r = 3 ft.
   H = 5 ft.

3) r = 7 yd.
   H = 2 yd.

4) r = 3 ft.
   H = 2 ft.

5) r = 6 in.
   H = 2 in.

6) r = 5 in.
   H = 1 in.

7) r = 3 ft.
   H = 6 ft.

8) r = 4 yd.
   H = 6 yd.

9) r = 7 in.
   H = 3 in.

10) r = 8 in.
    H = 2 in.

11) r = 6 ft.
    H = 5 ft.

12) r = 4 yd.
    H = 3 yd.

13) r = 1 ft.
    H = 3 ft.

14) r = 10 in.
    H = 12 in.

15) r = 1 ft.
    H = 10 ft.

16) d = 10 yd.
    H = 2 yd.

17) d = 20 ft.
    H = 5 ft.

18) d = 30 in.
    H = 1 in.

19) r = 2.1 ft.
    H = 2 ft.

20) r = 4 in.
    H = 3.1 in.

21) r = 1.1 ft.
    H = 2 ft.

22) r = 4 yd.
    H = 2.2 yd.

23) r = 6 ft.
    H = 5 ft.

24) r = $\frac{1}{4}$ in.
    H = 2 in.

PROBLEM SOLVING

Exercise C   Solve these area and volume word problems. Be sure that you include the units in your answer.

1) Find the volume of a can with a radius of 2 inches and a height of 5 inches.

2) Iwu's father asked him to compute the area of their patio. The patio was circular with a diameter of 18 feet. What was the area?

3) A can of Alpine soup has a radius of 2 inches and a height of 6 inches. A can of Family Brand soup has a radius of 2 $\frac{1}{2}$ inches and a height of 5 inches. Which can holds more soup? How much more?

4) Astronauts found a cylindrical spaceship with a diameter of 50 yards and a height of 200 yards. What is the volume of the spaceship?

5) There is a circular park in Chicago with a diameter of 119 yards. What is the area of the park?

Computing Units of Time

Time is measured the same all over the world. The same units—minutes, hours, days—are standard to time measurement.

1 minute = 60 seconds
1 hour = 60 minutes
1 day = 24 hours
1 week = 7 days
1 year = 52 weeks

When you add or subtract units of time, you often need to rename the units.

EXAMPLES

Subtract 6 minutes from 3 hours, 4 minutes.

```
    2        64
   3 hours  4 minutes    1 hour = 60 minutes
 −          6 minutes    60 minutes + 4 minutes = 64 minutes
   2 hours 58 minutes
```

Add 8 days, 18 hours to 6 days, 22 hours.

```
     8 days  18 hours    40 hours = 24 hours + 16 hours
  +  6 days  22 hours             = 1 day + 16 hours
    14 days  40 hours  =  15 days 16 hours
```

Exercise A   Add or subtract as shown. Write your answers in simplest form.

1)   28 minutes   7 seconds
      − 2 minutes   10 seconds

2)   15 minutes   45 seconds
      + 8 minutes   30 seconds

3)   6 hours   5 minutes
      +3 hours   8 minutes

4)   13 hours   3 minutes
       −2 hours   9 minutes

Exercise B Add or subtract as shown. Write your answers in simplest form.

1)   7 weeks   5 days
      −2 weeks   8 days

9)   2 days   8 hours
      +3 days   20 hours

2)   3 days   18 hours
      +2 days   21 hours

10)   4 years   8 weeks   1 day
       − 1 year   4 weeks   5 days

3)   15 weeks   5 days
      +   8 days

11)   6 weeks   6 days
       + 2 weeks   2 days

4)   7 years   24 weeks
      +   38 weeks

12)   8 years   30 weeks
       − 5 years   42 weeks

5)   9 years   5 weeks
      +2 years   9 weeks

13)   6 years   2 weeks
       − 5 years   4 weeks

6)   7 years   2 weeks
      −2 years   3 weeks

14)   10 weeks   5 days
       + 3 weeks   3 days

7)   5 years   5 weeks   2 days
      −   5 weeks   5 days

15)   2 days   12 hours
       + 1 day   16 hours

8)   4 years   2 days
      −   3 days

16)   12 years   3 weeks
       − 9 years   4 weeks

Elapsed time	**Elapsed time** is the amount of time that has passed from one given time to another given time.
How long an event lasts.	

EXAMPLES How much time has elapsed from the time shown on Clock A to the time shown on Clock B?

Clock A shows 5:15.   Clock B shows 7:25.

Always write the later time first.

$$
\begin{array}{r}
7{:}25 \\
-5{:}15 \\
\hline
2{:}10
\end{array}
$$

2:10 or 2 hours 10 minutes

How much time has elapsed from the time shown on Clock A to the time shown on Clock B?

Clock A shows 1:35.   Clock B shows 9:20.

Rename 1 hour to 60 minutes and add to the 20 minutes.

$$
\begin{array}{r}
\overset{8\ \ 80}{9{:}20} \\
-1{:}35 \\
\hline
7{:}45
\end{array}
$$

7:45 7 hours and 45 minutes have elapsed.

EXAMPLE

Clock A	Clock B

Clock A shows 11:15.   Clock B shows 1:28.

Add 12 hours to the 1 to work the problem.

```
  13
 1̸:28
−11:15
  2:13  2 hours and 13 minutes have elapsed.
```

Exercise A   Subtract to find how much time has elapsed
from the time shown on Clock A to the time shown on Clock B.

1)

4)

2)

5)

3)

6)

Exercise B Subtract to find the amount of time that has elapsed.

1) From   3:50 to   6:40
2) From   1:55 to   4:30
3) From   2:45 to   9:30
4) From 10:45 to   1:38
5) From   8:15 to 11:30
6) From   9:30 to 12:15
7) From 11:36 to   2:12
8) From   2:02 to   1:05

9) From   3:05 to   7:20
10) From   6:10 to   9:20
11) From   1:00 to   9:35
12) From   4:55 to   8:40
13) From   9:16 to   2:48
14) From 10:35 to 10:48
15) From   8:48 to   1:00
16) From   8:12 to 10:05

PROBLEM SOLVING

Exercise C Solve these problems about time. You will need to use the clock above each problem.

1) Lapeta put a turkey in the oven at the time shown. The turkey needs to roast for 5 hours 30 minutes. At what time should she take the turkey out of the oven?

3) Sophonie figures that it will take her 2 hours and 15 minutes to drive to Philadelphia. What time will it be when she arrives at Philadelphia?

2) Yunang's bus should arrive at 10:55. He looks to see what time it is now. How long will he have to wait?

4) Samuel went to sleep at 10:36 last night. When he woke up, he looked at the clock by his bed. How long did Samuel sleep?

Answer the questions about circles A, B, and C:

A

$$\pi = \frac{22}{7}$$

B

$$\pi = 3.14$$

C

$$\pi = 3.14$$

1) What is the diameter of A?

2) What is the circumference of A?

3) What is the circumference of B?

4) What is the area of C?

Find the volume for each:

5)

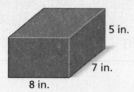

5 in.

7 in.

8 in.

6)

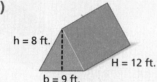

h = 8 ft.

H = 12 ft.

b = 9 ft.

7) r = 9 in.

H = 16 in.

Solve these problems:

8) Elisha's alarm clock woke him up at 7:30 A.M. He has to catch a bus at 1:15 P.M. How much time does he have before he catches the bus?

9)   9 hr.   6 min. 40 sec.
     +   55 min. 22 sec.
    _____

10)   13 hr.   6 min.
       − 5 hr.   8 min.
    _____

Test Taking Tip   Try making study flashcards for the formulas you have learned. On the front of the card identify the formula (area of a circle, for example). On the back of the card write the formula with two or three examples.

Chapter

11

Graphs

Pick up any newspaper or magazine. Study the weather or look at car sales trends. The information is often presented in a graph. To succeed in school and at work, you must be able to understand graphs. Creating graphs for yourself can help give you a clearer picture of how you are spending your money or how you are spending your time.

In Chapter 11, you will learn how to read and create many types of graphs. You will also learn how graphs are used to report information, and sometimes how they are used to mislead us.

Goals for Learning

▶ To read and construct pictographs from data in chart form

▶ To read and construct bar graphs and double bar graphs

▶ To read and construct divided bar graphs from data in chart form

▶ To read and construct line graphs and circle graphs

▶ To redraw and correct a misleading graph

Graphs are used to present information that can be read quickly. All graphs must have a title and a **scale** so that people will know what information is being presented. A **pictograph** is a graph that uses pictures to make it more attractive and interesting.

EXAMPLE

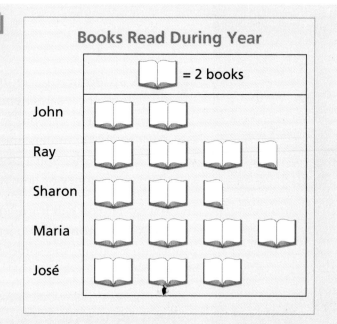

Books Read During Year

☐ = 2 books

John

Ray

Sharon

Maria

José

Often the pictures in pictographs stand for more than one item. In this pictograph, each picture stands for 2 books. John read 2 × 2, or 4, books.

Exercise A Use this pictograph to answer the questions below.

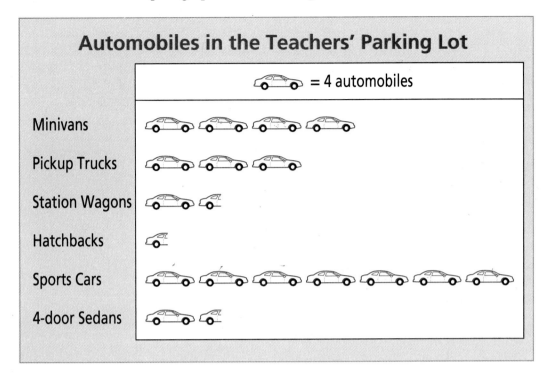

1) What is the title of this graph?

2) Where is the graph's scale?

3) What type of car do most of the teachers drive?

4) What type of car is driven least?

5) Why is part of a car drawn next to 4-door Sedans?

6) How many Pickup Trucks are in the parking lot?

7) About how many cars are in the parking lot?

Constructing Pictographs When you construct a pictograph, follow these steps:

Step 1 Decide how you are going to present the information.

Step 2 Choose a scale and a **symbol**.

Step 3 Graph the **data**.

Step 4 Put in the title.

Step 5 Put in the scale.

Exercise B Make a pictograph to show this information. Be sure that you include a title and a scale.

Cat Population of Five Streets	
Street	Number of Cats
Stricker	25
Fleet	5
Mount	20
Saratoga	10
Water	13

You might use a picture of a cat to stand for 5 cats.

Exercise C Make a pictograph to show this information. Round the numbers to the nearest 100.

Dog Population of Five Towns		
Town	Number of Dogs	Rounded Number
Sludge Creek	782	_____
Furnace Flats	415	_____
Rosetowne	1,276	_____
Millersville	804	_____
Magnolia	892	_____

Bar graph

A graph that compares amounts by using bars.

Pictographs take a long time to construct because each figure must be drawn accurately and put into the correct place. **Bar graphs**, however, are easier to construct. They are often used instead of pictographs to present information.

To tell how many objects are being represented in a bar graph, you compare the length of the bar to the scale.

EXAMPLE

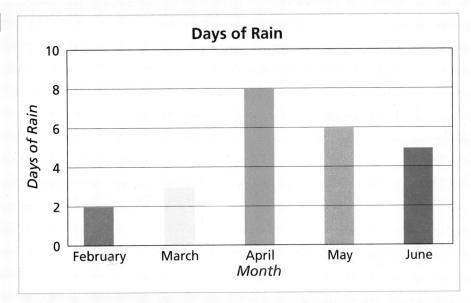

In this bar graph, April had eight days of rain. If the bar does not extend to the next line on the scale, estimate the value. In this bar graph, March had three days of rain. Use a straightedge to help you.

Exercise A Use this bar graph to answer the questions below.

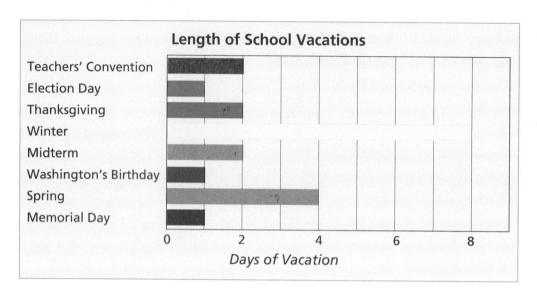

1) What is the graph's title?

2) Where is the scale of the graph?

3) What is the longest vacation?

4) How long is the midterm break?

5) How long is the spring vacation?

6) How many days of vacation come before the midterm break?

7) How many days of vacation are there in all?

8) How does the length of the midterm break compare to the
length of the spring vacation?

Using Vertical Bar Graphs Often, the bars are drawn up and down instead of across. This type of bar graph is called a vertical bar graph. You can tell the amount that each bar represents by comparing the height of the bar to the scale on the left.

Exercise B Use this bar graph to answer the questions below.

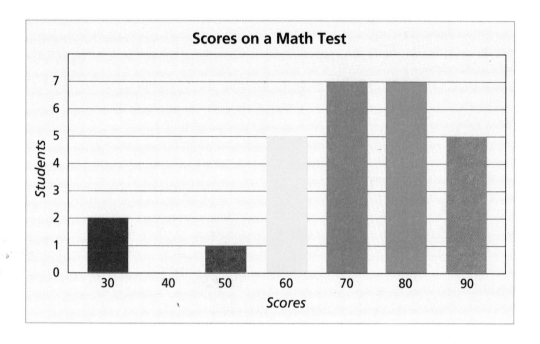

1) What is the title of this graph?

2) Where is the scale?

3) How many students scored a 90 on this test?

4) How many students got a 30?

5) Why is there no bar above the 40 on this graph?

6) How many students scored a 70 or an 80?

7) If 60 is the passing grade, how many students failed this test?

8) If 70 is the passing grade, how many students passed this test?

9) How many students took this test?

Calculator Practice

You know how to use a calculator to find the average of a set of numbers. You also know how to use your calculator's memory key. You can use both of these skills to calculate an average number or score from data you might find on a bar graph.

EXAMPLE   The results of a midterm test show the following scores: 2 students scored 100, 6 students scored 90, 8 students scored 80, 5 students scored 70, and 3 students scored 60. What is the average score?

Step 1   Add the scores for all the students. You will need to multiply the number of students by each score and add the products. Use the memory key to store and add each product.

Press 2   ×   100   =   M+
Press 6   ×   90   =   M+
Press 8   ×   80   =   M+
Press 5   ×   70   =   M+
Press 3   ×   60   =   M+
Press MR . The display reads 1910.

Step 2   Find the total number of student scores.
Press 2 + 6 + 8 + 5 + 3 =
The display reads 24.

Step 3   Divide the sum of the products by the total number of student scores.
Press MR ÷ 24 =
The display reads 79.583333. Round to the nearest whole number. The average score is 80.

Step 4   Press MC before starting the next problem.

Calculator Exercise   Use a calculator to find the average for each set of data. Round your answer to the nearest whole number.

1)

Score	Number of Students
88	3
82	4
79	6
75	7
68	9

2)

Age	Number of People
17 years	6
18 years	8
20 years	3
27 years	2
43 years	1

3)

Miles	Number of Runners
2	3
5	8
6	4
24	2

4)

High Temp.	Number of Days
70°	6
72°	1
76°	3
78°	6
92°	7
93°	4
95°	3

Constructing a Bar Graph   When you make a bar graph, follow these steps:

Step 1   Decide if you want to make a vertical or horizontal bar graph.

Step 2   Choose a scale.

Step 3   Label the vertical **axis** and horizontal axis.

Step 4   Draw the bars.

Step 5   Give the graph a title.

Axis
A line of reference on a graph.

Exercise C   Make a horizontal bar graph to show this information.

Softball Distance Throw	
Contestant	Distance
Mario	100 ft.
Jennifer	140 ft.
Brian	110 ft.
Heather	150 ft.
Rawkeem	170 ft.
Kim	125 ft.

Exercise D   Make a vertical bar graph to show this information.

High Jump	
Contestant	Height Jumped
Joe	54 in.
Luke	56 in.
Rita	48 in.
Anita	59 in.
Josh	63 in.
Yumi	52 in.

Divided bar graph	Sometimes more than one kind of information is presented in the same bar graph. One way this is done is with a **divided bar graph**. We use a divided bar graph when the total of the two parts is important. Use the **key** to determine what the bars in the graph stand for. A divided bar graph shows the information with a divided bar like this:
A graph that uses parallel bars to compare information.	

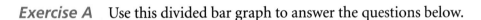

Key	
Area on a graph where the symbols are explained.	

Exercise A Use this divided bar graph to answer the questions below.

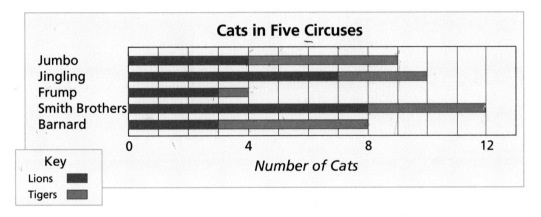

1) What is the title of this graph?

2) Where is the scale?

3) How many cats are in the Jingling Circus?

4) How many lions are in the Jumbo Circus?

5) How many tigers are in the Frump Circus?

6) What two circuses have the same number of lions?

7) Which circus has the most lions?

8) What two circuses have the same number of tigers?

9) What two circuses have more tigers than lions?

Using Multiple Bar Graphs   Another way to present more than one kind of information at a time is to use a **multiple bar graph**. We use a multiple bar graph when the comparison of the parts is important. A multiple bar graph shows the information with two or more bars side by side like this:

Exercise B   Use this multiple bar graph to answer the questions.

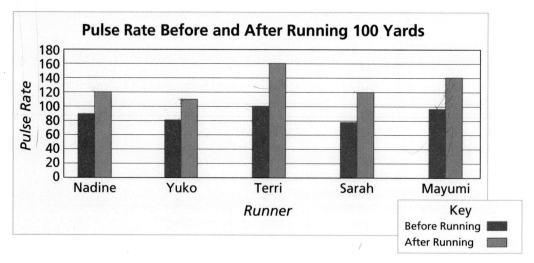

1) What is the title of this graph?

2) Where is the scale?

3) Whose pulse rate was the lowest before running?

4) Whose pulse rate was the lowest after running?

5) Whose pulse rate was highest before running?

6) Whose pulse rate was 110 beats after running?

7) Whose pulse rate was 90 beats before running?

8) Whose pulse rate increased the least?

9) Whose pulse rate increased the most?

10) Which runners had the same rate after running?

When making a bar graph, be sure to follow these steps:

Step 1   Decide if you want to make a vertical or a horizontal bar graph.

Step 2   Choose a scale.

Step 3   Label the vertical and horizontal axes.

Step 4   Draw the bars.

Step 5   Give the graph a title.

Exercise A   Make a divided bar graph to show this information.

Housing in the Jamala Islands		
Year	Owned	Rented
1960	7 million	9 million
1970	11 million	13 million
1980	15 million	20 million
1990	35 million	15 million

Exercise B   Make a multiple bar graph to show this information.

Scores on the Midterm and the Final		
Student	Midterm	Final
Sheila	80	85
Andy	70	80
Kim	65	90
Tony	60	75
Raj	70	75
Desi	75	80

Line graph

A graph that shows change in amounts with a solid line.

A **line graph** is used to show change over a period of time. Instead of drawing bars, a dot is placed at the correct height. Then the dots are connected in order from left to right. You can tell the number represented at a particular time. First find the time on a **horizontal axis**. Then go up the graph, and finally go over to the **vertical axis**. You can read the amount from this scale.

Horizontal axis

Line of reference parallel to the horizon.

Vertical axis

The line of reference that is up and down.

EXAMPLE

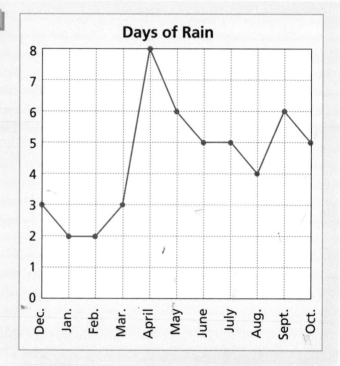

In this line graph, April had eight days of rain. June and July both had five days of rain.

Exercise A Use this line graph to answer the questions below.

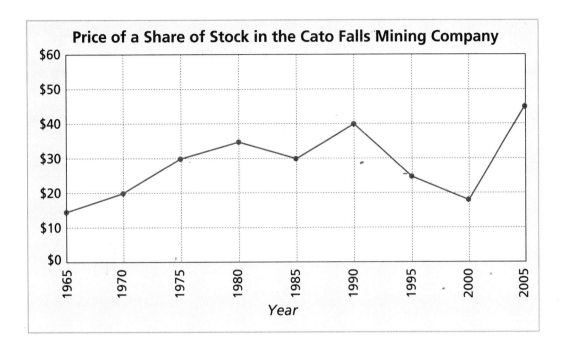

Price of a Share of Stock in the Cato Falls Mining Company

1) What is the title of this graph?

2) Where is the scale?

3) What was the price of a share of stock in 1975?

4) What was the price of a share of stock in 1995?

5) What was the approximate price of a share in 1972?

6) During what five-year period was the greatest increase in the price of a share of stock?

Constucting a Line Graph   When you make a line graph, follow these steps:

Step 1   Draw the horizontal and vertical axes.

Step 2   Choose a convenient scale for the numbers. You may need to round off large numbers.

Step 3   Enter these numbers on the vertical axis and the time units on the horizontal axis. Label the scales.

Step 4   Above each time, make a dot at the appropriate height.

Step 5   Connect the dots in order.

Step 6   Give the graph a title.

Exercise B   Make a line graph to show the following data.

1)

Yuri's Weight Loss	
Week of Diet	Yuri's Weight
0	205 lbs.
1	204 lbs.
2	201 lbs.
3	197 lbs.
4	195 lbs.
5	191 lbs.

2)

Average Monthly Temperature in Cincinnati	
January	29°
February	32°
March	42°
April	52°
May	64°
June	72°
July	76°
August	78°
September	69°
October	57°
November	41°
December	32°

Circle graph

A graphic way to compare amounts using segments of a circle.

Allotted

Assigned.

Sector

A part of a circle bounded by two radii.

A **circle graph** is used to show how the whole of something is divided into parts. You can guess how much is **allotted** to the different parts by comparing the sizes of the **sectors**. The exact allotment is usually shown in the graph by percent or a fraction.

The Wang Family Budget

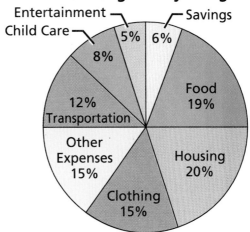

Exercise A   Use this circle graph to answer the questions.

1) What is the title of this graph?

2) What do the Wangs spend most of their money on?

3) How much do they spend for housing if their yearly income is $36,800?

4) What do they spend for food?

5) What do they spend for clothing?

6) How much do they save each year?

7) Make a chart to show how much the Wangs spend for each item in their budget if their yearly income is $36,800.

Exercise B Use this circle graph to answer these questions.

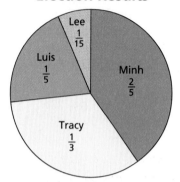

Student Government Election Results

1) What is the graph's title?

2) Who won the election?

3) Who got the fewest votes?

4) Who came in second?

5) If 1,095 votes were cast, how many votes did each person get?

Exercise C Copy this chart. Complete the missing information by multiplying the percent or the fraction by 360°. Round to the nearest degree.

Part of the Circle	$\frac{1}{3}$	$\frac{1}{2}$	$\frac{1}{6}$	$\frac{1}{12}$	10%	35%	5%	12%	32%
Number of Degrees									

Fractions   Percents

Constructing Circle Graphs   When you make a circle graph, follow these steps:

Step 1   Draw a conveniently sized circle. Mark the center with a dot.

Step 2   Find out how many degrees are in each sector. To do this, multiply the percent or the fraction by the 360° in a circle.

Step 3   Draw a radius.

Step 4   Use a protractor to measure and draw each sector. Use the center of the circle as the vertex of each angle.

Step 5   Label each sector and mark the appropriate percent or fraction.

Step 6   Give the graph a title.

Exercise D   Make a circle graph to show this information.

The Soler Family Budget	
Budget Item	Percent Allotted
Food	30%
Housing	25%
Clothing	20%
Car	10%
Savings	8%
Other	7%

Graphs That Mislead

Mislead

Cause a person to reach unrealistic conclusions.

Sometimes graphs are drawn so that they **mislead** the person who is reading them for information.

EXAMPLES

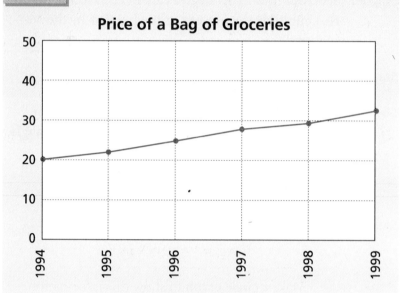

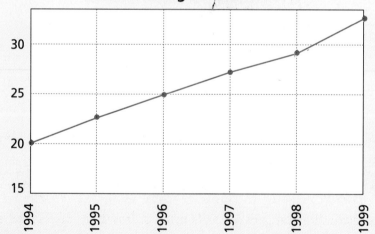

Graph A makes it appear that there was a slight increase in price. Graph B makes it appear there was a large increase in price. The vertical scales differ. These differences can mislead the person reading the graphs.

Exercise A Answer the questions below the graphs.

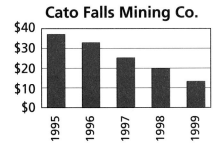

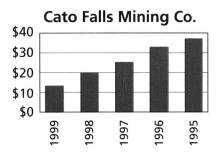

1) Which graph makes it appear that the price of a share of stock is going up?

2) Which graph makes the value of a share of stock appear to be decreasing?

3) How do the two graphs differ?

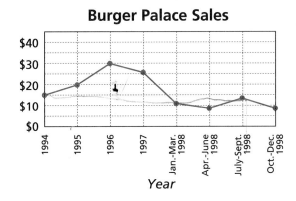

4) Does it appear that sales at Burger Palace for 1998 were more or less than sales for 1997?

5) What were the total sales during all of 1998?

6) Were the total sales for 1998 more or less than the total sales for 1997?

7) What is wrong with this graph?

Exercise B   Answer the questions about the graphs.

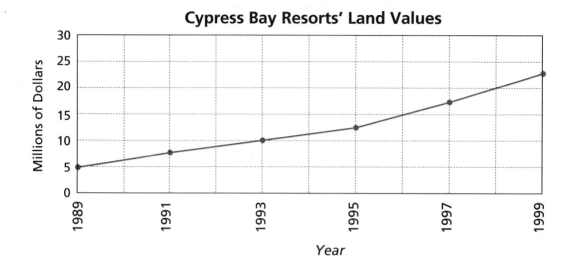

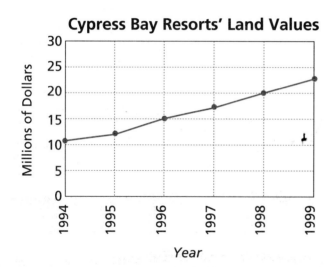

1) Which graph makes it appear that there has been a gradual increase in land values at Cypress Bay Resorts?

2) Which graph makes it appear that there has been a large increase in land values at Cypress Bay Resorts?

3) Which graph do you think a salesperson for Cypress Bay Resorts would use?

4) How do the two graphs differ?

Exercise C Answer the questions below this graph.

1) What is the title of this graph?

2) What is wrong with the vertical axis?

3) Name two things that are wrong with the horizontal axis.

4) How is the spacing on the horizontal and vertical axes different?

5) Redraw this graph so that it accurately shows the data. Make up a title for your graph.

Answer the following questions about pictographs:

1) If 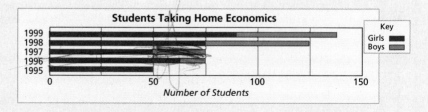 represents 4 cars, how many cars would be represented by ?

2) If ▯ represents 100 cans of soup, how many symbols would you draw to represent 875 cans of soup?

Make a vertical bar graph to show the information in this chart:

3)

Evan's Test Scores	
Test 1	85
Test 2	72
Test 3	90
Test 4	86
Test 5	92

Make a multiple bar graph to show the information in this chart:

4)

Scores on the Midterm and Final		
Student	Midterm	Final
Lance	65	85
Wanda	90	90
Maria	70	95
Emiko	80	70

Use this divided bar graph to find answers for the questions on page 265.

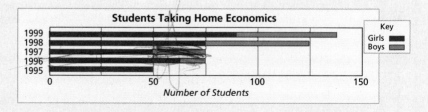

5) In what year did boys first take home economics?

6) How many girls took home economics in 1998?

7) How many students took home economics in 1997?

8) How many boys took home economics in 1998?

Make a line graph to show the information in this table:

9)

Pherooz's Weight Loss	
Week	Weight
1	185
2	183
3	180
4	175
5	178
6	170

Look at the graph. What is wrong with it? Make another graph that is correct.

10)

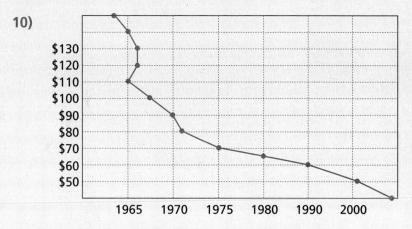

Test Taking Tip When you create a graph from a chart of data, check the number of facts you are supposed to record from the chart. Count to be sure you have the same number of facts on the graph.

Chapter

12

Scale Drawing

ave you ever wanted to plan an addition to your home, or design a deck, a building, or a landscape? Would you enjoy building model planes, trains, or automobiles? Does the idea of finding the best route for your next vacation sound like a smart idea? Whether you are creating plans or reading maps, being able to use a scale is helpful.

In Chapter 12, you will learn how to use floor plans, maps, scale models, and scale drawings. You will solve problems involving proportions and see how plans help designers, homeowners, and architects.

Goals for Learning

▶ To solve problems involving actual objects and models, using scale drawings and ratios

▶ To measure a drawing to the nearest eighth of an inch, and then solve a proportion to find the size of the actual object

▶ To use floor plans and ratios to determine the amount of carpet or tile needed to cover actual rooms

▶ To measure distances between two points on a map or drawing to the nearest eighth of an inch, and then use the scale to find the real distance

Scale

A ratio of the original size to the size on a map or model.

The **scale** of a model is a description of the size of the model in relation to the full-size object. This is a picture of a model steam engine made to a 1:288 scale. The scale 1:288 means that if a part of the model is 1 mm, the same part on the actual steam engine is really 288 mm.

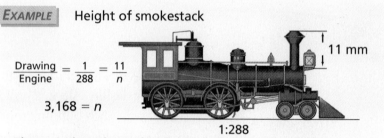

EXAMPLE   Height of smokestack

$$\frac{\text{Drawing}}{\text{Engine}} = \frac{1}{288} = \frac{11}{n}$$

11 mm

$$3{,}168 = n$$

1:288

The actual smokestack is 3,168 mm or 3.168 m high.

Exercise A   Use your metric ruler to measure the parts described on the drawing above. Then use a proportion to find the real-life sizes. Give your answers in meters.

1) Width of a window
2) Height of a window
3) Width of the cab
4) Width of the smokestack
5) Rear wheel diameter
6) Overall height
7) Length of the cab roof
8) Distance between the centers of the big wheels

Gauge

Scale of model trains.

Model railroaders use letters to describe their scales. Each scale is called a **gauge**. The chart tells what the scales mean. Use the ratios to find the model size or the actual size of a railroad car. In the chart below, the ratio tells how many model units to real units. If an O-gauge model is 1 inch long, the real one is 43.5 inches.

Gauge	Ratio
O	1:43.5
OO	1:76
HO	1:87
N	1:148
Z	1:220

An O-gauge railroad car measures 12 inches long. How many inches long is the real car?

$$\frac{\text{Model}}{\text{Real}} \quad \frac{1}{43.5} = \frac{12}{n}$$

$$n = 522 \text{ inches}$$

The car is 522 inches long.

A railroad car is 43.5 feet long. How many inches long is an HO-gauge model?

$$\frac{\text{Model}}{\text{Real}} \quad \frac{1}{87} = \frac{n}{43.5 \text{ ft.}}$$

$$\frac{1}{87} = \frac{n}{522 \text{ in.}}$$

$$\frac{522}{87} = n$$

$$6 = n$$

The model is 6 inches long.

Exercise B Use the ratios in the chart to answer these questions. Round to the nearest whole number if needed.

1) A switching engine is 49 feet long. About how many inches will the N-gauge model be?

2) An OO-gauge boxcar is 6 inches long. How many feet long is the real boxcar?

3) A caboose is 12 feet high. About how many inches high would the O-gauge model be?

4) A tank car is 37 feet long. About how many inches long would a Z-gauge model be?

5) About how many inches tall should the model people be in an OO-gauge layout if real people are about 6 feet tall?

6) About how many inches tall should the people be in an O-gauge layout?

7) An HO-gauge train car is 8 inches long. How many feet long is the real car?

8) About how many inches tall should a house be to fit into an HO-gauge train layout? The real house is 30 feet high.

9) A water tower in an OO-gauge layout is 3 inches tall. How many feet tall is the real water tower?

10) An O-gauge bridge is 24 inches long. How many feet long would the real bridge be?

The scale of some model trains is 1 foot to $\frac{1}{4}$ inch. This means that each foot on the real car is represented by $\frac{1}{4}$ inch on the model car.

This is a sketch of the side view of a caboose. You can use the measurements of the real car to find the measurements of the model car.

EXAMPLE   What is the width of the model's cupola?

$$\frac{\text{Real}}{\text{Model}} \qquad \frac{\frac{1}{1}}{\frac{1}{4}} = \frac{6}{n} \qquad \frac{1}{4} \times 6 = n$$

$$1\frac{1}{2} \text{ in.} = n$$

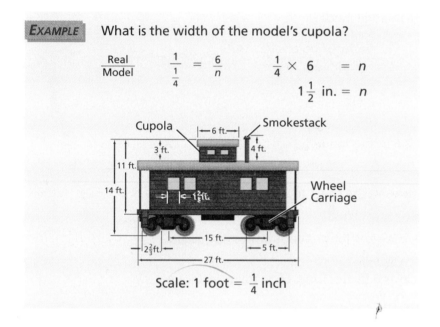

Scale: 1 foot = $\frac{1}{4}$ inch

Exercise C   Use the real measurements from the sketch and a proportion to find the sizes of these parts on the model.

1) Overall length of the caboose

2) Height of the smokestack

3) Diameter of a wheel

4) Overall height of the caboose

5) Height of the cupola

6) Width of a lower window

7) Distance between the centers of the wheel carriages

8) Width of the wheel carriages

9) Height of the car without the wheel carriages

10) Height of the wheel carriages

Calculator Practice   Use your calculator to solve a proportion with an unknown term.

Solve for *n*.

$$\frac{4}{5} = \frac{n}{20}$$

Multiply on the diagonal and divide by the third number.

Press 4 $\boxed{\times}$ 20 $\boxed{\div}$ 5 $\boxed{=}$
The display reads 16.
n = 16

$$\frac{n}{30} = \frac{5}{6}$$

Press 30 $\boxed{\times}$ 5 $\boxed{\div}$ 6 $\boxed{=}$
The display reads 25.
n = 25

Calculator Exercise   Use a calculator to solve for the unknown term in each proportion.

1) $\dfrac{n}{6} = \dfrac{15}{30}$

2) $\dfrac{5}{7} = \dfrac{n}{35}$

3) $\dfrac{8}{9} = \dfrac{n}{72}$

4) $\dfrac{6}{11} = \dfrac{n}{77}$

5) $\dfrac{9}{20} = \dfrac{n}{60}$

6) $\dfrac{18}{20} = \dfrac{n}{100}$

7) $\dfrac{35}{62} = \dfrac{n}{124}$

8) $\dfrac{12}{30} = \dfrac{96}{n}$

Scale drawing

A picture in which the relative sizes have been kept.

In a book, you might see a **scale drawing** like this one of a bird. A drawing that is the same size as the real-life object may be too large or too small to fit well into the book. Then the artist draws the object to scale and includes a scale with the drawing.

The scale of this drawing is 1:2. This means that each inch on the drawing represents two inches on the real-life object. The first number refers to the drawing. The second number refers to the real object.

If the first number in the scale is smaller than the second number, the real object is larger than the drawing. If the first number is larger, then the real object is smaller than the drawing. A scale of 1:1 means that the drawing is life-size.

You can find the actual size of the object drawn by measuring the drawing with a ruler and then using the scale to write a proportion.

EXAMPLE   How long is the bird above? The length of the drawing is $2\frac{5}{8}$ inches.

$$\frac{\text{Drawing}}{\text{Real}} \quad \frac{1}{2} = \frac{2\frac{5}{8}}{n}$$

$$2 \times 2\frac{5}{8} = n$$

$$5\frac{1}{4} = n$$

The bird is $5\frac{1}{4}$ inches long.

Exercise A   Measure the distance between the points of the arrows to the nearest $\frac{1}{8}$ inch. Use the scale to write a proportion. Solve the proportions to find the length of the real-life object in inches.

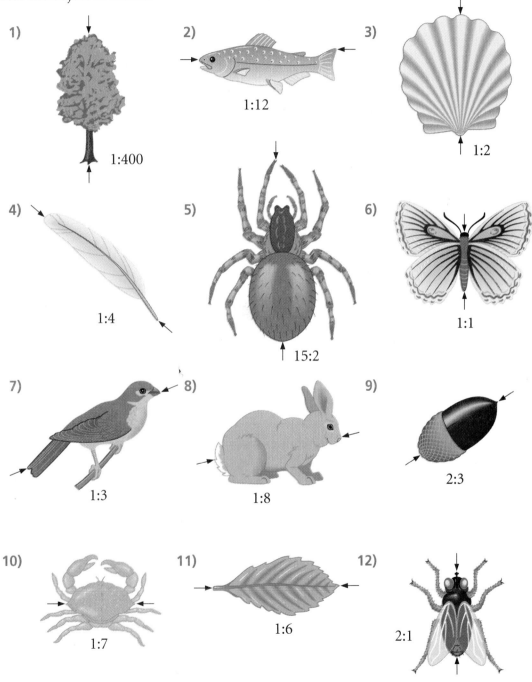

1)   1:400

2)   1:12

3)   1:2

4)   1:4

5)   15:2

6)   1:1

7)   1:3

8)   1:8

9)   2:3

10)   1:7

11)   1:6

12)   2:1

Dimensions

Measure, such as length, width, or height, of the size of an object.

Floor plans of houses and apartments are drawn to scale. They are used by construction workers, tenants, and interior decorators. These drawings can be used to plan improvements or arrange furniture. You can find the real **dimensions** of the rooms by measuring the drawing with a ruler and then solving a proportion.

EXAMPLE

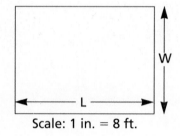

Scale: 1 in. = 8 ft.

Length of drawing = $1\frac{1}{2}$″   Width of drawing = $1\frac{1}{8}$″

$$\frac{\text{Drawing}}{\text{Real}} \quad \frac{1}{8} = \frac{1\frac{1}{2}}{n}$$

$$8 \times 1\frac{1}{2} = 1 \times n$$

$$8 \times \frac{3}{2} = n$$

$$12 = n$$

The living room is 12 feet long.

$$\frac{\text{Drawing}}{\text{Real}} \quad \frac{1}{8} = \frac{1\frac{1}{8}}{n}$$

$$8 \times 1\frac{1}{8} = 1 \times n$$

$$8 \times \frac{9}{8} = n$$

$$9 = n$$

The living room is 9 feet wide.

Exercise A Measure the length and width of each room to the nearest $\frac{1}{8}$ inch. Then use a proportion to find the real dimensions of each room using the scale 1 in. = 8 ft.

1) Living room
2) Dining room
3) Kitchen
4) Bath
5) Den
6) Bedroom

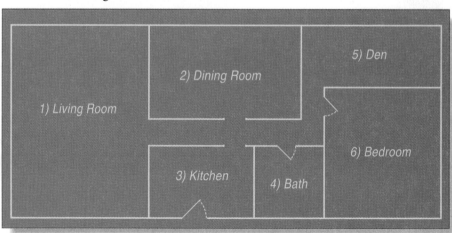

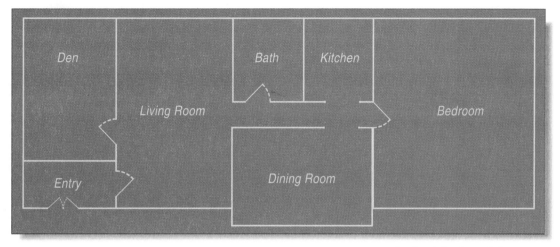

Scale: 1 inch = 8 feet

Exercise B   Use a ruler and the floor plan above to answer the questions.

1) What are the real-life dimensions of the den?

2) If you wanted to tile the entry with 1-foot by 1-foot tiles, how many tiles would you need?

3) How many square feet of carpet would be needed to install wall-to-wall carpeting in the dining room?

4) What would this be in square yards?

5) How much would it cost to install wall-to-wall carpeting in the living room and the den? The carpet costs $18 per square yard.

6) Tile costs 79¢ per square foot. How much would it cost to put tile in the kitchen?

7) What is the length and the width of the bedroom?

8) What is the length and width of the bath?

9) How much will it cost to carpet the dining room if the carpeting costs $14.75 per square yard?

10) How many square yards of carpeting would be needed to carpet the living room, the dining room, and the den?

Map distance

Space between two points as measured on a map.

You can find the shortest distance between two cities. First, measure the distance on the map. This is the **map distance**. Then multiply the map distance by the number of miles represented by one inch. This is the **real distance**. Make all your measurements to the nearest eighth of an inch.

Real distance

Actual space between two locations.

Scale: 1 inch = 880 miles

EXAMPLE   Distance between Washington, D.C. and Seattle

Map Distance: $2\frac{5}{8}''$

$2\frac{5}{8} \times 880 = \frac{21}{8} \times \frac{880}{1}$

$= 2{,}310$ miles

Exercise A   Copy and complete this chart.

Trip	Map Distance (inches)	Real Distance (miles)
1) Chicago to Washington, D.C.	_____	_____
2) Miami to Omaha	_____	_____
3) Dallas to San Francisco	_____	_____
4) Los Angeles to Miami	_____	_____
5) Omaha to Dallas	_____	_____
6) Boston to Dallas	_____	_____
7) Seattle to Los Angeles	_____	_____
8) Washington, D.C. to Miami	_____	_____

You can use a ruler to find the distance between two cities on a map. Then you multiply to find the actual distance.

The roads do not usually follow this straight line. To find the distance along the roads, you would add the **road distances** between each pair of arrows along your route.

Road distance

Space between two locations along a road indicated by a number on a map.

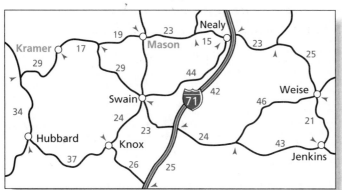

Scale: 1 inch = 32 miles

EXAMPLE The distance from Kramer to Mason = ■

Map distance: measurement $= \frac{7}{8}''$

$\frac{7}{8} \times 32 \; = 28$ miles

Road distance: 17 miles + 19 miles $= 36$ miles

Exercise B Copy and complete this chart. Make all measurements to the nearest eighth of an inch.

	Trip	Map Distance (inches)	Real Distance (miles)	Shortest Road Distance (miles)
1)	Kramer to Swain	_____	_____	_____
2)	Knox to Hubbard	_____	_____	_____
3)	Nealy to Weise	_____	_____	_____
4)	Jenkins to Swain	_____	_____	_____
5)	Swain to Weise	_____	_____	_____
6)	Nealy to Hubbard	_____	_____	_____
7)	Hubbard to Jenkins	_____	_____	_____

Answer these questions about scale models:

1) A real switching engine is 52 feet long. HO-gauge models are built to the scale of 1:87. About how many inches long would an HO model switching engine be?

2) The length of a real caboose is 27 feet. How long would the model be if the scale is 1 foot to $\frac{1}{4}$ inch?

3) An O-gauge car is $13\frac{1}{2}$ inches long. O-gauge models are built to the scale of 1:43.5. How long is the real car to the nearest $\frac{1}{4}$ inch?

4) A model tank is built to a 1:48 scale. How long would the real tank be if the model is $3\frac{1}{2}$ inches long? Give the answer in feet.

Use your ruler to measure the sizes of the rooms in the diagram below to the nearest eighth of an inch. Then answer these questions.

5) What is the length and width of the bathroom?

6) Tile costs 89¢ per square foot. How much would it cost to tile the kitchen?

7) What is the length and width of the living room?

8) What is the length and width of the dining room?

9) How many square yards of carpet are needed to cover the living room and dining room?

10) What is the perimeter of the bathroom?

11) Ceramic tile costs $1.29 per square foot. How much will it cost to tile the bath?

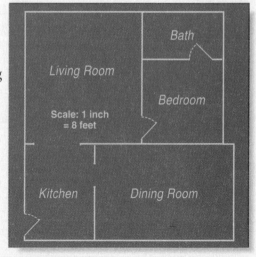

Find the map line distance and the shortest road distance between each pair of cities. Give answers in miles.

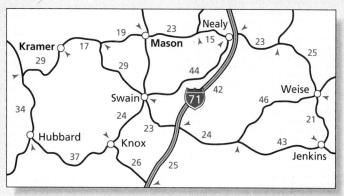

Scale: 1 inch = 32 miles

	map line distance	shortest road distance
12) Hubbard and Knox	_____	_____
13) Weise and Nealy	_____	_____
14) Mason and Hubbard	_____	_____
15) Jenkins and Knox	_____	_____
16) Kramer and Hubbard	_____	_____
17) Kramer and Weise	_____	_____

Measure the distance between the arrows to the nearest $\frac{1}{8}$ inch. Then find the lengths of the real-life creatures.

18)

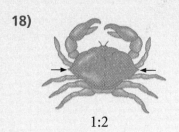

1:2

19)

2:3

20)

1:12

Chapter

13

Introduction to Algebra

When you read about an event that happened in the year 235 B.C., do you really have a good understanding of when that was? How many years ago was that? Time lines are like number lines. They both have numbers that go in different directions, and placement on the lines represent amounts or values.

In Chapter 13 you will learn more about the branch of mathematics called algebra. You will learn specific strategies for solving mathematical problems that include unknown quantities.

Goals for Learning

▶ To use number lines to help calculate and represent mathematical steps

▶ To compare integers, using symbols < and >

▶ To state the absolute value of any positive or negative integer

▶ To solve operations sentences with positive and negative integers

▶ To solve for a variable in an open sentence involving addition, subtraction, multiplication, and division

Sometimes we need to use a direction as well as an amount when we use numbers. Walking three steps to the right is the *opposite* of walking three steps to the left. A score of 35 points is the *opposite* of a score of 35 points in the hole.

Exercise A   Give the opposite of each phrase.

1) 3,000 feet above sea level

2) Twelve degrees below zero

3) Losing 5 yards on a down

4) Rewinding the tape to the beginning

5) Moving the clocks up 1 hour

Integers
All whole numbers and their opposites (. . . −2, −1, 0, 1, 2, . . .).

Going to the right is usually thought of as going in a positive direction. Going up is also thought of as a positive move. Going left or going down is going in a negative direction. We use **integers** when we want to talk about amounts with a direction. A number line can be used to show **positive integers** and **negative integers**.

Positive integers
Whole numbers greater than zero.

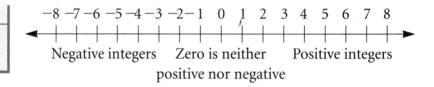

Negative integers   Zero is neither   Positive integers
positive nor negative

Negative integers
Whole numbers less than zero.

EXAMPLES   Each number below is listed with its opposite.

4, −4   −121, 121

−16, 16   53, −53

Exercise B   Name the opposite of each of these integers.

1) −8   **5)** 8   **9)** −24

2) 1   **6)** −12   **10)** −238

3) 17   **7)** −5   **11)** 14

4) −6   **8)** 108   **12)** 0

Any number plus its opposite is equal to zero. Any number plus zero is equal to that number.

EXAMPLES
$3 + -3 = 0$	$2 + 0 = 2$
$-5 + 5 = 0$	$0 + 7 = 7$
$9 + -9 = 0$	$8 + 0 = 8$

Exercise C   Find the sum of these integers.

1) $6 + -6$ **5)** $23 + 0$ **9)** $16 + -16$
2) $-12 + 12$ **6)** $8 + -8$ **10)** $0 + 3$
3) $0 + 76$ **7)** $-12 + 12$ **11)** $5 + -5$
4) $-7 + 0$ **8)** $0 + -11$ **12)** $-12 + 0$

On a number line, the larger of two numbers is the one that is to the right of the other number. Since the positive numbers are to the right of the negative numbers, we can say that any positive number is greater than any negative number.

$$-5 \; -4 \; -3 \; -2 \; -1 \quad 0 \quad 1 \quad 2 \quad 3 \quad 4 \quad 5 \quad 6 \quad 7 \quad 8$$

Using a number line, we can compare pairs of integers.

EXAMPLES
$+8$ and $+4$
$+8$ is farther to the right, so $+8 > +4$

-7 and $+4$
$+4$ is farther to the right, so $-7 < +4$

-3 and -7
-3 is farther to the right, so $-3 > -7$

Exercise D   Use a number line to help you compare each pair of integers, using $>$ or $<$.

1) $-3 \quad +2$ **6)** $-7 \quad -2$ **11)** $-6 \quad 0$
2) $+8 \quad +1$ **7)** $+3 \quad -1$ **12)** $-2 \quad -8$
3) $-9 \quad -4$ **8)** $+6 \quad -9$ **13)** $-36 \quad +4$
4) $-5 \quad +5$ **9)** $+5 \quad -9$ **14)** $-58 \quad -72$
5) $+6 \quad +8$ **10)** $+6 \quad 0$ **15)** $+23 \quad -468$

Use a number line to help you think through these problems.

EXAMPLES If you begin at 6 and move three spaces to the right, you will end at 9.

Write an addition sentence: +6 + +3 = +9

If you begin at 4 and move three spaces to the left, you will end at 1.

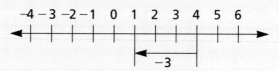

Write an addition sentence: +4 + −3 = +1

Exercise A Write an addition sentence to describe each move. Be sure to include the answer in your sentence.

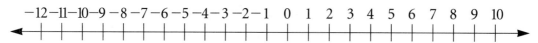

1) Begin at +5. Move +3.

2) Begin at +7. Move −7.

3) Begin at −7. Move +4.

4) Begin at +1. Move −8.

5) Begin at −8. Move +5.

6) Begin at −4. Move +5.

7) Begin at +2. Move −8.

8) Begin at −6. Move −3.

9) Begin at −4. Move −5.

10) Begin at −6. Move 0.

A number line can be used to understand adding integers. The first addend tells us where to begin. The second addend tells us which direction and how far to move. The place we stop is the sum of the integers.

$+6 + -8 = \blacksquare$
Begin at $+6$ and move -8.

$$-2\ -1\quad 0\quad 1\quad 2\quad 3\quad 4\quad 5\quad 6\quad 7$$

-8

Stop at -2 so $+6 + -8 = -2$.

$-3 + -4 = \blacksquare$
Begin at -3 and move -4.

$$-8\ -7\ -6\ -5\ -4\ -3\ -2\ -1\quad 0\quad 1$$

-4

Stop at -7 so $-3 + -4 = -7$.

Exercise B   Use the number line to help you find the sums.

1) $+5 + -7$

2) $-4 + -4$

3) $+6 + +3$

4) $-7 + +3$

5) $+3 + +3$

6) $-6 + -1$

7) $-4 + -6$

8) $-8 + +9$

9) $+7 + -7$

10) $+9 + -9$

11) $-7 + -2$

12) $+4 + -8$

13) $+3 + +2$

14) $-7 + -2$

15) $+8 + -6$

16) $+4 + -9$

17) $-5 + -5$

18) $+1 + -9$

19) $-10 + +7$

20) $-2 + -5$

21) $-3 + -2 + +6$

22) $+4 + -8 + +7$

23) $-5 + -3 + +6$

24) $-8 + +5 + +7$

The **absolute value** of a number is the distance that the number is from zero. The absolute value of a number is always positive.

Absolute value

The distance a number is from zero.

EXAMPLES $|+6| = 6$ $|-3| = 3$ $|0| = 0$

The absolute value symbol is a pair of vertical lines.

Exercise C   Give the absolute value of each number.

1) $|-4|$

2) $|+8|$

3) $|+108|$

4) $|+6|$

5) $|-108|$

6) $|+11|$

7) $|0|$

8) $|-3|$

9) $|-273|$

10) $|+3|$

11) $|+23|$

12) $|-19|$

When you use the number line to add two integers with the same sign, you move in the same direction. When you add two numbers with the same signs, you are also adding the absolute values of the numbers. The sign of the answer is the same as the signs of the two addends.

EXAMPLES $+3 + +2 = \blacksquare$

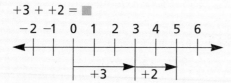

$+3 + +2 = +5$
Both move to the right. The sum is positive.

$-4 + -2 = \blacksquare$

$-8\ -7\ -6\ -5\ -4\ -3\ -2\ -1\ \ \ 0$

$-4 + -2 = -6$
Both move to the left. The sum is negative.

When you add two numbers with unlike signs on the number line, you first go one direction and then the other. When you add two numbers with unlike signs you subtract the absolute values of the numbers. The sign of the answer is the same as the sign of the number with the larger absolute value.

 EXAMPLES $-6 + {}^+4 = \blacksquare$

$$-6\ -5\ -4\ -3\ -2\ -1\quad 0\quad 1$$

$-6 + {}^+4 = -2$

Move left and then right. The sum is negative.

$${}^+5 + {}^-2 = \blacksquare$$

$$-2\ -1\quad 0\quad 1\quad 2\quad 3\quad 4\quad 5\quad 6$$

${}^+5 + {}^-2 = {}^+3$

Move right and then left. The sum is positive.

You can position a negative or a positive sign in two places: $^-8$ or -8 and $^+3$ or $+3$. For example, you could write $^-8 - {}^-8 = {}^-16$ or $^+3 + {}^+3 = {}^+6$. The problems may be less confusing if you write the numbers in parentheses like $(-4) + (+6)$ instead of $-4 + {}^+6$.

Exercise D   Find the sums.

1) $(-3) + (+8)$

2) $(-28) + (-36)$

3) $(+52) + (+38)$

4) $(-1) + (-2)$

5) $(-92) + (+203)$

6) $(-7) + (-9)$

7) $(-2) + (-5)$

8) $(+27) + (-45)$

9) $(-38) + (+19)$

10) $(+6) + (-203)$

11) $(+4) + (+23)$

12) $(-24) + (+6)$

13) $(-206) + (+27)$

14) $(+16) + (-33)$

15) $(0) + (-6)$

We can think of a subtraction problem as one where we try to find a missing addend. In the problem $8 - 2$, we think of 8 as the sum and 2 as one addend. The answer to the problem is the missing addend.

EXAMPLES　Two plus what number equals 8?

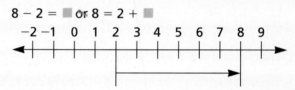

$$8 - 2 = \blacksquare \text{ or } 8 = 2 + \blacksquare$$

On the number line, this problem would begin at 2. What would you do to get to 8? You would go six places to the right. The answer is +6. Using a number line can help you find the answers to subtraction problems.

$$(+4) - (+9) = \blacksquare$$

Begin at +9. Go to +4. Move 5 to the left.
$$(+4) - (+9) = -5$$

$$(-5) - (+3) = \blacksquare$$

Begin at +3. Go to −5. Move 8 to the left.
$$(-5) - (+3) = -8$$

$$(+3) - (-2) = \blacksquare$$

Begin at −2. Go to +3. Move 5 to the right.
$$(+3) - (-2) = +5$$

Exercise A Use a number line to find the answers to these subtraction problems.

1) $(-2) - (+5)$

2) $(-5) - (-5)$

3) $(+6) - (+2)$

4) $(+2) - (+7)$

5) $(-7) - (+3)$

6) $(+6) - (+8)$

7) $(+8) - (+9)$

8) $(-1) - (+8)$

9) $(+4) - (-6)$

10) $(-8) - (-6)$

11) $(-3) - (-5)$

12) $(+4) - (-4)$

13) $(-5) - (-1)$

14) $(-1) - (+7)$

15) $(+4) - (+1)$

16) $(-9) - (+3)$

The answer to $(+2) - (-4)$ is the same as the answer to $(+2) + (+4)$. The answer to $(+2) - (+4)$ is the same as the answer to $(+2) + (-4)$. Subtraction problems can also be solved by solving a related addition problem instead. To subtract a number, add its opposite.

EXAMPLES

$(+2) - (-4) = (+6)$
$(+2) + (+4) = (+6)$

$(+2) - (+4) = (-2)$
$(+2) + (-4) = (-2)$

Exercise B Solve these subtraction problems by changing to adding the opposite.

1) $(-23) - (-16)$

2) $(+17) - (-46)$

3) $(-26) - (+51)$

4) $(+42) - (+38)$

5) $(-35) - (-23)$

6) $(+18) - (+35)$

7) $(-45) - (+26)$

8) $(-73) - (-43)$

9) $(+82) - (-37)$

10) $(-52) - (+36)$

11) $(+35) - (+28)$

12) $(-23) - (-44)$

13) $(+16) - (+39)$

14) $(+92) - (-54)$

15) $(-64) - (+31)$

16) $(+43) - (-12)$

We can use positive and negative integers to help us solve word problems.

> **EXAMPLE** A football team gained 3 yards on the first down, lost 5 yards on the second down, and gained 7 yards on the third down. How many yards did they gain?
> $(+3) + (-5) + (+7) = 5$
> They gained 5 yards.

PROBLEM SOLVING

Exercise A Write an addition sentence and solve each problem.

1) On Monday the temperature goes up 7°, by Thursday the temperature goes up another 4°, and by Sunday the temperature goes down 2°. How much has the temperature changed over the course of the week?

2) On Friday your checking account balance is $122. On Saturday you shop at the mall and write two checks for $17 and $31. What is your checking account balance now?

3) During the course of the game, the team scores 56 points, then they lose 18 points, and finally they score 32 more points. What is their final score?

4) Marta takes a three-part physical endurance test. In part 1 she loses 18 points. In part 2 she gains 22 points, and in part 3 she gains 4 points. What is Marta's score on the endurance test?

5) The Giants lose 12 yards on the first down in the football game. They gain 7 yards on the second down. On the third down they gain 8 yards. What is the total yardage gained by the Giants?

6) Hector works on the 4th floor of a high rise building. He needs to go up 9 floors to get to the cafeteria for lunch, and then go down 5 floors to attend a meeting. On what floor does the meeting take place?

7) Sun Ling owes her brother $37. She earns $18, and then earns $21. How much money does Sun Ling have now?

8) Kwon has 82 books in his collection. He donates 26 paperbacks to the library book drive, and recycles 4 that are too worn out to keep. Kwon then goes to the bookstore and buys 3 books. How many books are now in his collection?

The multiplication of positive and negative integers is just like the multiplication of whole numbers.

EXAMPLES

> **Rule** The product of two numbers with like signs will be positive.
>
> $(+3) \times (+7) = +21$
> $(-3) \times (-7) = +21$
>
> Both signs are the same so the product is positive.

EXAMPLES

> **Rule** The product of two numbers with unlike signs will be negative.
>
> $(-5) \times (+2) = -10$
> $(+2) \times (-6) = -12$
>
> Both signs are different so the product is negative.

Exercise A Find the products.

1) $(-2) \times (-6)$
2) $(+3) \times (-3)$
3) $(+3) \times (+7)$
4) $(-5) \times (-3)$
5) $(-6) \times (-4)$
6) $(-3) \times (-1)$
7) $(+10) \times (-2)$
8) $(-4) \times (-5)$
9) $(-4) \times (+6)$
10) $(+6) \times (+12)$
11) $(-1) \times (-1)$
12) $(-4) \times (-13)$

13) $(-7) \times (-7)$
14) $(-7) \times (+6)$
15) $(+5) \times (+8)$
16) $(+9) \times (-8)$
17) $(+4) \times (-18)$
18) $(+45) \times (-2)$
19) $(-6) \times (-9)$
20) $(-11) \times (-11)$
21) $(+11) \times (-11)$
22) $(-7) \times (+10)$
23) $(+22) \times (-2)$
24) $(+3) \times (-35)$

Sometimes it may be necessary to multiply with more than two numbers. Simply multiply the first two numbers and replace them with their product.

EXAMPLE $(-3) \times (-5) \times (-2)$

$\underbrace{}$

$(+15) \times (-2) = -30$

Exercise B   Find the products.

1) $(-4) \times (-3) \times (+3)$

2) $(+5) \times (-2) \times (-5)$

3) $(+5) \times (-1) \times (-1)$

4) $(-2) \times (-3) \times (-1)$

5) $(+6) \times (-4) \times (-3)$

6) $(-6) \times (+6) \times (-9)$

7) $(-4) \times (-4) \times (-4)$

8) $(+8) \times (+1) \times (-10)$

9) $(-2) \times (+4) \times (-1)$

10) $(-12) \times (-12) \times (-1)$

11) $(-3) \times (-1) \times (-12)$

12) $(+11) \times (-11) \times (-1)$

13) $(+13) \times (-2) \times (-1)$

14) $(-16) \times (+11) \times (+2)$

15) $(-3) \times (-4) \times (-9)$

16) $(-7) \times (-5) \times (-1)$

17) $(-5) \times (+5) \times (-1)$

18) $(+6) \times (+2) \times (-1)$

19) $(-4) \times (-1) \times (-5)$

20) $(+11) \times (-1) \times (+4)$

21) $(-30) \times (-10) \times (-3)$

22) $(+12) \times (+4) \times (-20)$

23) $(-22) \times (-10) \times (-1)$

24) $(-3) \times (-2) \times (-14)$

Commutative property

States that two numbers may be added or multiplied in either order.

The addition and multiplication operations have special properties. The **commutative property** states that two numbers may be added in either order.

EXAMPLES Commutative Property of Addition

$$5 + 4 = 4 + 5$$

9　　　9　Both sums equal 9.

$$(+2) + (-7) = (-7) + (+2)$$

−5　　　　　−5　Both sums equal −5.

$$(-4) + (-3) = (-3) + (-4)$$

−7　　　　　−7　Both sums equal −7.

The commutative property also states that two numbers may be multiplied in either order.

EXAMPLES Commutative Property of Multiplication

$$4 \times 6 = 6 \times 4$$

24　　　24　Both products equal 24.

$$(-7) \times (-2) = (-2) \times (-7)$$

14　　　　　14　Both products equal 14.

$$(-3) \times (+5) = (+5) \times (-3)$$

−15　　　　　−15　Both products equal −15.

The **associative property** allows you to add with different groupings. Sometimes this property is called the grouping property.

EXAMPLE   Associative Property of Addition

$$(2 + 3) + 4 = 2 + (3 + 4)$$
$$5 + 4 = 2 + 7$$
$$9 = 9$$

Both sums equal 9. Adding the 2 and 3 first or adding the 3 and 4 first does not change the final answer.

The associative property also allows you to multiply with different groupings.

EXAMPLE   Associative Property of Multiplication

$$(4 \times 5) \times 2 = 4 \times (5 \times 2)$$
$$20 \times 2 = 4 \times 10$$
$$40 = 40$$

Both products equal 40. Multiplying the 4 and 5 first or multiplying the 5 and 2 first does not change the final answer.

Exercise A   Write the name of the property demonstrated. Refer to the examples if necessary.

1) $2 + 6 = 6 + 2$

2) $5 + (6 + 2) = (5 + 6) + 2$

3) $8 + 1 = 1 + 8$

4) $8 \times 4 = 4 \times 8$

5) $12 + 5 + 2 = 12 + 2 + 5$

6) $10 \times 9 = 9 \times 10$

7) $(9 + 2) + 3 = 9 + (2 + 3)$

8) $(8 + 2) + 5 = 8 + (2 + 5)$

9) $(3 \times 4) = (4 \times 3)$

The **distributive property** applies to problems that mix multiplication and addition or multiplication and subtraction. The distributive property allows you to multiply each term in parentheses by a single factor.

Distributive property

The product of a number and a sum or difference of numbers $a \times (b + c)$ or $a \times (b - c)$ is the same as the sum or difference of the products $(a \times b) + (a \times c)$ or $(a \times b) - (a \times c)$.

EXAMPLES   Distributive Property of Multiplication

$$2 \times (4 + 3) = 2 \times 4 + 2 \times 3$$
$$2 \times 7 = 8 + 6$$
$$14 = 14$$

Recall the Order of Operations from Chapter 1. Multiply 2×4 and 2×3 before adding. Then add the products $8 + 6$.

Both solutions equal 14. Instead of adding the 4 and 3 in parentheses first, you can multiply each by the 2 and then add. The final answer does not change.

$$4 \times (6 + 2) = 4 \times 6 + 4 \times 2$$
$$24 + 8$$
$$32$$

$$5 \times (9 - 2) = 5 \times 9 - 5 \times 2$$
$$45 - 10$$
$$35$$

Exercise B   Use the distributive property of multiplication to simplify these expressions. Show your steps as shown in the examples above.

1) $5 \times (7 + 5)$

2) $6 \times (8 + 10)$

3) $3 \times (12 - 10)$

4) $5 \times (6 - 2)$

5) $4 \times (7 + 2)$

6) $7 \times (6 + 2)$

7) $8 \times (11 - 4)$

8) $4 \times (11 + 3)$

9) $7 \times (10 - 2)$

10) $5 \times (12 - 4)$

11) $8 \times (5 - 2)$

12) $18 \times (2 + 3)$

13) $5 \times (20 - 5)$

14) $15 \times (3 - 1)$

15) $9 \times (8 + 3)$

16) $3 \times (4 + 9)$

Division of positive and negative integers requires the use of the same rules used in multiplication.

EXAMPLES

    Rule The quotient of two numbers with like signs will be positive.

$$(-15) \div (-5) = +3$$
$$(+16) \div (+2) = +8$$

Both signs are the same so the quotient is positive.

EXAMPLES

    Rule The quotient of two numbers with unlike signs will be negative.

$$(-12) \div (+4) = -3$$
$$(+14) \div (-2) = -7$$

The signs are unlike so the quotient is negative.

Division problems can be expressed as fractions.

EXAMPLES $(+15) \div (-3)$ is the same as $\frac{15}{-3}$ and $-\frac{15}{3} = -5$

$$\frac{-12}{-4} = +3 \qquad \frac{-17}{18} = -\frac{17}{18}$$

Exercise A   Solve for the quotients.

1) $(-16) \div (-8)$	**9)** $(+24) \div (-6)$	**17)** $(-39) \div (-3)$
2) $(-9) \div (+3)$	**10)** $(-7) \div (-7)$	**18)** $(-28) \div (-4)$
3) $(-9) \div (-9)$	**11)** $(-1) \div (-1)$	**19)** $(+30) \div (-15)$
4) $(+36) \div (+2)$	**12)** $(-6) \div (+3)$	**20)** $(+21) \div (-7)$
5) $(+30) \div (+3)$	**13)** $(+88) \div (-11)$	**21)** $(-10) \div (-1)$
6) $(+35) \div (-7)$	**14)** $(+34) \div (-17)$	**22)** $(-61) \div (+1)$
7) $(+52) \div (-2)$	**15)** $(+82) \div (-2)$	**23)** $(+85) \div (-5)$
8) $(-32) \div (+32)$	**16)** $(-77) \div (-11)$	**24)** $(-90) \div (-2)$

Exercise B   Simplify these fractions by dividing.

1) $\dfrac{-28}{+4}$

2) $\dfrac{+35}{-7}$

3) $\dfrac{-60}{-1}$

4) $\dfrac{-14}{-7}$

5) $\dfrac{-32}{-2}$

6) $\dfrac{-56}{+2}$

7) $\dfrac{+78}{-2}$

8) $\dfrac{-21}{+3}$

9) $\dfrac{-25}{-5}$

10) $\dfrac{+52}{-26}$

11) $\dfrac{-44}{+11}$

12) $\dfrac{-17}{-1}$

13) $\dfrac{-24}{-12}$

14) $\dfrac{-88}{+44}$

15) $\dfrac{+46}{-23}$

16) $\dfrac{+52}{+26}$

Exercise C   Simplify these fractions.

1) $\dfrac{-14}{+5}$

2) $\dfrac{+33}{-10}$

3) $\dfrac{-19}{-12}$

4) $\dfrac{+22}{-10}$

5) $\dfrac{-78}{-11}$

6) $\dfrac{+22}{+12}$

7) $\dfrac{-10}{+4}$

8) $\dfrac{-11}{+10}$

9) $\dfrac{-10}{-10}$

10) $\dfrac{+18}{-12}$

11) $\dfrac{+55}{-11}$

12) $\dfrac{+57}{-23}$

13) $\dfrac{-200}{+20}$

14) $\dfrac{+140}{+70}$

15) $\dfrac{-80}{-12}$

16) $\dfrac{+34}{-16}$

17) $\dfrac{-26}{-19}$

18) $\dfrac{+57}{-27}$

19) $\dfrac{-70}{+30}$

20) $\dfrac{-71}{-20}$

Variable

A symbol, usually a letter, that can stand for different values.

A **variable** is a letter such as *a*, *b*, *n*, *x*, or *y* that stands for an unknown number. You can use any letter or symbol to stand for an unknown number. When you know the value of the variable, you can replace the letter with a number.

All numbers can be represented on the number line.

EXAMPLES   Graph $x = 3$ on the number line.

Step 1   Use a number line like the one shown.

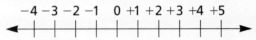

Step 2   Locate the $x = 3$ and draw a shaded circle as shown.

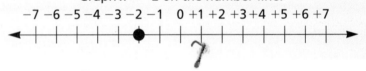

Graph $x = -2$ on the number line.

Exercise A   Draw number lines to graph these values.

1) $x = 6$ 8) $x = -1$

2) $x = 5$ 9) $x = -3$

3) $x = -7$ 10) $x = 3$

4) $x = 7$ 11) $x = -4$

5) $x = 4$ 12) $x = -5$

6) $x = -6$ 13) $x = 0$

7) $x = -2$ 14) $x = 1$

Ordered pair
Two numbers that give the location of a point on a grid.

Origin
The point on a grid with the coordinates (0, 0).

x-axis
The horizontal line on a grid that passes through the origin.

x-coordinate
The first number in an ordered pair describing the location of a point.

y-axis
The vertical line on a grid that passes through the origin.

y-coordinate
The second number in an ordered pair describing the location of a point.

When a vertical number line is drawn so that it crosses a horizontal number line at zero, it forms a grid. The horizontal line is called the **x-axis**. The vertical line is called the **y-axis**. The point where the two lines cross at zero is the **origin**.

Any point on the grid can be named by its **x-coordinate** and its **y-coordinate**. The x-coordinate is the first number and the y-coordinate is the second number in an **ordered pair (x, y)**. For x, move to the right or left on the horizontal number line. For y, move up or down on the vertical number line.

EXAMPLE Graph the ordered pairs $(-3, -2)$, $(-2, 2)$, $(0, 1)$, $(3, 4)$, and $(4, -1)$.

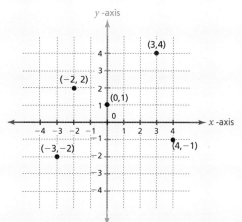

Exercise A   Graph the ordered pairs.

1) $(-2, 2)$, $(0, 2)$, $(2, 2)$

2) $(3, 3)$, $(3, 0)$, $(3, -3)$

3) $(-2, 2)$, $(0, 0)$, $(2, -2)$

4) $(-2, 0)$, $(0, 2)$, $(2, 4)$

5) $(-2, -1)$, $(-1, 1)$, $(0, 3)$

6) $(-1, 1)$, $(0, -2)$, $(1, -5)$

Equation
Two or more mathematical expressions separated by equal signs.

An **equation** is a mathematical sentence that says two expressions are equal. For example, $13 + 5 = 18$. When an equation includes at least one variable, we call it an **open sentence**.

Equations with variables are easy to solve using opposites. Remember the opposite of $+8$ is -8 because when you add them together the answer is zero. The opposite of -5 is $+5$ because $-5 + 5 = 0$ or $(-5) + (+5) = 0$.

Open sentence
An equation with an unknown.

EXAMPLES

Solve the equation $n + 5 = +18$.

In the equation $n + 5 = 18$ we must remove the $+5$ from the equation by adding the opposite -5 to both sides of the equation.

$$
\begin{array}{rl}
n + 5 &= +18 \\
\underline{-5} & \underline{-5} \\
n + 0 &= +13 \quad \text{because } 18 - 5 = 13 \\
n &= +13 \quad \text{because } 13 - 0 = 13
\end{array}
$$

Check: $13 + 5 = +18$ ✓

Find x for $x - 7 = +10$.

Recall that subtraction problems can be solved by changing to add the opposite. Think of $x - 7 = (+10)$ as $x + (-7) = (+10)$.

$$
\begin{array}{rl}
x - 7 &= +10 \\
\underline{+7} & \underline{+7} \\
x &= +17 \quad \text{because } 10 + 7 = 17
\end{array}
\qquad
\begin{array}{rl}
\text{Think: } x + (-7) &= +10 \\
\underline{+7} & \underline{+7} \\
x &= 17
\end{array}
$$

Check: $17 - 7 = +10$

Find a for $a + 5 = -11$.

$$
\begin{array}{rl}
a + 5 &= -11 \\
\underline{-5} & \underline{-5} \quad \text{Add } -5 \text{ to both sides of the equal sign.} \\
a &= -16 \quad \text{because } -11 - 5 = -16
\end{array}
$$

Check: $-16 + 5 = -11$

Exercise A Solve for the variable. Refer to the examples if you need help.

1) $x + 2 = +10$

2) $a + 6 = +20$

3) $t + 2 = +18$

4) $n + 5 = +22$

5) $x + 1 = +20$

6) $y + 7 = +30$

7) $a + 8 = +38$

8) $c + 10 = +25$

9) $r + 20 = +30$

10) $s + 7 = +17$

11) $n + 3 = +28$

12) $x + 30 = +30$

13) $y + 32 = +90$

14) $b + 9 = +39$

15) $r + 34 = +54$

16) $p + 45 = +60$

17) $v + 2 = +32$

18) $w + 12 = +21$

19) $x + 10 = +10$

20) $s + 4 = +5$

Exercise B Solve for the variable. Check your answers.

1) $d - 5 = +30$

2) $a - 10 = +22$

3) $f - 1 = +2$

4) $x - 13 = +23$

5) $g - 5 = +20$

6) $t - 1 = +30$

7) $y - 28 = +40$

8) $m - 2 = +26$

9) $n - 23 = +1$

10) $x - 17 = +30$

11) $a - 7 = +7$

12) $b - 1 = +1$

13) $u - 3 = +3$

14) $w - 7 = 0$

15) $c - 9 = +11$

16) $m - 1 = 0$

17) $h - 3 = +30$

18) $k - 5 = +2$

19) $x - 12 = +3$

20) $y - 5 = +2$

Exercise C   Solve for the variable. Check your answers.

1) $p - 7 = -10$

2) $q - 4 = -4$

3) $a + 5 = -11$

4) $m + 3 = -5$

5) $r - 5 = -30$

6) $d + 1 = -1$

7) $x - 6 = -50$

8) $h + 2 = -3$

9) $x + 10 = -3$

10) $j - 3 = -19$

11) $z + 11 = -12$

12) $b + 17 = -33$

13) $s - 29 = -9$

14) $n - 21 = -3$

15) $u + 1 = -1$

16) $f - 14 = -14$

17) $x - 1 = -1$

18) $k + 120 = -100$

Sometimes the open sentence may be in the form of $-5 + x = 12$. Solving for the variable requires the same basic operation as before.

EXAMPLES   Solve for the variable.

$$-5 + a = 12$$

$$
\begin{array}{rl}
-5 + a &= 12 \\
+5 & +5 \\
\hline
a &= 17
\end{array}
$$
Add +5 to both sides of the equation.

Check: $-5 + 17 = 12$

$$
\begin{array}{rl}
-6 + x &= -5 \\
+6 & +6 \\
\hline
x &= +1
\end{array}
$$
Add on both sides of the equation.

Check: $-6 + 1 = -5$

$$
\begin{array}{rl}
20 &= a - 7 \\
+7 & +7 \\
\hline
+27 &= a
\end{array}
$$
Add on both sides of the equation.

Check: $20 = 27 - 7$

$$
\begin{array}{rl}
8 + x &= -10 \\
-8 & -8 \\
\hline
x &= -18
\end{array}
$$
Add on both sides of the equation.

Check: $8 + (-18) = -10$

$$
\begin{array}{rl}
-16 &= c + 5 \\
-5 & -5 \\
\hline
-21 &= c
\end{array}
$$
Add on both sides of the equation.

Check: $-16 = -21 + 5$

Exercise D Solve for the variable. Check your answers.

1) $8 + x = 20$
2) $-5 + y = -15$
3) $20 = a + 4$
4) $8 = x - 15$
5) $-30 = c - 31$
6) $-5 + x = 0$
7) $-8 = x - 21$
8) $-10 + y = 10$
9) $-9 + c = 21$
10) $-16 = c + 5$
11) $-7 = x - 5$
12) $-10 = y - 10$
13) $9 = a - 20$
14) $-6 = x + 1$
15) $-25 + c = 50$
16) $-1 = c - 1$

PROBLEM SOLVING

Exercise E Write an open sentence for each word problem and solve the equation.

1) Sumi has $243 in her checking account. She needs to write a check for $324. How much money does she need to deposit to prevent her check from bouncing?

2) Antonio listens to the evening weather report and hears that the temperature has dropped 18 degrees since the day's high. The current temperature is -16 degrees. What was the high temperature for the day?

3) After selling 24 calendars for the community center fund-raiser, Amy has 14 left. How many calendars did she have before she sold any?

4) Wally lost 25 pounds but he gained a few pounds on vacation. Now his net weight loss is 17 pounds. How many pounds did he gain on vacation?

Some open sentences require the use of multiplication or division to solve for the variable. Write expressions like $2 \times n = 12$ without the multiplication symbol. Numbers are understood to be positive of the sign is omitted.

EXAMPLES $+2 \times +n$ is the same as $2n$.   Rewrite without the multiplication symbol. The number is positive.

$-3 \times +p$ is the same as $-3p$.

Use division to solve for the variable.

EXAMPLES   Find y for $2y = 12$.
Rewrite without the multiplication symbol.

$\frac{2y}{2} = \frac{12}{2}$ Divide both sides by $+2$.

$y = 6$ because $12 \div 2 = 6$

Check: $2 \times 6 = 12$

Find a for $3a = 36$.

$\frac{3a}{3} = \frac{36}{3}$ Divide both sides by $+3$.

$a = 12$ because $36 \div 3 = 12$

Check: $3 \times 12 = 36$

Find x for $-7x = 20$.

$\frac{-7x}{-7} = \frac{20}{-7}$

$x = \frac{20}{-7}$ or $-\frac{20}{7}$

Check: $-7 \times \frac{-20}{7} = 20$

In algebra, improper fractions are preferred rather than mixed numbers, therefore, answers like $-\frac{20}{7}$ are in an acceptable form.

You can also use multiplication to solve for the variables.

EXAMPLES   Find n for $n \div 2 = 12$.

$$\frac{n}{2} = 12 \qquad \text{Rewrite in vertical form.}$$

$$2 \times \frac{n}{2} = 12 \times 2 \qquad \text{Multiply both sides by } +2.$$

$$n = 24 \qquad \text{because } 12 \times 2 = 24$$

Check: $\frac{24}{2} = 12$

Find x for $\frac{x}{-5} = -12$.

$$\frac{x}{-5} = -12$$

$$-5 \times \frac{x}{-5} = -12 \times -5 \quad \text{Multiply both sides by } -5.$$

$$x = +60 \qquad \text{because } -12 \times -5 = +60$$

Check: $\frac{+60}{-5} = -12$

Exercise A   Solve for the variable. Check your answers.

1) $5x = 40$

2) $6a = 54$

3) $5s = 20$

4) $6r = 30$

5) $12t = 24$

6) $6x = 42$

7) $2a = 56$

8) $3b = 96$

9) $19z = 38$

10) $8x = 72$

11) $4w = 16$

12) $13a = 130$

13) $\frac{b}{10} = 5$

14) $\frac{x}{22} = 2$

15) $\frac{r}{12} = 4$

16) $\frac{n}{11} = 8$

17) $\frac{n}{10} = 6$

18) $\frac{x}{4} = 23$

19) $\frac{a}{21} = 3$

20) $\frac{b}{48} = 2$

21) $\frac{t}{7} = 9$

22) $\frac{r}{2} = 23$

23) $\frac{n}{5} = 9$

24) $\frac{x}{10} = 10$

Exercise B   Solve for the variable. Check your answers.

1) $12x = -36$

2) $-3a = -24$

3) $\frac{r}{-10} = 4$

4) $\frac{x}{4} = -3$

5) $\frac{y}{20} = 4$

6) $7b = 63$

7) $-5f = -20$

8) $\frac{s}{3} = -8$

9) $25p = -100$

10) $\frac{n}{-2} = -24$

11) $13u = -42$

12) $-16w = -64$

13) $\frac{x}{-12} = 6$

14) $\frac{n}{-20} = -1$

15) $-2x = -30$

16) $-5t = -55$

17) $\frac{n}{7} = -4$

18) $\frac{a}{-16} = 5$

19) $-2a = 66$

20) $8a = -96$

21) $-34d = -68$

22) $\frac{b}{-5} = -20$

23) $\frac{n}{10} = -3$

24) $8p = -64$

25) $-3r = -15$

26) $\frac{a}{2} = -21$

27) $-\frac{a}{2} = -21$

28) $\frac{a}{-2} = 21$

29) $-4a = -1$

30) $-2g = -7$

31) $\frac{s}{-6} = -5$

32) $-1a = -44$

33) $\frac{n}{-19} = -5$

34) $-7x = 63$

35) $\frac{v}{2} = -2$

36) $-5y = -25$

37) $\frac{b}{2} = -34$

38) $-1y = -20$

39) $\frac{w}{16} = -4$

40) $2x = -7$

41) $9r = -8$

42) $-4v = -9$

43) $-3b = 40$

44) $-4x = 9$

45) $-2a = 5$

Calculator Practice   Use your calculator to solve for the variable.

EXAMPLES

$7n = 20$
Press 20 $\div$ 7 $=$
The display reads 2.8571428.
Round to the nearest tenth.
$n = 2.9$

$\frac{x}{14} = 3$
Press 3 $\times$ 14 $=$
The display reads 42.
$x = 42$

Calculator Exercise   Use a calculator to solve for the variable. Round your answer to the nearest tenth, if necessary.

1) $23x = 50$

2) $3c = 38$

3) $\frac{a}{9} = 4$

4) $31n = 85$

5) $\frac{x}{12} = 5$

6) $\frac{z}{3} = 17$

7) $18a = 52$

8) $\frac{x}{4} = 9$

9) $16c = 32$

10) $\frac{n}{8} = 48$

11) $5p = 30$

12) $\frac{k}{3} = 22$

13) $\frac{d}{5} = 36$

14) $14f = 8$

15) $28r = 103$

Lesson 12 — Solving Two-Step Equations

Equations in the form of $2x + 5 = 25$ can best be solved using two steps as shown.

EXAMPLES $2x + 5 = 25$

Solution:

$$2x + 5 = 25$$
$$\underline{\quad -5 \quad -5 \quad} \qquad \textbf{Step 1} \quad \text{Add } (-5) \text{ to both sides.}$$
$$2x = 20$$

$$\frac{2x}{2} = \frac{20}{2} \qquad \textbf{Step 2} \quad \text{Divide both sides by 2.}$$

$$x = 10$$

Check: $(2 \times 10) + 5 = 20 + 5 = 25$

$$5y - 6 = 20$$

Solution:

$$5y - 6 = 20$$
$$\underline{\quad +6 \quad +6 \quad} \qquad \textbf{Step 1} \quad \text{Add } (+6) \text{ to both sides.}$$
$$5y = 26$$

$$\frac{5y}{5} = \frac{26}{5} \qquad \textbf{Step 2} \quad \text{Divide both sides by 5.}$$

$$y = \frac{26}{5} \qquad \text{Leave as an improper fraction}$$

Check: $(5 \times \frac{26}{5}) - 6 = 26 - 6 = 20$

$$-25 = 3a - 2$$

Solution:

$$-25 = 3a - 2$$
$$\underline{\quad +2 \qquad\qquad +2 \quad} \quad \textbf{Step 1} \quad \text{Add } (+2) \text{ to both sides.}$$
$$-23 = 3a$$

$$-\frac{23}{3} = \frac{3a}{3} \qquad \textbf{Step 2} \quad \text{Divide both sides by } +3.$$

$$-\frac{23}{3} = a \qquad \text{Leave as an improper fraction}$$

Check: $-25 = (3 \times -\frac{23}{3}) - 2 = -23 - 2$

Exercise A Solve for the variable. Check your answers.

1) $2a - 6 = 30$

2) $5y + 10 = -20$

3) $2c - 1 = 9$

4) $3a + 3 = -15$

5) $3c - 1 = 11$

6) $5x + 2 = 22$

7) $6x - 1 = -19$

8) $-6 + 2x = 20$

9) $13 + 3x = -5$

10) $3a + 1 = 22$

11) $6x + 2 = 20$

12) $3c + 2 = -19$

13) $9y + 18 = 0$

14) $2y - 3 = 20$

15) $10c + 1 = 81$

16) $7a - 4 = 30$

17) $3 + 2n = 31$

18) $-8 + 11n = 25$

EXAMPLE

$$-2a + 3 = 13$$
$$\underline{\qquad -3 \quad -3}$$
$$-2a = 10$$

Step 1 Add (-3) to both sides.

$$\frac{-2a}{-2} = \frac{10}{-2}$$

Step 2 Divide both sides by -2.

$$a = -5$$ because $(+10) \div (-2) = -5$

Check: $(-2 \times -5) + 3 = 10 + 3 = 13$

Exercise B Solve for the variable. Check your answers.

1) $-3a - 1 = 1$

2) $-2a + 2 = 18$

3) $-9a - 2 = 34$

4) $-1a - 6 = 20$

5) $-6c + 10 = 40$

6) $-6a - 1 = -17$

7) $-4a + 2 = 20$

8) $4 - 3a = 40$

9) $-1c + 2 = 30$

10) $-2x + 3 = -25$

Combining like terms is similar to adding or subtracting integers.

EXAMPLES | Remember $(-2) + (-5) = -7$
Then $(-2a) + (-5a) = -7a$
or $-2a - 5a = -7a$

Notice that the addition sign is not always shown when you add a negative integer.
$(-2a) + (-5a)$ is the same as $-2a - 5a$.

$$-3a - 6a = -9a \qquad\qquad -9x + 2x = -7x$$
$$-4a + 5a = 1a \qquad\qquad 4a - 5a = -1a$$
$$\text{or } -4a + 5a = a \qquad\qquad \text{or } 4a - 5a = -a$$

We usually refer to "1a" or "−1a" as simply "a" or "−a."

Exercise A   Simplify by combining like terms.

1) $+3a - 4a$

2) $+6x - 4x$

3) $+9y - 3y + 2y$

4) $+y + 2y$

5) $-17c + 7c$

6) $-8c - 2c + 10c$

7) $+25a + 2a + 3a$

8) $-3c - 6c + 8c$

9) $+8c - 2c$

10) $-10x - 10x$

11) $-12c + 12c$

12) $-9c - 2c$

13) $-15c + 5c - 5c$

14) $-13x + 2x - 3x$

15) $+16a - 20a$

16) $+11y - 2y + 3y$

Sometimes when you combine like terms, other variables may be present.

EXAMPLES   Simplify $+7a + 3c + 4a - 9c$ by combining like terms.

$+7a + 4a + 3c - 9c$ Arrange like terms together, then combine like terms.

$+11a - 6c$

Simplify $-8x + 3y - 2x - 10y$ by combining like terms.

$-8x - 2x + 3y - 10y$ Arrange like terms together, then combine like terms.

$-10x - 7y$

Other terms without variables may also be present. Combine as you would with variables.

EXAMPLE   Simplify $+5a + 2c - 8a + 5c + 6 - 8$

$+5a - 8a + 2c + 5c + 6 - 8$ Arrange like terms.

$-3a + 7c - 2$

Exercise B   Simplify by combining like terms.

1) $-3a + 9c + 8c$

2) $+4x + 2 + 5x$

3) $-5c + 7c + 6c$

4) $+4a - 6a - 2a + 3$

5) $+4 - 5c + 2c - 6c + 2$

6) $+30c + 2c - 6c + 4c$

7) $-6x + 2y + 8y - 3x$

8) $+3y - 8y + 6 - 9$

9) $+5a + 8a - 2a + 6a$

10) $+5 - 8x - 2x + 3x + 7x + 6$

11) $-6y - 3y + 6y + 6x$

12) $+4c + 5c + 2c - 9c + 1$

1) Find the absolute value of $+7$.

2) Find the absolute value of -8.

3) Find the opposite of -31.

Compare the pairs of integers with $>$ or $<$.

4) $-6 \quad -4$

5) $+2 \quad -5$

Give the absolute value.

6) $|-2|$

7) $|+13|$

Perform the indicated operations.

8) $(-6) + (-7)$

9) $(+5) - (-7)$

10) $-3 + 5$

11) $+3 - 4$

12) $(-2) \times (-5)$

13) $(+10) \times (-2)$

14) $(-8) \div (-4)$

15) $(-9) \div (-3)$

16) $(-64) \div (+4)$

Find the value for the variable.

17) $n - 12 = 20$

18) $a + 6 = -10$

19) $3 \times n = -18$

20) $-5x = 30$

21) $5 = 3a + 5$

22) $-3x + 5 = 20$

Combine like terms.

23) $-3a - 4c + 7a$

24) $-8a - 3 + 7a - 9a + 7$

25) Construct a number line with the graph of $x = -3$

Solve each problem.

26) The team loses 38 points and then loses 16 points. They finally score 88 points, and then lose just 6 points. What is the team's final score?

27) You are in the basement of the office building gathering some old paperwork. Next you go up 9 floors to your office, and down 2 floors to drop off your mail. On what floor is the mailroom?

28) The football team loses 11 yards on the first down of the game. On the second down they gain 15 yards, and on the third down they lose 18 yards. What is the team's total gain or loss of yardage?

Graph each set of ordered pairs.

29) $(3,3), (3,-3), (-3,-3), (-3,3)$

30) $(0,4), (4,0), (0,-4), (-4,0)$

| Test Taking Tip | Whenever you solve an open sentence and find the value of a variable, always check your answer. Substitute the value you found for the variable in the equation. Then, evaluate each side of the equation and be sure that the two sides are equal. |

Whole Numbers

Exercise A Write the name of the place for each underlined digit.

1) 50,7<u>1</u>3
2) 71,3<u>7</u>8
3) 6,502,33<u>1</u>
4) 1<u>1</u>2,450
5) <u>7</u>0,300
6) <u>4</u>00,045
7) <u>3</u>,060,017
8) 9,064,4<u>3</u>7
9) 8<u>8</u>,675,000
10) 5<u>0</u>5,600
11) 600,<u>4</u>65
12) 74,023,7<u>6</u>9
13) 7,<u>6</u>48,493
14) 20,2<u>3</u>6,200
15) 4,90<u>3</u>,002

Exercise B Round each number to three different places.

		Tens	Hundreds	Thousands
1)	567	____	____	____
2)	7,098	____	____	____
3)	6,005	____	____	____
4)	765,365	____	____	____
5)	36,667	____	____	____
6)	906,380	____	____	____
7)	326,511	____	____	____
8)	65,409,811	____	____	____
9)	65,800,409	____	____	____
10)	43,000	____	____	____
11)	16	____	____	____
12)	453	____	____	____

Whole Numbers

Exercise C Add.

1) 4 +9	**2)** 0 +8	**3)** 2 +4	**4)** 9 +0	**5)** 6 +7	**6)** 6 +1	**7)** 4 +6	**8)** 5 +7
9) 1 +1	**10)** 1 +2	**11)** 1 +9	**12)** 7 +0	**13)** 1 +6	**14)** 2 +2	**15)** 7 +2	**16)** 0 +5
17) 9 +4	**18)** 0 +1	**19)** 0 +7	**20)** 3 +8	**21)** 4 +0	**22)** 9 +1	**23)** 9 +5	**24)** 7 +9
25) 5 +8	**26)** 0 +2	**27)** 7 +7	**28)** 2 +9	**29)** 3 +3	**30)** 8 +8	**31)** 6 +5	**32)** 9 +9
33) 2 +3	**34)** 8 +5	**35)** 8 +4	**36)** 5 +0	**37)** 3 +4	**38)** 7 +4	**39)** 1 +8	**40)** 0 +0
41) 4 +8	**42)** 6 +0	**43)** 9 +2	**44)** 3 +5	**45)** 9 +6	**46)** 0 +4	**47)** 8 +1	**48)** 4 +2

Exercise D Write these addends in vertical form. Then add.

1) 23 + 467 + 829

2) 5,602 + 910 + 874

3) 1,035 + 267 + 8,412

4) 3,567 + 8,103 + 103

5) 7,108 + 468 + 2,081

6) 4,017 + 3,008 + 26

7) 429 + 207 + 4,610

8) 4,191 + 468 + 462

9) 305 + 8,135 + 607

10) 981 + 628 + 6,740

11) 43 + 638 + 9,005

12) 611 + 683 + 60

13) 487 + 36 + 8,739

14) 236; 487; 7,105; 238

15) 4,083; 1,032; 6,297; 42

16) 726; 2,913; 6,213; 781

17) 468; 2,963; 2,903; 76

18) 1,711; 4,804; 1,357; 9; 1

19) 521; 26; 4,835; 6,291

20) 9,183,629; 396,298

21) 67,037; 7,038; 5,013

22) 11,038; 5,073; 643,509

23) 51,602; 40,050; 64,576

24) 102; 64; 8; 5,009; 68,308

Exercise E   Write these problems vertically. Then subtract.

1) 263 − 28
2) 4,820 − 785
3) 9,163 − 562
4) 5,032 − 863
5) 9,100 − 1,629
6) 4,103 − 1,263
7) 92,063 − 4,845
8) 8,300 − 402
9) 200,342 − 198,342
10) 673,902 − 570,942
11) 105,031 − 97,025
12) 10,000 − 5,460
13) From 9,126 subtract 358

14) Subtract 923 from 8,203
15) Subtract 6,855 from 10,000
16) From 2,913 subtract 809
17) Subtract 2,098 from 4,083
18) From 7,023 subtract 298
19) From 30,356 subtract 8,735
20) From 29,803 subtract 8,135
21) Subtract 9,898 from 19,200
22) From 33,600 subtract 699
23) Subtract 3,032 from 31,011
24) From 1,200 subtract 994
25) From 293 subtract 82
26) From 70,311 subtract 3,983

Exercise F   Multiply.

1) 7 × 5
2) 5 × 3
3) 2 × 0
4) 3 × 1
5) 2 × 7
6) 3 × 7
7) 5 × 5

8) 1 × 4
9) 4 × 3
10) 3 × 2
11) 4 × 8
12) 5 × 0
13) 9 × 2
14) 3 × 5

15) 9 × 6
16) 0 × 4
17) 8 × 1
18) 4 × 2
19) 6 × 6
20) 3 × 9
21) 1 × 9

22) 7 × 0
23) 1 × 6
24) 2 × 2
25) 7 × 2
26) 0 × 5
27) 9 × 4
28) 0 × 1

29) 0 × 7
30) 3 × 8
31) 3 × 6
32) 7 × 1
33) 6 × 2
34) 4 × 5
35) 7 × 8

36) 1 × 5
37) 5 × 9
38) 1 × 0
39) 2 × 5
40) 2 × 8
41) 6 × 8
42) 1 × 3

43) 0 × 9
44) 7 × 3
45) 5 × 4
46) 0 × 6
47) 7 × 6
48) 6 × 9
49) 8 × 0

Whole Numbers

Exercise G Write these problems in vertical form. Then multiply.

1) 38×29
2) 42×35
3) 271×34
4) 715×42
5) 962×43
6) $8,910 \times 23$
7) $50,203 \times 9,015$
8) $6,044 \times 1,032$
9) $3,104 \times 1,090$
10) $4,570 \times 2,740$
11) $3,672 \times 1,010$
12) $5,401 \times 300$
13) 385 and 27
14) 761 and 39
15) 640 and 20
16) 6,035 and 52
17) 7,803 and 120
18) 1,760 and 87
19) 13,206 and 7,214
20) 3,203 and 670
21) 6,625 and 550
22) 1,030 and 2,037
23) 6,601 and 4,110
24) 309 and 7,104
25) 203 and 4,670
26) 176 and 245
27) 6,107 and 723
28) 87,161 and 409

Exercise H Copy these problems and divide.

1) $1,080 \div 8$
2) $954 \div 9$
3) $1,172 \div 4$
4) $2,877 \div 7$
5) $2,496 \div 8$
6) $18,009 \div 29$
7) $72,980 \div 178$
8) $16,426 \div 43$
9) $30,000 \div 50$
10) $6,399 \div 81$
11) $8,925 \div 85$
12) $6,820 \div 62$
13) $16,856 \div 28$
14) $5,332 \div 43$
15) $6,750 \div 54$
16) $31,356 \div 78$
17) $56,960 \div 80$
18) $398,888 \div 56$
19) $86,388 \div 276$
20) $113,764 \div 239$
21) $21,627 \div 27$
22) $32,240 \div 52$
23) $19,076 \div 38$
24) $26,659 \div 53$
25) $9,672 \div 62$
26) $42,840 \div 21$
27) $7,440 \div 62$
28) $19,872 \div 32$
29) $60,600 \div 30$
30) $220,320 \div 72$

Whole Numbers

Exercise I   Write the value of each expression.

1) 5^3

2) 6^2

3) 8^3

4) 7^3

5) 9^2

6) 8^4

7) 9^3

8) 12^2

9) 11^2

10) 13^2

11) 14^2

12) 4^5

13) 20^2

14) 40^3

15) 25^2

16) 26^2

17) 11^3

18) 10^3

19) 15^4

20) 25^3

21) 7^4

22) 18^3

23) 24^5

24) 48^3

25) 72^3

26) 36^4

27) 30^5

28) 85^2

29) 125^3

30) 200^6

Exercise J   Find the answers. Perform the operations in the correct order.

1) $33 - 8 \times 2 \div 4$

2) $15 + 6 \times 2 - 6$

3) $5^2 + 8^2 \div 4 - 2$

4) $12^1 - 8 \times 4 \div 2^2$

5) $2^5 \div 8 - 12 \div 12 + 2$

6) $36 \div 3 - 6 + 2 \times 2^3$

7) $35 \div 7 \times 2 + 16 \div 4^1 - 1$

8) $25 - 2^3 + 3^2 \times 2 \div 3$

9) $16 - 4^2 + 6^2 \times 2 \div 4 - 8$

10) $50 + 25 - 8^2 + 4 \times 3^3$

11) $35 - 4^2 + 6 \times 2^3 \div 6$

12) $13 \times 3 - 6 \times 2^3 \div 12$

13) $26 + 3 \times 10 \div 2 - 48 \div 16$

14) $3^2 + 2^2 + 6^2 \times 2 - 4^2$

15) $2^3 + 3^3 \div 9 - 2$

16) $32 - 2^4 + 3 \times 6$

17) $13 - 6^2 \div 6 + 8 \times 2^3$

18) $5^2 - 6^2 \div 2 + 8 \times 4 \div 2 + 3$

19) $25 - 5^3 \div 25 + 8 - 2^3$

20) $36 + 8 \times 5 \div 2^3 - 6 \times 2$

21) $5^2 - 4 \times 3^2 \div 2 + 12^2 \times 2^2 \times 2$

22) $8^2 - 2^4 \div 2 + 64 \div 4$

23) $12^2 \div 16 \times 2^2 - 10^2 \div 20$

24) $9 - 6^2 \div 4 + 12 \times 4 \div 2^4 - 3$

Fractions

Exercise A   Express these fractions in higher terms.

1) $\frac{3}{4} = \frac{\blacksquare}{24}$

2) $\frac{2}{7} = \frac{\blacksquare}{56}$

3) $\frac{5}{7} = \frac{\blacksquare}{84}$

4) $\frac{8}{9} = \frac{\blacksquare}{108}$

5) $\frac{6}{7} = \frac{\blacksquare}{63}$

6) $\frac{5}{8} = \frac{\blacksquare}{96}$

7) $\frac{11}{12} = \frac{\blacksquare}{132}$

8) $\frac{5}{23} = \frac{\blacksquare}{92}$

9) $\frac{4}{9} = \frac{\blacksquare}{126}$

10) $\frac{17}{24} = \frac{\blacksquare}{120}$

11) $\frac{16}{17} = \frac{\blacksquare}{51}$

12) $\frac{31}{34} = \frac{\blacksquare}{102}$

13) $\frac{19}{20} = \frac{\blacksquare}{80}$

14) $\frac{13}{15} = \frac{\blacksquare}{45}$

15) $\frac{7}{8} = \frac{\blacksquare}{104}$

16) $\frac{8}{22} = \frac{\blacksquare}{110}$

Exercise B   Rename these fractions in simplest form.

1) $\frac{24}{56}$

2) $\frac{38}{82}$

3) $\frac{45}{55}$

4) $\frac{72}{81}$

5) $\frac{46}{62}$

6) $\frac{34}{68}$

7) $\frac{77}{121}$

8) $\frac{33}{132}$

9) $\frac{18}{99}$

10) $\frac{36}{128}$

11) $\frac{98}{147}$

12) $\frac{42}{105}$

13) $\frac{26}{52}$

14) $\frac{36}{75}$

15) $\frac{13}{104}$

16) $\frac{21}{147}$

Exercise C   Rename these mixed numbers as improper fractions.

1) $5\frac{4}{6}$

2) $4\frac{3}{4}$

3) $6\frac{3}{8}$

4) $8\frac{2}{7}$

5) $8\frac{5}{6}$

6) $2\frac{4}{5}$

7) $9\frac{6}{7}$

8) $16\frac{2}{3}$

9) $33\frac{5}{6}$

10) $19\frac{11}{12}$

11) $13\frac{10}{14}$

12) $34\frac{15}{16}$

13) $10\frac{5}{20}$

14) $14\frac{10}{11}$

15) $10\frac{1}{8}$

16) $14\frac{1}{2}$

Exercise D   Rename these improper fractions as mixed numbers or whole numbers.

1) $\frac{16}{5}$

2) $\frac{17}{8}$

3) $\frac{19}{7}$

4) $\frac{23}{5}$

5) $\frac{29}{11}$

6) $\frac{32}{6}$

7) $\frac{49}{16}$

8) $\frac{108}{9}$

9) $\frac{92}{4}$

10) $\frac{73}{6}$

11) $\frac{205}{15}$

12) $\frac{69}{13}$

13) $\frac{67}{57}$

14) $\frac{156}{12}$

15) $\frac{36}{8}$

16) $\frac{75}{12}$

Fractions

Exercise E   Express the following mixed numbers in simplest form.

1) $5\frac{4}{3}$

2) $8\frac{9}{5}$

3) $\frac{12}{16}$

4) $12\frac{10}{9}$

5) $15\frac{14}{10}$

6) $16\frac{10}{14}$

7) $33\frac{23}{20}$

8) $27\frac{24}{12}$

9) $18\frac{44}{11}$

10) $52\frac{20}{6}$

11) $34\frac{7}{3}$

12) $10\frac{9}{27}$

13) $51\frac{48}{15}$

14) $28\frac{45}{60}$

15) $36\frac{8}{44}$

16) $64\frac{35}{7}$

17) $13\frac{26}{5}$

18) $22\frac{26}{20}$

19) $38\frac{44}{14}$

20) $15\frac{37}{15}$

21) $39\frac{45}{9}$

22) $17\frac{32}{15}$

23) $63\frac{58}{50}$

24) $28\frac{45}{10}$

25) $74\frac{80}{10}$

26) $40\frac{30}{13}$

27) $25\frac{20}{5}$

28) $54\frac{35}{6}$

29) $13\frac{54}{80}$

30) $75\frac{42}{38}$

31) $14\frac{6}{15}$

32) $63\frac{36}{34}$

Exercise F   Multiply these mixed numbers. Write your answers in simplest form.

1) $\frac{2}{7} \times 2\frac{6}{7}$

2) $\frac{3}{4} \times 3\frac{1}{2}$

3) $\frac{3}{5} \times 2\frac{3}{4}$

4) $\frac{2}{3} \times 22\frac{1}{2}$

5) $1\frac{1}{3} \times \frac{1}{2}$

6) $2\frac{3}{4} \times \frac{6}{11}$

7) $2\frac{1}{5} \times \frac{10}{22}$

8) $1\frac{4}{5} \times \frac{2}{9}$

9) $2\frac{7}{8} \times \frac{16}{23}$

10) $3\frac{3}{8} \times \frac{8}{12}$

11) $5\frac{2}{5} \times 1\frac{1}{9}$

12) $4\frac{1}{5} \times 1\frac{3}{7}$

13) $2\frac{4}{5} \times 1\frac{11}{14}$

14) $5\frac{2}{8} \times 2\frac{2}{7}$

15) $6\frac{6}{7} \times 2\frac{2}{6}$

16) $1\frac{1}{2} \times 1\frac{7}{9}$

17) $3\frac{1}{5} \times 1\frac{9}{16}$

18) $4\frac{1}{2} \times 1\frac{1}{15}$

19) $7\frac{1}{5} \times 1\frac{2}{3}$

20) $5\frac{1}{4} \times 2\frac{1}{7}$

21) $3\frac{3}{7} \times 2\frac{1}{3}$

22) $5\frac{5}{8} \times 1\frac{7}{9}$

23) $3\frac{4}{9} \times \frac{27}{62}$

24) $\frac{8}{12} \times 3\frac{2}{16}$

Fractions

Exercise G   Divide these mixed numbers. Write your answers in simplest form.

1) $2\frac{1}{5} \div \frac{11}{15}$ **5)** $1\frac{1}{2} \div \frac{6}{7}$ **9)** $4\frac{5}{7} \div 1\frac{1}{14}$

2) $3\frac{2}{3} \div \frac{22}{24}$ **6)** $2\frac{3}{5} \div \frac{2}{15}$ **10)** $2\frac{1}{6} \div 5\frac{4}{7}$

3) $7\frac{1}{2} \div \frac{5}{6}$ **7)** $5\frac{2}{12} \div \frac{62}{3}$ **11)** $1\frac{7}{9} \div 4\frac{4}{5}$

4) $8\frac{2}{3} \div \frac{13}{15}$ **8)** $3\frac{5}{9} \div 2\frac{2}{3}$ **12)** $5\frac{3}{12} \div 2\frac{1}{4}$

Exercise H   Change to common denominators and add. Write your answers in simplest form.

1) $\frac{2}{3} + \frac{1}{5}$ **5)** $\frac{6}{7} + \frac{1}{14}$ **9)** $\frac{1}{8} + \frac{5}{6}$

2) $\frac{3}{9} + \frac{1}{5}$ **6)** $\frac{2}{11} + \frac{3}{22}$ **10)** $\frac{2}{12} + \frac{1}{9}$

3) $\frac{5}{9} + \frac{2}{6}$ **7)** $\frac{6}{13} + \frac{2}{26}$ **11)** $\frac{5}{72} + \frac{2}{9}$

4) $\frac{4}{12} + \frac{1}{4}$ **8)** $\frac{10}{24} + \frac{3}{12}$ **12)** $\frac{6}{7} + \frac{3}{8}$

Exercise I   Change to common denominators and subtract. Write your answers in simplest form.

1) $6\frac{1}{5} - 4\frac{2}{3}$ **9)** $7\frac{8}{17} - 1\frac{21}{34}$ **17)** $2\frac{1}{7} - 1\frac{4}{9}$

2) $9\frac{2}{3} - 4\frac{7}{8}$ **10)** $36\frac{1}{7} - 2\frac{3}{8}$ **18)** $12\frac{5}{16} - 2\frac{2}{3}$

3) $8\frac{5}{6} - 1\frac{7}{18}$ **11)** $19\frac{2}{9} - 4\frac{1}{2}$ **19)** $19 - 14\frac{11}{15}$

4) $5\frac{13}{15} - \frac{27}{30}$ **12)** $5\frac{3}{16} - 2\frac{5}{8}$ **20)** $10\frac{2}{3} - 4\frac{19}{20}$

5) $21\frac{4}{7} - 2\frac{2}{3}$ **13)** $7\frac{2}{5} - 3\frac{22}{45}$ **21)** $5\frac{4}{9} - 2\frac{2}{3}$

6) $14\frac{1}{6} - 3\frac{5}{8}$ **14)** $40 - 16\frac{1}{3}$ **22)** $5\frac{1}{7} - 3\frac{5}{6}$

7) $11\frac{3}{4} - 5\frac{16}{18}$ **15)** $23\frac{2}{5} - 5\frac{1}{3}$ **23)** $17\frac{5}{16} - 2\frac{2}{3}$

8) $8\frac{2}{15} - 2\frac{9}{20}$ **16)** $14\frac{2}{7} - 9\frac{3}{5}$ **24)** $17 - 12\frac{5}{13}$

Decimals

Exercise A   Write the name of the place for each underlined digit.

1) 57.4̲5392

2) 56.48̲39

3) .100̲98

4) .008̲974

5) .560̲985

6) 453.05̲67

7) .5608̲9

8) .84̲7109

9) .75̲7056

10) 1.1019̲8

11) 564.31̲

12) 7.4507̲8

13) .40̲1015

14) .5̲60902

15) 14.02̲

16) .07575̲2

Exercise B   Complete the chart by rounding each decimal to the places named.

		Tenths	Hundredths	Thousandths
1)	47.7581	_____	_____	_____
2)	5.04745	_____	_____	_____
3)	85.86086	_____	_____	_____
4)	14.06	_____	_____	_____
5)	47.5	_____	_____	_____
6)	4.00987	_____	_____	_____
7)	.88809	_____	_____	_____
8)	5.46469	_____	_____	_____
9)	9.87431	_____	_____	_____
10)	6.9874909	_____	_____	_____

Decimals

Exercise C   Write these problems in vertical form. Then add.

1) 2.3 + 4 + 5.98
2) 5 + .46 + .045
3) .3409 + 6.6 + .08
4) 43.4 + .048 + 3
5) 6.6 + 9.02 + 5
6) 9.4 + .45 + 7
7) 6 + 8.9 + .02
8) .553 + .09 + 3.7
9) 4 + 1.09 + .06
10) 6.4 + .3 + .56
11) 57.3 + 5.6 + 7
12) 9 + .6 + .32 + .07
13) 3.4, 2.04, 5.67

14) 364, 5.607, 3.04
15) 45.402, 6.907, 97
16) 6.4, 50, 7.2, 6.04
17) 47.02, 64, 70.2
18) 63.5, 70.3, 86.03
19) .004, .056, 3.02
20) 4.56, 8.023, .0304
21) 8.45, .0081, .06
22) 67.7, 60, .046, 85
23) 42.4, 66.78, .632
24) 56.4, .004, .3045
25) .05, .044, .1
26) 3.5, 6, 7.89, 10

Exercise D   Write these problems in vertical form. Then subtract.

1) 13.5 − 2.4
2) 37.8 − 2.67
3) 4.9 − 2.34
4) 3.62 − .8
5) 19.4 − .36
6) 67.8 − .07
7) 46.78 − 9
8) .4507 − .23
9) 564 − 56.7
10) 5.9 − .67
11) .007 − .0023
12) 6.8 − 5.78
13) From 2 subtract .8
14) From 3.4 subtract 2.43
15) Subtract .34 from 3.8

16) From .46 subtract .097
17) From .362 subtract .08
18) Subtract .362 from 1
19) Subtract .464 from 8.09
20) From 23 subtract 21.8
21) Subtract 6 from 24.6
22) From 3.4 subtract .935
23) From 6.7 subtract .465
24) Subtract 5 from 46.78
25) From 87.09 subtract 9.8
26) From 46.9 subtract 9
27) Subtract 3.58 from 36
28) Subtract .36 from 6
29) From 3.4 subtract .0056
30) From 3 subtract .456

Decimals

Exercise E Write these problems in vertical form. Then multiply.

1) 2.3 × 6.3

2) 4.2 × .41

3) .26 × 3.4

4) 4.62 × 1.2

5) 5.8 × .2

6) 60.9 × .03

7) .983 × 2.8

8) .803 × 6.91

9) 5.03 × .071

10) 89.6 × .003

11) 28.4 × .34

12) 5.02 × 2.3

13) .68 × 7.9

14) .08 × 64

15) 36.5 × 8.8

16) 3.8 and 6.2

17) 9.08 and .3

18) .523 and .02

19) 6.21 and .28

20) 5.36 and 9.6

21) 9.86 and 1.2

22) 2.61 and .25

23) 8.2 and 93

24) 128 and 2.9

25) 4.63 and 1.9

26) 5.5 and 4.7

27) 80.3 and .34

28) 74.2 and 6.7

29) 2.34 and 9.04

30) 3.46 and 3.56

Exercise F Write these numbers in scientific notation.

1) 2,350

2) 46,800

3) 383,000

4) 84,100,000

5) 76,004

6) 357,000

7) 340,000,000

8) 72,300,000

9) 64,200

10) 83,020,000

11) 654,000

12) 2,100,000,000

13) 519

14) 700

15) 750,000

16) 423,000,000

Decimals

Exercise G   Write these decimals in scientific notation.

1) .4506

2) .00076

3) .0000003

4) .00000452

5) 45.58

6) .7809

7) .000000457

8) .000917

9) .75053

10) .00004079

11) 508.04

12) .9407

Exercise H   Copy these problems and divide.

1) 25.74 ÷ 9

2) 1.75 ÷ 5

3) 16.48 ÷ 8

4) 9.269 ÷ 23

5) 2,527.7 ÷ 92

6) 179.4 ÷ 39

7) 80.28 ÷ 36

8) 62.4 ÷ 15

9) 1.15 ÷ 50

10) 133.14 ÷ 42

11) 1.984 ÷ 16

12) 1.95 ÷ 15

Exercise I   Copy these problems and divide.

1) 1.3 ÷ .5

2) .008 ÷ .4

3) 15.06 ÷ .6

4) 5.6 ÷ .16

5) .192 ÷ 2.4

6) .1446 ÷ .002

7) .322 ÷ .07

8) .06 ÷ 2

9) .134 ÷ .02

10) 2.9 ÷ 5.8

11) .004 ÷ .08

12) .2268 ÷ .081

Decimals

Exercise J   Find the answers.

1) .8 − .3

2) .3 + .6

3) 4 × .02

4) .4 + 9

5) .267 ÷ 3

6) 12.37 − .283

7) .3 × .2

8) .04 + 1.6

9) 405 ÷ 90

10) .046 × .003

11) 16 − .37

12) 12.5 × .367

13) .0036 ÷ .2

14) 29.06 − 9.9

15) .204 + 1.35

16) 42.81 ÷ .3

17) 1.3 − .42

18) .048 ÷ 5.4

19) .48 × 3.7

20) 7 + 3.92

21) 3.0612 ÷ 4

22) 5.036 − 3.27

23) .26 × .3

24) 29.8 + 4.73

25) .004 + 36.49

26) 46.86 ÷ 1.1

27) 24 − .362

28) 28.2 × .038

29) 5.7 − .604

30) 6.3 ÷ 8.4

31) .8 + .6

32) .23 × .9

33) .37 − .04

34) .47 + .06

35) 91.8 ÷ 36

36) .46 − .38

37) 5 × .018

38) 1.42 + 8

39) 5 ÷ 8

40) 8 − 3.4

41) .32 × .16

42) .205 + 4.378

43) .09 ÷ 4.5

44) .07 − .0634

45) 1.82 + 138

46) .003 × .08

Percents

Exercise A   Rename each percent as a decimal.

1) 8%

2) 42%

3) 105%

4) 246%

5) .9%

6) $32\frac{5}{8}\%$

7) 25.3%

8) .046%

9) 346%

10) $\frac{3}{4}\%$

Exercise B   Rename each percent as a fraction in simplest form.

1) 8%

2) 68%

3) 1.35%

4) $83\frac{1}{3}\%$

5) $2\frac{1}{2}\%$

6) $1\frac{7}{8}\%$

7) $\frac{3}{4}\%$

8) $2\frac{2}{3}\%$

9) $\frac{5}{9}\%$

10) $105\frac{1}{3}\%$

Exercise C   Rename each number as a percent.

1) .05

2) .4

3) 1.36

4) $.16\frac{2}{3}$

5) .056

6) .00036

7) .43

8) 3.24

9) $1.16\frac{2}{3}$

10) .572

Percents

Exercise D Fill in the missing fractions, decimals, and percents in this chart.

	Fraction	Decimal	Percent
1)	$\frac{5}{8}$		
2)		.4	
3)			$11\frac{2}{3}\%$
4)		.025	
5)			$3\frac{1}{3}\%$
6)		1.6	
7)			1.32%
8)			$\frac{3}{4}\%$
9)	$\frac{3}{200}$		
10)		.45	
11)			124%
12)	$\frac{4}{11}$		
13)		1.08	
14)	$\frac{7}{25}$		
15)			48%
16)		.0036	
17)	$\frac{3}{20}$		
18)			4.5%

Percents

Exercise E   Find the percentage.

1) 42% of 150 is ____

2) ____ is 30% of 96

3) ____ is 8% of 45

4) $22\frac{1}{2}$% of 28 is ____

5) 4.6% of 15 is ____

6) ____ is 106% of 35

7) ____ is .4% of 750

8) $\frac{3}{4}$% of 200 is ____

9) $2\frac{1}{2}$% of 1,600 is ____

10) 18% of 75 is ____

Exercise F   Find the base.

1) 30% of ____ is 27

2) 36 is 45% of ____

3) $2\frac{1}{2}$ is 20% of ____

4) 15% of ____ is 27

5) $6\frac{2}{3}$% of ____ is 4

6) 13 is $12\frac{1}{2}$% of ____

7) 21 is 4.2% of ____

8) 35% of ____ is 56

9) 8% of ____ is 16

10) 63 is 28% of ____

Exercise G   Find the rate.

1) ____% of 32 is 12

2) 34 is ____% of 40

3) 6 is ____% of 45

4) ____% of 126 is 18

5) ____% of 72 is 24

6) $2\frac{1}{2}$ is ____% of 10

7) ____% of 81 is 36

8) ____% of 63 is 42

9) 18 is ____% of 150

10) 10.40 is ____% of 52

Percents

Exercise H   Find the missing numbers.

1) 8% of 95 is ____

2) ____% of 54 is 9

3) 52% of ____ is 13

4) ____ is 42% of 60

5) 35% of ____ is 483

6) 2 is ____% of 40

7) ____% of 40 is 3

8) .3 is 6% of ____

9) 5 is ____% of 80

10) $37\frac{1}{2}$% of 108 is ____

11) $2\frac{2}{3}$ is ____% of $13\frac{1}{3}$

12) $\frac{4}{5}$ is 16% of ____

13) 4.5% of 160 is ____

14) 20% of ____ is 6

15) ____ is 9% of 500

16) ____% of $12\frac{1}{2}$ is 3

17) 4.3 is 4.3% of ____

18) 6 is ____% of $12\frac{1}{2}$

19) ____% of .3 is .015

20) 45 is .9% of ____

21) ____ is .02% of 500

22) $16\frac{2}{3}$ is ____% of 100

23) .03% of ____ is .003

24) ____ is 120% of 35

Exercise I   Fill in the missing amounts in these discount problems.

	List Price	Discount Rate	Discount	Sale Price
1)	$145.00	20%		
2)	$26.50	40%		
3)	$80.00		$16.00	
4)	$75.50	10%		
5)	$300.00	$33\frac{1}{3}$%		
6)	$45.00	$13\frac{1}{3}$%	$6.00	
7)	$18.00	$3\frac{1}{3}$%		
8)			$5.00	$45.00
9)	$38.50	24%		
10)			$5.46	$40.04

Percents

Exercise J   Solve these sales tax problems. Remember that you round up when you are working in sales tax problems.

1) Jacket costs $68.00.   Tax _____

Tax rate of 5%   Cost after tax _____

2) Boots cost $125.00.   Tax _____

Tax rate of 3%   Cost after tax _____

3) CD player costs $137.50.   Tax _____

Tax rate of 7%   Cost after tax _____

4) CDs cost $37.89.   Tax _____

Tax rate of 3%   Cost after tax _____

5) Sports car costs $28,650.00. Tax _____

Tax rate of 7%   Cost after tax _____

6) Tape costs 69 cents.   Tax _____

Tax rate of 3%   Cost after tax _____

Exercise K   Compute the total interest.

1) $84 at 7% for 4 years

2) $39 at 12% for 4 months

3) $38 at 11% for 5 years

4) $428 at 8% for 3 years

5) $52 at 5% for 1 year

6) $608 at 7% for 9 months

7) $300 at 12% for 18 months

8) $45 at 8% for 1 year

9) $53 at 14% for 4 years

10) $76 at 9% for 5 years

11) $730 at 12% for 1 year

12) $204 at 8% for 4 years

13) $48 at 10% for 3 months

14) $20 at $6\frac{1}{2}$% for 8 years

15) $445 at 9% for 6 months

16) $400 at 13% for 15 months

17) $638 at $11\frac{1}{2}$% for 4 years

18) $636 at 9% for $1\frac{1}{2}$ years

19) $804 at $4\frac{1}{2}$% for 2 years

20) $600 at 9% for 3 years

Percents

Exercise L   Solve these problems.

1) Joe buys a TV for $300. He is going to pay $30 per month. He will pay $1\frac{1}{2}$% finance charge on the unpaid balance each month. Fill in this chart to show how Joe will pay for the TV.

Month	Previous Balance	Finance Charge	Before Payment	Monthly Payment	New Balance
January	$300.00	$4.50	$304.50	$30.00	$274.50
February	$274.50	_____	_____	$30.00	_____
March	_____	_____	_____	$30.00	_____
April	_____	_____	_____	$30.00	_____
May	_____	_____	_____	$30.00	_____
June	_____	_____	_____	$30.00	_____
July	_____	_____	_____	$30.00	_____
August	_____	_____	_____	$30.00	_____
September	_____	_____	_____	$30.00	_____
October	_____	_____	_____	$30.00	_____
November	_____	_____	_____	_____	$0.00

2) Scott charges a $480 refrigerator on his credit card. The finance rate is $1\frac{1}{2}$% per month. He plans to pay $80 per month. Make a chart to show how Scott will pay for the refrigerator.

Percents

Exercise M   Solve these commission problems.

1) Marie receives a 6% rate of commission for selling a house. What is her commission for selling a $165,000 house?

2) Rashaan sells 9 electric drills at $29.95 each and 7 power saws at $39.95 each. How much is he paid if he receives a 6% rate of commission?

3) Miguel receives a different rate of commission for selling different items. Figure out his total commission for the sales in this chart.

Item	Machinery	Safety Supplies	Abrasives	Power Tools
Total Sales	$2,033.05	$254.15	$2,916.22	$3,011.88
Rate of Commission	18%	12%	14%	25%

4) Gwen receives a weekly salary of $95 plus 8% of all of her sales over $500. What are Gwen's weekly earnings if she sells $942.37 worth of merchandise?

5) Sam sells $7,896 worth of reference books. He is paid 2% for his first $4,000 of sales and 6% on all sales over $4,000. What is Sam's total commission?

6) Inga is paid $102 per week plus 1% of her sales. How much does she get paid for one week if she sells $2,908 worth of merchandise?

7) Li Chen is a salesperson for the Connally Machinery Company. She is paid a 2% rate of commission on the first $2,000 and 4% on all sales over $2,000. How much commission does she receive for $5,987 in sales?

8) A purchasing agent receives $4\frac{1}{2}\%$ for buying produce for her clients. What is her commission for buying 860 cartons of peaches for $16.85 per carton?

Exercise A   Give the best name for each polygon.

1)

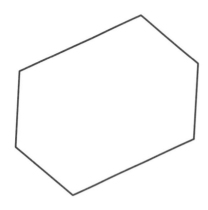

4)

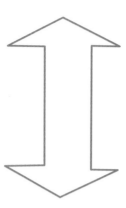

2)

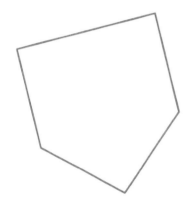

5)

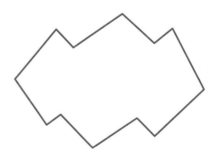

3)

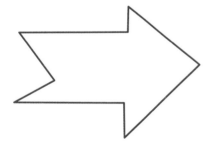

Exercise B   Use the sides of the triangle to give the best name for each.

1)

3)

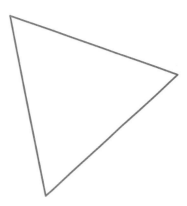

2)

4)

Geometry

Exercise C   Use the angles of the triangle to give the best name for each.

1)

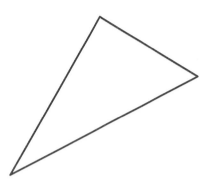

4)

2)

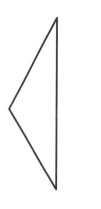

5)

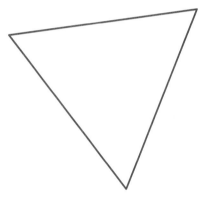

3)

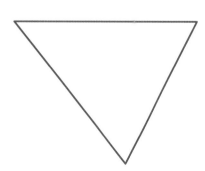

Exercise D   Give the best name for each quadrilateral.

1)

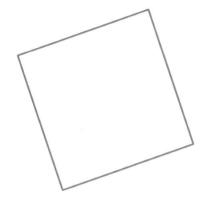

4)

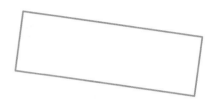

2)

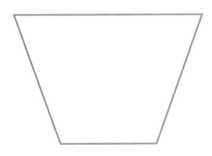

5)

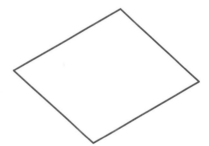

3)

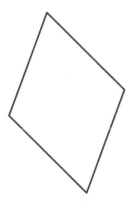

Geometry

Exercise E Use the diagram to answer each question.

1) Which line is parallel to $\overleftrightarrow{GF}$?

2) Which line is perpendicular to $\overleftrightarrow{FC}$?

3) What kind of angle is ∠ GBA?

4) What kind of triangle is Δ ADE?

5) Where does $\overleftrightarrow{AB}$ intersect $\overleftrightarrow{FE}$?

6) What kind of quadrilateral is ABFE?

7) If ∠ BCE is 52°, what is the measure of ∠ GBD?

8) What kind of triangle is Δ BCF?

9) What kind of angle is ∠ DCF?

10) What kind of triangle is Δ DBG?

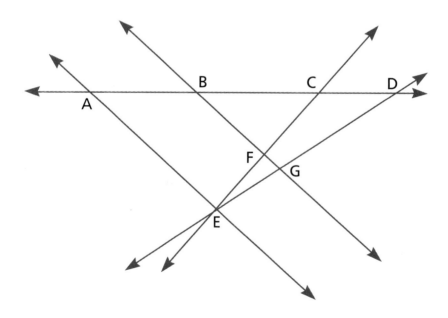

Exercise A   Use your ruler to measure the length of each pencil to the nearest tenth of a centimeter.

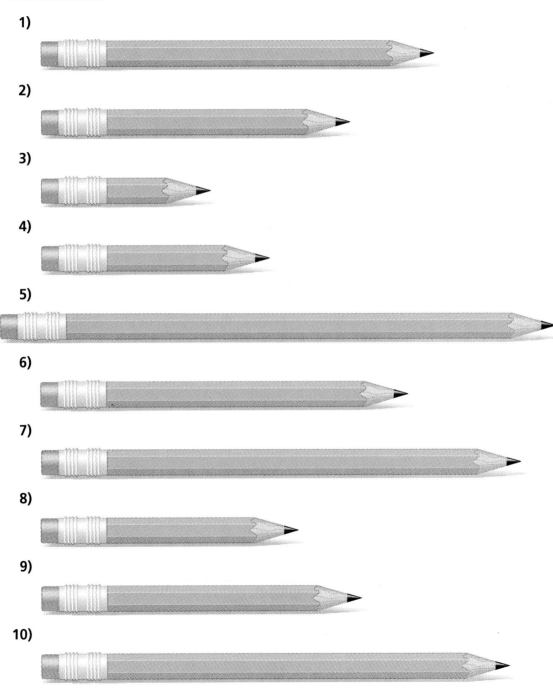

1)

2)

3)

4)

5)

6)

7)

8)

9)

10)

Measurement

Exercise B   Circle the most reasonable measurement for each.

1) Fat in a bowl of cereal.

     5 mg   5 g   5 kg

2) Water in a water balloon.

     .6 ml   .6 l   .6 kl

3) Height of a doorknob.

     1 cm   1 m   1 km

4) A glass of milk.

     .4 ml   .4 l   .4 kl

5) Length of a blackboard.

     6 cm   6 m   6 km

6) Gas in a car's tank.

     15 ml   15 l   15 kl

7) Height of a mountain.

     1.4 cm   1.4 m   1.4 km

8) Vanilla extract used to make cookies.

     5 ml   5 l   5 kl

9) Distance to the next city.

     18 cm   18 m   18 km

10) Length of your foot.

     21 cm   21 m   21 km

11) Weight of a sack of potatoes.

     3.8 mg   3.8 g   3.8 kg

12) Water in a town's reservoir.

     5,800 ml   5,800 l   5,800 kl

13) Height of a stepladder.

     1.9 cm   1.9 m   1.9 km

14) Perfume in a bottle.

     .5 ml   .5 l   .5 kl

15) Length of a ladybug.

     .3 cm   .3 m   .3 km

16) Fruit punch in a bowl.

     5 ml   5 l   5 kl

Exercise C Find the perimeter of each polygon.

1)

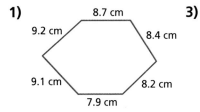

8.7 cm

9.2 cm

8.4 cm

9.1 cm

8.2 cm

7.9 cm

3)

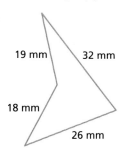

19 mm

32 mm

18 mm

26 mm

5)

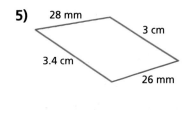

28 mm

3 cm

3.4 cm

26 mm

2)

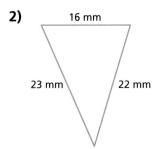

16 mm

23 mm

22 mm

4)

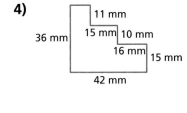

36 mm

11 mm

15 mm 10 mm

16 mm

15 mm

42 mm

6)

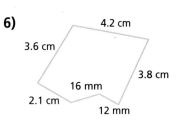

4.2 cm

3.6 cm

3.8 cm

16 mm

2.1 cm

12 mm

Exercise D Find the area of each polygon. Include the proper units in your answer.

1)

14 cm

14 cm

3)

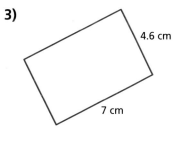

4.6 cm

7 cm

5)

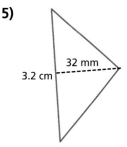

32 mm

3.2 cm

2)

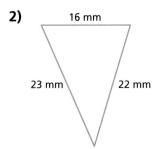

3.2 cm

7.5 cm

4)

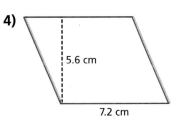

5.6 cm

7.2 cm

6)

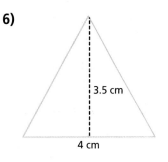

3.5 cm

4 cm

Exercise E   Measure the height of each plant to the nearest sixteenth of an inch. Measure from the bottom of the pot to the highest point of the plant.

1)

4)

7)

10)

8)

2)

5)

9)

3)

6)

Exercise F Find the perimeter of each polygon.

1)

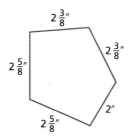

$2\frac{3}{8}''$
$2\frac{3}{8}''$
$2\frac{5}{8}''$
$2''$
$2\frac{5}{8}''$

3)

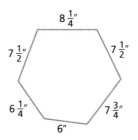

$8\frac{1}{4}''$
$7\frac{1}{2}''$
$7\frac{1}{2}''$
$6\frac{1}{4}''$
$7\frac{3}{4}''$
$6''$

5)

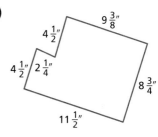

$9\frac{3}{8}''$
$4\frac{1}{2}''$
$4\frac{1}{2}''$ $2\frac{1}{4}''$
$8\frac{3}{4}''$
$11\frac{1}{2}''$

2)

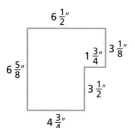

$6\frac{1}{2}''$
$6\frac{5}{8}''$
$1\frac{3}{4}''$ $3\frac{1}{8}''$
$3\frac{1}{2}''$
$4\frac{3}{4}''$

4)

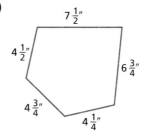

$7\frac{1}{2}''$
$4\frac{1}{2}''$
$6\frac{3}{4}''$
$4\frac{3}{4}''$
$4\frac{1}{4}''$

6)

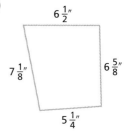

$6\frac{1}{2}''$
$7\frac{1}{8}''$
$6\frac{5}{8}''$
$5\frac{1}{4}''$

Exercise G Find the area of each polygon. Include the proper units in your answer.

1)

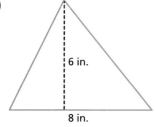

6 in.

8 in.

3)

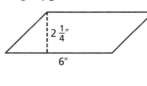

$2\frac{1}{4}''$
6''

5)

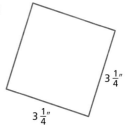

$3\frac{1}{4}''$
$3\frac{1}{4}''$

2)

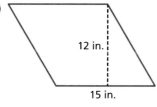

12 in.

15 in.

4)

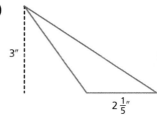

3''

$2\frac{1}{5}''$

6)

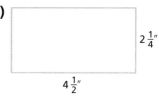

$2\frac{1}{4}''$
$4\frac{1}{2}''$

Exercise A   Construct a vertical bar graph to display the following information.

Favorite Pizza Topping	
Topping	Frequency
Pepperoni	8
Green Peppers	6
Onions	4
Extra Cheese	5
Mushrooms	2
Hot Peppers	7

Exercise B   Construct a horizontal bar graph to display the following information.

Favorite Snowball Flavors	
Flavor	Frequency
Root Beer	12
Lemon Lime	9
Strawberry	6
Egg Custard	15
Cherry	7
Sky Blue	8

Exercise C   Construct a circle graph to display the Mallory family budget.

Mallory Family Budget	
Expense	Amount
Food	$12,000
Clothing	$8,000
Housing	$24,000
Entertainment	$1,200
Savings	$2,000
Other	$800

0008/7

Exercise D   Construct a line graph to display the following data.

Average Monthly Temperature in San Juacinto			
Month	Temperature	Month	Temperature
January	34°	July	92°
February	28°	August	94°
March	42°	September	86°
April	56°	October	72°
May	82°	November	51°
June	87°	December	44°

Algebra

Exercise A   Simplify by adding.

1) $(-4) + (-1)$

2) $(+1) + (-1)$

3) $(+12) + (-2)$

4) $(-18) + (-2)$

5) $(+15) + (-17)$

6) $(-6) + (+5)$

7) $(-3) + (+11)$

8) $(-10) + (-10)$

9) $(-17) + (-11)$

10) $-3 + 5 - 2 + 5$

11) $+2 - 20 - 11$

12) $+30 - 32$

13) $-1 - 4 + 3 + 1$

14) $+4 - 5 + 3 - 1$

15) $+1 + 3 - 2 - 2$

16) $+3 - 3 + 3 + 4$

17) $-3 + 5 + 6 - 1$

18) $+3 + 3 - 7 - 1$

Exercise B   Combine like terms.

1) $-3a - 4a + 3$

2) $-4c + c - 3c$

3) $-4c + 3c - 8c$

4) $+3 - 4 + 3a - 5a + 1$

5) $+n - 7n + 10 + n$

6) $-x + 7x - 3x$

7) $-3a - 3a + 2a + 3$

8) $-4x + 4x - 10$

9) $-a + 3a - a + 1$

10) $+14x + 3y + 3x - 2y$

11) $+6x + 7y - 4x - 8y - 2$

12) $+x - 3 + 5y - 5 - 2x$

13) $+3x - 2y - 5x - y + 3$

14) $-3a - 2b + 4a - 5 - 5b + 1$

15) $+6y + 3c + 5c - 7y + 8 - 10$

16) $+z - 5v + 2v - z - 5 + v - 1$

17) $-6c - a - 3a + c$

18) $+1 - 20c + 6a - 14a - 3 + 7c$

Algebra

Exercise C Remove parentheses and combine like terms.

1) $4(4 + 6)$

2) $10(12 - 8)$

3) $-1(12 - 5)$

4) $+7(-3 + 5)$

5) $5(10a - 1)$

6) $-4(5c - 6)$

7) $+7(8a - 9)$

8) $-(-5 - 6a)$

9) $-(5x - 7) - 3$

10) $+2(-1 + 7c) + 4$

11) $-3(-2 + 9a) - 2$

12) $-5(6 - 1)$

13) $2(10 - 5)$

14) $-1(-3 - 5)$

15) $+5(-19 + 18)$

16) $-6(21a + 1)$

17) $9(5b - 1)$

18) $(5a - 3)3$

19) $(3a - 9)(-5)$

20) $-(-2c - 5) - 5$

21) $+5(1 + x) - 4$

22) $-2(-4 + 17z) + 20$

Exercise D Solve for the unknown.

1) $x + 4 = 10$

2) $a - 5 = -12$

3) $-4 + n = -3$

4) $-3 + a = -16$

5) $-3 + 8 - x = 15$

6) $x - 10 = 10$

7) $x + 17 = 0$

8) $-1 + 2 + x = 10$

9) $x - 7 = 20 - 18$

10) $3x - 4 = 14$

11) $2c - 3 = +15$

12) $+2 + 3x = 20$

13) $12 = 3x - 3$

14) $3x + 1 = 17$

15) $4a - 1 = 15$

16) $5x + 10 = 20$

17) $5 + 2x = 35$

18) $-2 + 3x = -17$

Calculator Handbook

There are many kinds of electronic calculators. Each calculator is a little different from others. Some have more keys than others. The keys may be placed differently. You may have to press the keys in a certain order. Most calculators, however, are very similar.

Here is a calculator that has the basic functions you find on most calculators.

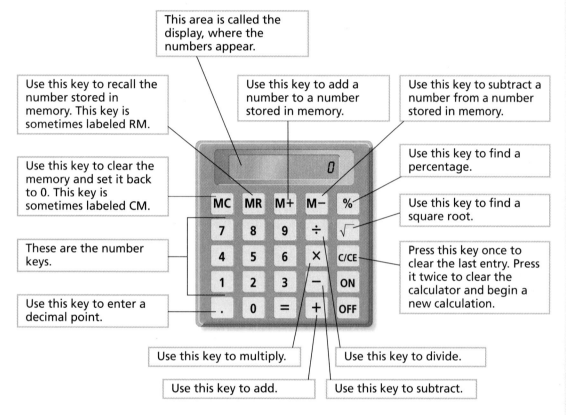

This area is called the display, where the numbers appear.

Use this key to recall the number stored in memory. This key is sometimes labeled RM.

Use this key to add a number to a number stored in memory.

Use this key to subtract a number from a number stored in memory.

Use this key to clear the memory and set it back to 0. This key is sometimes labeled CM.

Use this key to find a percentage.

Use this key to find a square root.

These are the number keys.

Press this key once to clear the last entry. Press it twice to clear the calculator and begin a new calculation.

Use this key to enter a decimal point.

Use this key to multiply.

Use this key to divide.

Use this key to add.

Use this key to subtract.

You can use a calculator to help you do arithmetic quickly and accurately. In many cases, you key the calculation the same way you would write it on paper.

Press 23 + 61 =
The display will read 84.
23 + 61 = 84

Press 98 − 18 =
The display will read 80.
98 − 18 = 80

Press 12 × 12 =
The display will read 144.
12 × 12 = 144

Press 63 ÷ 9 =
The display will read 7.
63 ÷ 9 = 7

It's a good idea to look at the display after you key in each number. It helps to check that you haven't pressed a wrong key by mistake.

The $\sqrt{}$ key will give you the square root of a number.

Example What is the square root of 81?
Press *8 1* $\sqrt{}$
The display will read *9*.

The % key will help you find a percentage. The % key works differently on different kinds of calculators. You may need to press = after % on some calculators. The examples show how the key works on most calculators.

Examples What is 25 percent of 44?
Press *44* × *25* %
The display will read *11*.

What is 10 percent more than 50?
Press *50* + *10* %
The display will read *55*.

What is 20 percent less than 65?
Press *65* − *20* %
The display will read *52*.

If you are going to use the same number, or constant, in a series of calculations, you can store it in memory. Remember to clear the memory by pressing MC before you begin.

Examples What is 18 times 4? 18 times 12? 18 times 31?

Press *18* M+ C/CE
The display reads *0*. The number 18 is stored in memory.

Press MR × *4* = The display reads *72*.
Press MR × *12* = The display reads *216*.
Press MR × *31* = The display reads *558*.

You can add to or subtract from the number in memory by using the M+ and M− keys. Remember to clear the memory by pressing MC before you begin.

Press	Display	Number in Memory
22	*22*	0
M+	*22*	22
6	*6*	22
M+	*6*	28
20	*20*	28
M−	*20*	8

Glossary

A

Absolute value—the distance a number is from zero (p. 286)

Acute angle—an angle whose measure is less than 90 degrees (p. 162)

Acute triangle—a triangle with three acute angles (p. 169)

Addend—one of the numbers being added (p. 7)

Addition—the arithmetic operation of combining numbers to find their sum or total (p. 7)

Allotted—assigned (p. 257)

Angle—two rays with the same endpoint (p. 160)

Area—the amount of space inside a shape, measured in square units (p. 184)

Associative property—allows you to add or multiply with different groupings. The final answer does not change. (p. 294)

Average—the number obtained by dividing the sum of two or more quantities by the number of quantities (p. 27)

Axis (*plural:* **axes**)—a line of reference on a graph (p. 250)

B

b—an abbreviation for base (p. 216)

Bar graph—a graph that uses bars to compare amounts or sizes (p. 245)

Base (b)—1. one side of a polygon used to find area (p. 216)

   2. the amount you are taking a part or percent of (p. 138)

C

Capacity—the amount a container will hold when full (p. 191)

Centimeter (cm)—a measure of length about equal to the width of a large paper clip (p. 179)

Circle—a plane figure whose points are equally distant from the center (p. 162)

Circle graph—a graphic way to compare amounts using segments of a circle (p. 257)

Circumference—distance around a circle (p. 226)

cm—an abbreviation for centimeter (p. 179)

cm²—square centimeter (p. 184)

cm³—cubic centimeter (p. 187)

Commission—percentage of total sales (p. 154)

Common denominators—common multiples of two or more denominators (p. 73)

Common factors—for any two numbers, all the numbers that divide evenly into both numbers (p. 49)

Commutative property—states that two numbers may be added or multiplied in either order (p. 293)

Comparison—examining two numbers to see which is larger (p. 116)

Composite number—a number with more than two factors (p. 38)

Cone—a solid figure with a circular base connected to a vertex, forming a point (p. 172)

Conversion factor—number you multiply by to change to another unit of measure (p. 182)

Conversions—changes to a different unit of measure (p. 124)

Convert—change to an equivalent measure (p. 192)

Cross product—the answer obtained by multiplying the denominator of one fraction with the numerator of another (p. 57)

Cube—a prism with square sides and faces (p. 172)

Cubic units—units used to measure volume (p. 187)

Currency—money (p. 124)

Customary—usual or common; ordinary (p. 178)

Cylinder—a solid figure with two equal circular bases that are parallel (p. 172)

D

Data—information (p. 244)

Decimal places—positions to the right of a decimal point (p. 87)

Degree—a measure of angles; $\frac{1}{360}$ of a circle (p. 162)

Denominator—the number below the fraction bar that tells the number of parts to the whole (p. 56)

Diameter—distance across a circle through the center (p. 226)

Difference—answer to a subtraction problem (p. 10)

Digit—one of the characters used to write a numeral (p. 2)

Dimensions—measure, such as length, width, or height, of the size of an object (p. 274)

Discount—a reduction made from the regular price (p. 148)

Discount rate—percent that the price is reduced (p. 148)

Distributive property—in a problem that mixes multiplication with addition or subtraction, allows you to multiply each term in parentheses by a single factor (p. 295)

Divided bar graph—a graph that uses parallel bars to compare information (p. 251)

Dividend—number being divided (p. 20)

Divisibility—able to be divided evenly (p. 42)

Divisible—able to be divided without remainder (p. 42)

Division—the arithmetic operation that finds how many times a number is contained in another number (p. 20)

Divisor—number by which you are dividing (p. 20)

E

Elapsed time—how long an event lasts (p. 235)

Equation—a mathematical sentence that says two expressions are equal (p. 300)

Equilateral triangle—a triangle with three equal sides (p. 169)

Exponent—number that tells the times another number is a factor (p. 30)

F

Factors—numbers being multiplied in a multiplication problem (p. 14)

Finance charge—cost for borrowing money (p. 153)

Finance rate—percent charged for borrowing money (p. 153)

Fluid ounce—unit of liquid capacity equal to $\frac{1}{16}$ of a pint (p. 202)

Fraction—part of a whole number (p. 56)

Fractional form—expressed as a fraction (p. 116)

G

g—an abbreviation for gram (p. 178)

Gallon—unit of liquid capacity (p. 202)

Gauge—scale of model trains (p. 268)

GCF—an abbreviation for greatest common factor (p. 49)

Geometry—the study of points, lines, angles, surfaces, and solids (p. 160)

Gram (g)—measure of mass about equal to the weight of a paper clip (p. 178)

Graph—a visual way to show information (p. 242)

Greatest common factor (GCF)—largest factor of two numbers (p. 49)

H

h—an abbreviation for height (p. 216)

Height (h)—distance from bottom to top (p. 216)

Hexagonal prism—a prism with hexagonal faces (p. 172)

Horizontal—parallel to the horizon (p. 8)

Horizontal axis—line of reference parallel to the horizon (p. 254)

I

Improper fraction—a fraction whose numerator is equal to or greater than its denominator (p. 60)

Infinite—without end or limit (p. 37)

Integers—whole numbers and their opposites (p. 282)

Intersecting lines—lines that cross in the same plane (p. 161)

Invert—change positions (p. 70)

Isosceles triangle—a triangle with two equal sides (p. 169)

K

Key—area on a graph where the symbols are explained (p. 251)

kg—an abbreviation for kilogram (p. 195)

Kilogram (kg)—measure of mass about equal to the weight of four rolls of quarters (p. 195)

Kiloliter (kL)—measure of capacity about equal to that of a small wading pool (p. 191)

Kilometer (km)—measure of distance about equal to five city blocks or a little more than a half mile (p. 181)

kL—an abbreviation for kiloliter (p. 191)

km—an abbreviation for kilometer (p. 181)

km²—square kilometer (p. 184)

L

l—an abbreviation for length (p. 184)

L—an abbreviation for liter (p. 178)

LCD—an abbreviation for least common denominator (p. 73)

LCM—an abbreviation for least common multiple (p. 48)

Least common denominator (LCD)—smallest denominator that is a multiple of two denominators (p. 73)

Least common multiple (LCM)—smallest number that two numbers will divide (p. 48)

Length (l)—distance from end to end (p. 184)

Less than (<)—smaller than (p. 57)

Like denominators—having the same denominators (p. 71)

Linear measurement—the length of a line between fixed points (p. 206)

Line graph—a graph that shows change in amounts with a solid line (p. 254)

Line segment—part of a line (p. 160)

List price—regular price (p. 148)

Liter (L)—measure of capacity about equal to that of a coffee can (p. 178)

M

m—an abbreviation for meter (p. 178)

m²—square meter (p. 184)

m³—cubic meter (p. 187)

Map distance—space between two points as measured on a map (p. 276)

Mass—measure of matter (p. 195)

Meter (m)—measure of length about equal to the height of a doorknob (p. 178)

Metric system—system of measurement based on powers of ten; gram and meter are basic units (p. 178)

mg—an abbreviation for milligram (p. 195)

Milligram (mg)—measure of mass about equal to $\frac{1}{10}$ of a grain of rice (p. 195)

Milliliter (mL)—measure of capacity about equal to that of an eyedropper (p. 191)

Millimeter (mm)—measure of length about equal to the width of the wire in a paper clip (p. 179)

Mislead—to lead in the wrong direction or to a mistaken belief (p. 260)

Mixed number—number composed of a whole number and a fraction (p. 60)

Mixtures—combinations of two or more items (p. 121)

mL—an abbreviation for milliliter (p. 191)

mm—an abbreviation for millimeter (p. 179)

mm²—square millimeter (p. 184)

mm³—cubic millimeter (p. 187)

Multiple bar graph—a bar graph with more than one kind of bar that compares information (p. 252)

Multiples—the product of a given number and a whole number (p. 37)

Multiplication—the arithmetic operation combining numbers by adding one number to itself many times (p. 14)

N

n—a letter used to stand for an unknown number (p. 120)

Negative exponent—an exponent less than zero; used to express small numbers (p. 100)

Negative integers—whole numbers less than zero (p. 282)

Numerator—the number above the fraction bar that tells how many parts are used (p. 56)

O

Obtuse angle—angle with a measure between 90 and 180 degrees (p. 162)

Obtuse triangle—a triangle with one obtuse angle (p. 169)

Open sentence—an equation with at least one variable or unknown (p. 300)

Order—sequence from smallest to largest (p. 7)

Ordered pair—pair of x- and y-coordinates that name a point on a grid (p. 299)

Origin—the point where horizontal and vertical number lines cross at zero (p. 299)

Ounce—unit of weight equal to $\frac{1}{16}$ of a pound (p. 203)

P

Parallel lines—lines that are always the same distance apart; parallel lines never meet (p. 161)

Parallelogram—a four-sided polygon with two pairs of equal and parallel sides (p. 170)

Partial products—answers obtained by multiplying a factor by a digit in the other factor (p. 16)

Percent (%)—part per one hundred (p. 130)

Percentage—result obtained by multiplying a number by a percent (p. 138)

Perimeter—distance around (p. 210)

Perpendicular lines—intersecting lines that cross and form four right angles (p. 161)

Pi (π)—ratio of the circumference to the diameter (p. 227)

Pictograph—a graph that uses pictures or symbols to show information (p. 242)

Pint—measure of liquid capacity (p. 202)

Place value—worth based on position in a numeral (p. 2)

Plane—a flat surface that extends forever in all directions (p. 160)

Polygon—a closed plane figure with three or more sides (p. 168)

Positive integers—whole numbers greater than zero (p. 282)

Power of ten—product of multiplying ten by itself one or more times (p. 100)

Prefix—set of letters placed before a word to make a new word; often used in the metric system (p. 178)

Previous balance—amount owed before a payment is made (p. 153)

Prime factorization—showing a number as the product of its prime numbers (p. 46)

Prime number—a number with only two factors (p. 38)

Principal—amount borrowed or invested (p. 152)

Prism—a solid figure with two parallel faces that are polygons of the same shape (p. 172)

Product—answer to a multiplication problem (p. 14)

Proportion—two equal ratios (p. 118)

Protractor—a tool used to draw or measure angles (p. 164)

Pyramid—a solid figure with a base that is a polygon and triangular sides (p. 172)

Q

Quadrilaterals—polygons with four sides (p. 170)

Quart—measure of liquid capacity (p. 202)

Quotient—answer to a division problem (p. 20)

R

Radius (*plural:* **radii**)—distance from the center of a circle to the edge of a circle (p. 226)

Rate—percent (p. 138)

Rate of commission—percent used to compute commissions (p. 154)

Rate of interest—percent paid or charged for the use of money (p. 152)

Ratio—comparison of two numbers using division (p. 116)

Ray—a line that has a beginning point but no end (p. 160)

Real distance—actual distance between two locations (p. 276)

Rectangle—a four-sided polygon with four right angles and the opposite sides equal (p. 170)

Rectangular prism—a prism with rectangular faces (p. 172)

Reflex angle—an angle whose measure is between 180 and 360 degrees (p. 162)

Remainder—amount left over when dividing (p. 22)

Rename—to express in a form that is equal to the original (p. 11)

Repeating decimal—a decimal where the same series of digits repeat (p. 111)

Rhombus—a polygon with four equal sides and the opposite angles equal (p. 170)

Right angle—an angle whose measure is 90 degrees (p. 162)

Right triangle—a triangle with one right angle (p. 169)

Road distance—space between two locations along a road indicated by a number on a map (p. 277)

Index

fractions in simplest form, 59, 131, 156
improper fractions as mixed numbers, 62
mixed numbers as improper fractions, 60–61
multiplying with, 16
percents to decimals and fractions, 131–32
subtracting fractions with, 79–81
Rounding
decimals, 89–92, 134–35, 137
whole numbers, 4–5, 19, 244, 249, 258
Ruler, 179, 204–05

S

Scale
defined, 242, 268
in floor plans, 274–75
in maps, 276–77
Scale drawing, 268–76
Scale models, 268–71
Scientific notation, 100–01
Simple interest, 152
Simplest form
defined, 59
renaming fractions in, 59, 131, 156
writing mixed numbers in, 63
Solid figures, 172–73
Special properties, 293–95
Sphere, 172–73
Square unit, 184
Subtraction
of decimals, 95–96, 148–49, 153
defined, 10
of fractions, 75–80
with linear measurements, 207–08
of mixed numbers, 75–81, 83
of positive and negative integers, 288–89
solving equations using, 300–03
of whole numbers, 10–13, 32–33, 207–08, 222, 233–37, 239, 283–90, 300, 302, 316

T

Tables. *See* Charts and tables
Test Taking Tips, 33, 53, 83, 113, 127, 157, 175, 199, 223, 239, 265, 279, 313
Time, 233–37
Triangle, 168–69, 216–17
Triangular prism, 172–73, 221

U

Units
of capacity, 192–94
cubic, 187
square, 184
time, 233–34
Unlike denominators, 73–74, 77–78

V

Variables
in algebra problems, 298–311
defined, 298
in floor plans, 274
missing numbers as, 120
in percent problems, 138–47
in proportions, 121, 124, 126
in scale drawings, 272–73
in scale models, 268–71
Volume
customary units of, 219–21
of cylinder, 231–32
defined, 187
metric units of, 187–90
of rectangular prism, 219–20
of triangular prism, 221

W

Weight, 195, 203
Whole numbers, 1–33
adding, 7–9, 41, 43, 53, 179, 183, 207–08, 210–12, 215, 222, 233–34, 239, 275, 277, 284–87, 290, 300–03, 315
averaging, 27–29
defined, 3
dividing, 20–26, 32–33, 42–45, 47, 59, 62, 65, 137, 202–03, 206, 209, 222, 268, 270–71, 296–97, 304–07, 312, 317
exponents of, 30
infinite set of, 39
multiplying, 14–19, 57–58, 60–61, 64, 66–70, 118–20, 132, 146–47, 184–90, 193, 197, 199, 202–03, 206, 208–09, 213–15, 218–20, 222–23, 238, 269, 271, 274–77, 291–95, 316–17
order of operations and, 31
place values and, 2
reading and writing, 3–6, 314
rounding, 3–6, 314
subtracting, 10–13, 207–08, 222, 233–37, 239, 288–89, 300–03, 316

Y

Yard, 206

Z

Zero, 7, 23